The Complete Book of

Hot Wheels™

Bob Parker

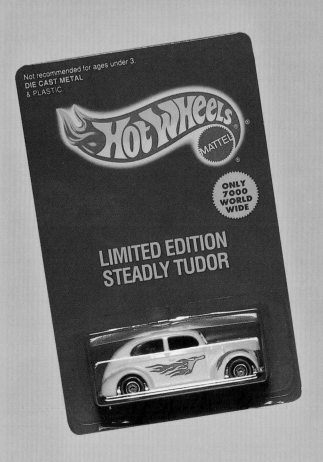

With Price Guide

Schiffer Publishing Ltd

77 Lower Valley Road, Atglen, PA 19310

ACKNOWLEDGMENTS

I am grateful to each of the following individuals for their efforts on behalf of this work: Frank Veres for overseeing all of the photography; Jerilynn Prokop for her review of the manuscript; Charlie Tulchin, Tony Cataldo, Bill Keller, Joe Altieri, and Jim Yun for supplying models from their respective collections to be photographed; Kyp Seiferth for the use of his camera; Jesse Thompson, Jim Wilson, and the staff at Milford Camera for their cooperation and expertise; and Charles Kitson not only for helping with the variation guide, but for his ideas, support, and extraordinary commitment to this project.

"Hot Wheels"   "Fat Daddy Sizzlers"   "Crack-Ups"
"Spectraflame"   "Flying Colors"   "Color Racers"
"Gran Prix"   "Super Chromes"   "Action Command"
"Heavyweights"   "Mean Machines"   "Speed Demons"
"Spoilers"   "Night Ridin' Sizzlers" "XV Racers"
"Gran Toros"   "Scene Machines"   "Flip-Outs"
"Sizzlers"   "Golden Machines"   "Park N' Plates"
"Hot Birds"   "Scorchers"   "California Customs"
"Hotline"   "Workhorses"   "Super California
"Earthshakers"   "Hi-Rakers"   Customs"
"RRRumblers"   "Hot Ones"   "Gleam Team"
"Drivin' Gear"   "Steering Rigs"   "Pro Circuit"
"Farbs"   "Truck Co."   "Revealers"
"Hot Shots"   "Speed Machines"   "Tatoo Machines"
"Chopcycles"   "Real Riders"   "Color FX"
"Zowees"   "Ultra Hots"   "Top Speed"
"Revvers"

are trademarks of Mattel Inc., El Segundo, CA. 90245 U.S.A.

DEMOLITION MAN is a trademark of Warner Bros.

*Many of the Hot Wheels items described and pictured in this book have imprints, designs, and logos of various other companies which are trademarks of those companies. Also the names of makes and models of actual vehicles are trademarks of the manufacturers of those vehicles.

Library of Congress Cataloging-in-Publication Data

Parker, Bob, 1967-
    The complete book of Hot Wheels : with price guide / Bob Parker.
      p. cm.
    ISBN 0-88740-827--3 (paper)
    1. Hot Wheels toys--Collectors and collecting. 2. Automobiles-
-Models--Collectors and collecting. I. Title.
TL237 .2. P37   1995
629.22' 12--dc20   95-19706
                    CIP

Book Design by (M_J) Hannigan

ISBN: 0-88740-827-3

Printed in China

DEDICATION

TO MOM, FOR YOUR LOVING SUPPORT AND PATIENCE.

CONTENTS

Introduction 3
History 3
1668 4
1969 6
1970 10
1971 15
1972 20
1973 21
1974 23
1975 26
1976 29
1977 32
1978 34
1979 36
1980 39
1981 41
1982 44
1983 47
1984 50
1985 53
1986 57
1987 59
1988 61
1989 63
1990 65
1991 67
1992 70
1993 72
1994 74
25th Anniversary / Vintage Series 76
Packaged Cars 78
Promos 80
Limited Edition 83
Miscellaneous 85
Hot Wheels Variation Guide 95
Bibliography .... Inside Back Cover

Published by Schiffer Publishing Ltd.
77 Lower Valley Road
Atglen, PA 19310
Please write for a free catalog.
This book may be purchased from the publisher.
Please include $2.95 postage.
Try your bookstore first.

We are interested in hearing from authors
with book ideas on related topics.

INTRODUCTION

The toys pictured and described in this book provide a guide to collectors of Mattel's Hot Wheels. As with other die-cast cars, Hot Wheels are produced with many interior and exterior variations. The color pictures represent almost all of the various castings manufactured from the first car produced in 1968 through the 1994 model year. In addition, a guide listing the many variations is included to help collectors sort through the vast and rapidly growing world of Hot Wheels. Lists of other toys produced by Mattel and of interest to Hot Wheels collectors are included.

In 1993 Mattel celebrated 25 years of Hot Wheels. Hot Wheels cars first appeared in stores in 1968 and were an instant success with consumers and collectors. Enthusiasm for these unique toy vehicles has not waned as new products continue to line store shelves and the number of serious collectors grows rapidly here and abroad. The scope of Hot Wheels collecting is international as collectors can be found throughout the world.

The exciting hobby of collecting Hot Wheels is enjoyed by people of all ages. This book should increase their knowledge, interest, and enjoyment of collecting Hot Wheels.

HISTORY

Throughout the 1950s and 60s Lesney's Matchbox cars were the most well known and collectible die-cast cars. Elliot Handler, one of the founders of Mattel, is credited with the birth of Hot Wheels cars. In 1966, Handler and Mattel began research and development on a line of die-cast cars that would be added to the list of quality toys produced by the company. When Hot Wheels were introduced in 1968 as the fastest metal cars in the world, their special torsion bar suspensions and low-friction wheel bearings quickly established Mattel's competitive edge in the die-cast market. Lesney soon changed the style of Matchbox cars from regular wheels to new "Superfast" wheels to compete with the new Mattel cars.

A total of 16 cars made up the original Hot Wheels line. Models were produced at factories located in the United States and Hong Kong, with the country of manufacture cast on the base. In addition to the special wheels and suspension, California styling and "Spectraflame" paint colors contributed to the quick success of Hot Wheels. Each of the cars was available in most of the optional colors offered, including green, light green, olive green, blue, light blue, aqua, red, brown, gold, pink, purple, and magenta. Various interior, base, and window variations were available as well. Special mag wheels and red line tires made the Hot Wheels line more distinctive. In retail stores the cars were sold separately in blisterpacks with a collector's button for about $1.00. A four-digit numbering system was developed to help identify the cars.

Sales of Hot Wheels were even greater than anticipated, and, soon sets including track and other accessories were produced to enhance the Hot Wheels line.

The first Hot Wheels car to come off the production line in 1968 was the Custom Camaro. Many of the original 16 cars in the 1968 line featured detailed engines and moveable parts. The custom cars were available with a black painted roof to simulate a vinyl top. The other cars produced in 1968 were based on actual and experimental show cars. To keep up with consumer demand, these popular cars were manufactured in both the United States and Hong Kong. Minor variations exist in the cars produced in the two different countries. The most recognizable difference is that U.S. versions are less detailed. With the instant success of the cars, Mattel began to produce track sets and accessory packs to supplement the vehicles. Additionally, several storage and carrying cases were marketed, the most popular being the famous, wheel-shaped Rally Case.

TRACK SETS
#6200 Strip Action Set
#6201 Stunt Action Set
#6202 Drag Race Action Set
#6223 Hot Curves Race Action Set

POP UP SETS
#5134 Service Station
#5135 Speed Shop
#5136 House and Car Port
#5141 Speedway Action Set

ACCESSORIES
#6224 Hot Strip Track
#6225 Full Curve Pak
#6226 Daredevil Loop Pak
#6227 Half Curve Pak
#6475 Hot Strip Super Pak

CASES
#5137 12 Car Rally Case
#5138 24 Car Case
#5139 Pop Up 12 Car Case

6205 Custom Cougar

6206 Custom Mustang

6206 Custom Mustang - open hood scoop

6206 Custom Mustang - louvered rear window

6207 Custom T-Bird

6210 Deora

6208 Custom Camaro

6211 Custom Barracuda

6208 Custom Camaro - white enamel

6212 Custom Firebird

6209 Silhouette

6214 Ford J-Car

6213 Custom Fleetside

6215 Custom Corvette

6218 Custom Eldorado

6216 Python

6219 Hot Heap

6217 Beatnik Bandit

6220 Custom Volkswagen

1969

As the popularity of Hot Wheels increased so did the number of cars in the 1969 line. There were 24 new cars added, bringing the total to 40. Several custom cars, along with three classic street rods, were included. So, too, were eight new race cars which made up the Grand Prix series. The Volkswagen Beach Bomb was a popular car that was produced in two different castings; the rarest model had two surf boards sticking out of the back window. Very few of these models are in existence, as the more common version had the surf boards mounted on the side of the vehicle. Models continued to be produced in both the United States and Hong Kong. Many new sets and cases were manufactured and sold in 1969.

TRACK SETS
#6280 Double Dare Race Set
#6281 Hot Curves Race Action Set
#6290 Super-Charger Sprint Set
#6291 Super-Charger Speedway-Freeway Set
#6292 Super-Charger Grand Prix Race Set

ACCESSORIES
#6283 Jump Ramp Pak
#6284 Trestle Pak
#6285 Competition Pak

CASES
#5142 24 Car Super Rally Case
#5143 12 Car Adjustable Case
#5144 24 Car Adjustable Case
#5145 48 Car Adjustable Case

OTHER HOT WHEELS ITEMS
#5146 Custom Shop Showcase Plaque
#5147 Car Carrier Showcase Plaque
#5158 Action City
#5159 Talking Service Center
#5439 Hot Wheels Wipe-Out Race Game

6250 Classic '32 Ford Vicky

6251 Classic '31 Ford Woody

6252 Classic '57 T-Bird

6253 Classic '36 Ford Coupe

6254 Lola GT70

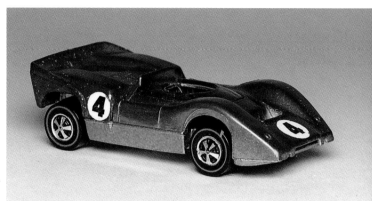

6255 McLaren M6A

6256 Chapparal 2G

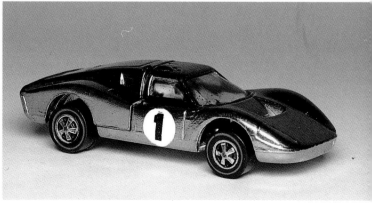

6257 Ford Mark IV

6258 Twinmill

6262 Lotus Turbine

6259 Turbofire

6263 Indy Eagle

6260 Torero

6264 Brabham-Repco F1

6261 Splittin' Image

6265 Shelby Turbine

8

6266 Custom Continental Mark III

6274 Volkswagen Beach Bomb

6267 Custom AMX

6275 Mercedes-Benz 280SL

6288 Custom Charger

6276 Rolls-Royce Silver Shadow

6269 Custom Police Cruiser

6277 Maserati Mistral

1970

In 1970, production of Hot Wheels continued in both the U.S. and Hong Kong and 36 new Hot Wheels were added along with several new series. The Heavyweights were a line of futuristic trucks. The Spoilers were a group of cars with front and rear spoilers and exposed engines. The first in a series of Snake and Mongoose cars was introduced. These models were popular because of the racing rivalry between Don "The Snake" Prudhomme and Tom "The Mongoose" McEwen. The Sky Show Fleetside was unique as it was sold only in a special set with small plastic airplanes that would launch from a ramp attached to the vehicle. The Heavy Chevy, Boss Hoss, and King Kuda with special chrome paint finishes could be found only in Club Kits which were offered to collectors through the mail. The Club Kits also contained a collector's book, Hot Wheels decal, and membership certificate. A fast food restaurant chain called Jack-in-the-Box was the first company to use a Hot Wheels car in a promotion. In 1970 a line of 1/43-scale die-cast cars called Gran Toros was produced. Sold under the Hot Wheels name, there were a total of 25 of these detailed cars manufactured through 1972. Sizzlers cars made their debut in 1970. The cars were made out of plastic and contained chargeable batteries that powered small motors. Sets and accessories for both Sizzlers and the regular Hot Wheels line were available.

SETS
#6429 Super-Charger Race Set
#6430 Super-Charger Rally'n Freeway Set
#6431 Sizzlin' Six Set
#6436 Sky Show Set
#6437 Drag Chute Stunt Set
#6438 Mongoose vs. Snake Drag Race Set
#6439 Rod Runner Speedway Set
#6440 Dual-Lane Rod Runner Race Set
#6441 Super-Charger Speed Test Set
#6442 Road Trials Set
#6443 Hi-Performance Set
#6446 Dual-Lane Rod Runner Drag Set
#6447 Indy Team Gift Set

ACCESSORIES
#6270 Lap Counter
#6294 Super-Charger
#6295 2-Way Super-Charger
#6297 Racing Stickers Pak
#6473 Decal Pak
#6475 Hot Strip Track Super Pak
#6476 Dual-Lane Lap Counter
#6477 Dual-Lane Curve Pak
#6479 Rod Runner
#6480 Dual-Lane Rodd Runner
#6481 Tune-Up Tower
#6482 Bridge Pak
#6483 Speedometer
#6484 Dual-Lane Speedometer

CASES
#4975 12 Car Collector's Race Case
#4976 24 Car Collector's Race Case
#4977 48 Car Collector's Race Case
#4978 72 Car Collector's Race Case
#4979 Speed Shop

SIZZLERS
#6500 Ford MK IV
#6501 Angeleno M70
#6502 Mustang Boss Hoss
#6503 Firebird Trans-Am
#6504 Revvin' Heavin
#6505 Hot Head

SIZZLERS SETS AND ACCESSORIES
#6510 National Champ Race Set
#6512 Laguna Oval Set
#6513 Newport Pacer Set
#6514 California 8 Race Set
#6506 Dual-Lane Speed Brake with Esses
#6507 Power Pit
#6511 Juice Machine
#6515 Single Speed Brake with Esses

GRAN TOROS
#6601 Ferrari Can Am
#6602 Astro II Chevy
#6603 T'rantula
#6604 Torpedo
#6605 Lamborghini Miura
#6606 Chapparal 2G
#6607 Ford MK II
#6608 Abarth 695 SS
#6611 Mustang Boss Hoss
#6612 Alpha Romeo 33/3
#6613 Porsche Carrera
#6614 Ferrari P4
#6615 Twinmill
#6616 Silhouette
#6617 Toyota 2000 GT
#6618 Lotus Europa
#6621 Ferrari 512S
#6622 Mercedes C-111
#6623 Porsche 917
#6624 Abarth 3000
#6625 Mantis
#6626 McLaren M8D Can Am
#6627 De Tomaso Pantera
#6628 Chapparal 2J Can Am
#6629 Lola T212 Can Am

GRAN TOROS SETS AND ACCESSORIES
#6680 Strip Action Set
#6681 Drag Race Set
#6690 Hot Strip Track Pak
#6691 Competition Pak

6400 Red Baron

6404 Classic Nomad

6401 The Demon

6405 Nitty Gritty Kitty

6402 Paddy Wagon

6407 TNT-Bird

6403 Sand Crab

6408 Heavy Chevy

6189 Heavy Chevy (Club Kit)

6190 King Kuda (Club Kit)

6409 Snake

6412 Light My Firebird

6410 Mongoose

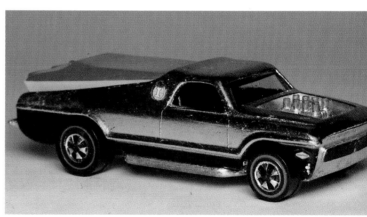

6413 Seasider

6411 King Kuda

6414 Mighty Maverick

6416 Porsche 917

6421 Jack "Rabbit" Special

6417 Ferrari 312P

6422 Swingin' Wing

6419 Peepin' Bomb

6423 Mantis

6420 Carabo

6424 Tri Baby

6436 Sky Show Fleetside

6436 Sky Show Fleetside

6450 Tow Truck

6451 Ambulance

6452 Cement Mixer

6453 Dump Truck

6454 Fire Engine

6455 Moving Van

6456 Mod Quad

6469 Fire Chief Cruiser

6457 Whip Creamer

6499 Boss Hoss (Club Kit)

6459 Power Pad

1971

In 1971, 35 new models were introduced. More vehicles were added to the Heavyweights and Spoilers series. The Snake and Mongoose lines were expanded with two dragsters and two funny cars. The dragsters were only available in unique two-packs or in the Wild Wheelie Set. This was the last year collector's buttons were sold with the cars; however, some plastic buttons were made before this practice was discontinued. It was also the last year Hot Wheels were manufactured in the United States. Mattel introduced many new items in 1971, including Hot Birds Airplanes, Hotline Trains, and Earthshakers construction vehicles. RRRumblers, a series of die-cast motorcycles with plastic drivers, were added to the growing Hot Wheels family. A complete line of sets and accessories was also available for these products.

SETS
#6037 Mongoose and Snake Wild Wheelie Set
#6427 Show Team (4 Pack)
#6428 Go Team (4 Pack)
#6429 Ontario Team (4 Pack)
#6493 Flyin' Circus Set

ACCESSORIES
#6013 Victory Pak
#6015 Danger Changer
#6034 Big Belter and Matchmaker
#6115 Crossover Pak
#6492 Joiner Pak

SIZZLERS
#6519 Side Burn
#6520 Spoil Sport
#6526 Backfire
#6527 Anteater
#6528 Cuda Trans-Am
#6529 Camaro Trans-Am
#6532 Indy Eagle
#6538 Ferrari 512S
#6550 Live Wire
#6551 Straight Scoop
#6552 Hot Wings

SIZZLERS SETS AND ACCESSORIES
#6453 High-Winder Set
#6009 Fat Track Big O Set
#6563 Fat Track Super Circuit Race Set
#6562 Fat Track California 500 Layout
#6559 Fat Track Big O Layout
#6560 Fat Track California 500 Layout
#5932 Car and Juice Machine
#6036 Fat Track Scramble Start
#6534 U-Turn Pak
#6539 Fat Track Good-Timer
#6542 High-Winder Pak
#6548 Fat Track Curve Pak
#6554 Fat Track Strip Track
#6555 Fat Track Lap Computer
#6561 Power Pit
#6594 Fat Track Post Pak
#5499 Race Case

HOT BIRDS AIRPLANES, SETS, AND ACCESSORIES
#6075 Sky Scraper
#6076 Cloud Hopper
#6078 Ski Gull
#6079 Maching Bird
#6080 Regal Eagle
#5939 Air Race Set
#5940 Sky Command Set
#6056 Control Tower
#6057 Sky Line And Hook Pad
#6069 Flight Deck
#6071 Sky Solo Set
#6072 On Target Set
#6073 Joy Rider
#5846 Collectors Case

HOTLINE TRAINS, SETS, AND ACCESSORIES
#6564 Speed Chief
#6565 Tail Waggin'
#6566 Freight Crate
#6567 Rockin' Roller
#6568 Mad Flatter
#6569 Folks Wagon
#5620 Mountain Tunnel Set
#6570 Thunder Run Set
#6572 Mighty Mover Set
#6582 Great Freight Set
#6584 High-Tail Hauler Train And Layout Set
#6571 Railtrack Pak
#6576 Curve Pak
#6577 Rail-Router
#6578 Signal Tower
#6579 Big Tipper with Train Brake
#6580 Bridge 2-Pak
#6581 Quick-Switch Pak
#5845 Hotline Train Case

EARTHSHAKERS
#5975 Ground Hog with Blade
#5976 Ground Hog with Scoop and Scraper
#5977 Ground Hog with Scoop and Dumper
#5978 Construction Set

RRRUMBLERS, SETS, AND ACCESSORIES
#6010 Road Hog
#6011 High Tailer
#6031 Mean Machine
#6032 Rip Snorter
#6048 3-Squealer
#6049 Torque Chop
#6012 Stunt Rider Set
#6033 Mean Mountain Set
#6047 Dizzy Dare Set
#5847 Roarin' 8 Collector's Case

5178 Bugeye

5953 Snake 2

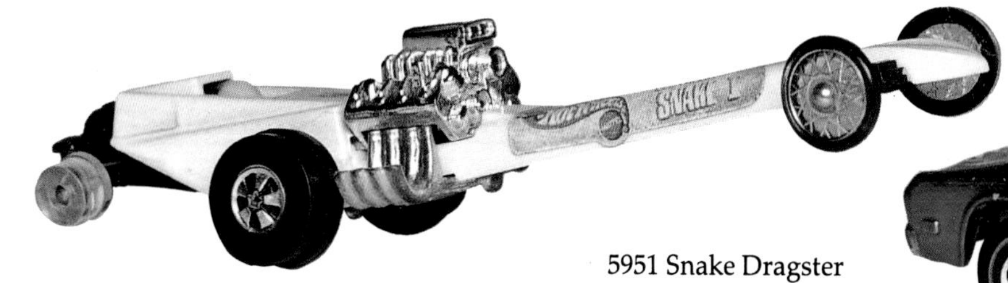

5951 Snake Dragster

5954 Mongoose

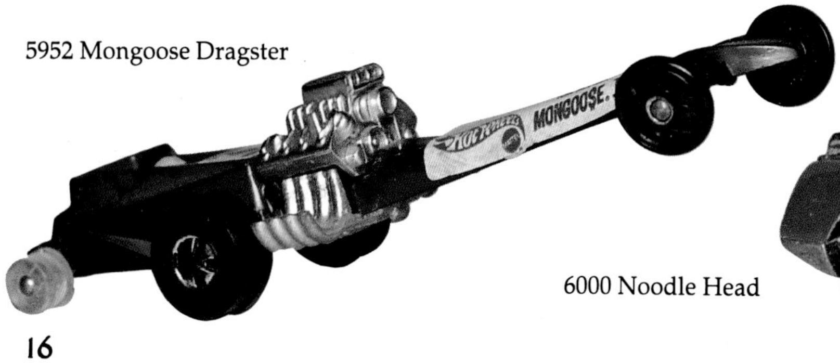

5952 Mongoose Dragster

6000 Noodle Head

16

6001 What-4

6020 Snorkel

6003 Six Shooter

6175 The Hood

6006 Special **Delivery**

6176 Short Order

6018 Fuel Tanker

6019 Team Trailer

6177 T-4-2

6179 Jet Threat

6183 Pit Crew Car

6184 Ice T

6185 Mutt Mobile

6186 Rocket-Bye-Baby

6187 Bye-Focal

6188 Strip Teaser

6192 Waste Wagon

6193 Scooper

6194 Racer Rig

6461 Grass Hopper

6407 Boss Hoss

6466 Cockney Cab

6418 Sugar Caddy

6467 Olds 442

6468 S'Cool Bus

6458 Hairy Hauler

6460 AMX/2

6471 Evil Weevil

6472 Classic Cord

19

1972

The year 1972 brought the first major change to Hot Wheels. Buttons were no longer produced and a new blisterpack was designed for the vehicles. The cars were produced with an attachment that allowed them to be used with an accessory called Drivin' Gear. A new Snake and Mongoose were two of only seven new cars. The cars produced in 1972 were only available for one year. The Sizzler and RRRumbler lines expanded with new vehicles and sets, and, once again, Mattel added several new lines that appealed to Hot Wheels collectors. Chopcycles were motorcycles powered like the Sizzlers cars. Farbs were a series of four cars in the shape of humans and were known as "Fantastic Car Kooks". Hot Shots featured "Ripfire" motors on larger-scale plastic dragsters.

SETS AND ACCESSORIES
#5645 Bug Bite Set
#5824 Zappit Pak
#5870 Drivin' Gear
#6692 Snake Bite Set

SIZZLERS
#5879 Flat Out
#5884 Up Roar
#5885 Double Boiler
#6553 Co-Motion

SIZZLERS SETS
#5924 Mad Scatter Set
#5979 Fat Track Control Set
#6596 Fat Track Super Control Set
#6642 Fat Track Breakin' 8 Set

RRRUMBLERS/SETS
#5947 Bold Eagle
#5948 Choppin Chariot
#5873 Devil's Deuce
#5883 Roamin Candle
#5949 Revolution
#5872 Straight Away
#5866 Bold Eagle Set
#5867 Dude Feud Set

CHOPCYCLES/SETS
#5628 Mighty Zork
#5629 Blown Torch
#5844 Speed Steed
#5871 Bruiser Cruiser
#5605 Hairy Hurdle Set
#5609 Rip Rider Set

FARBS/SETS
#5854 Hot Rodney
#5850 Hy Gear
#5851 Myles Ahead
#5853 Red Catchup
#5864 Head-Over-Heals-Set
#5865 Human Race Set

HOT SHOTS/SETS
#5857 Sound Breaker
#5858 Heatwave
#5876 Purple Rage
#5877 Red Alert
#6695 Winning Streak
#6696 Masked Bandit
#5868 Cool Duel Set
#5869 Flash Dash Set

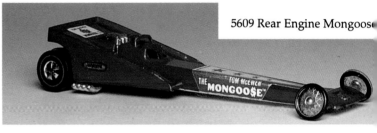

5609 Rear Engine Mongoose

5856 Rear Engine Snake

5881 Open Fire

6005 Funny Money

6021 Ferrari 512S

6022 Side Kick

6169 Mercedes-Benz C-111

1973

There were only three new castings produced in 1973. Mattel re-issued many of the earlier castings with new names. Enamel paint was used as the spectraflame colors were discontinued. The cars were very plain; most did not have stickers, decals, or imprints. Limited production and availability make the 1973 cars extremely rare collectibles. Mattel teamed with Shell Oil Co. and produced a set of ten cars to be used in a nationwide promotion. The models were packaged in small plastic bags and each car was available in a variety of colors. Zowees were small vehicles, some of which were also part of a Shell promotion, while some were sold in retail stores. New Chopcycles, RRRumblers, and Hot Shots were introduced. Revvers, a line of self-propelled vehicles, and Sizzlers with large tires, named Fat Daddy Sizzlers, also made their appearance in 1973.

SETS AND ACCESSORIES
#8232 Campground Set
#8227 24 Car Collector's Case

FAT DADDY SIZZLERS
#4943 Fire Works
#4944 Needle Nose
#4945 Ram Rocket
#4946 Hiway Hauler
#4947 Red Baron
#4948 Law Mill
#5630 Steering Trailer Set

SIZZLERS SETS
#8221 Road Chase Set
#8222 Super Road Chase Set
#8223 Target Set
#8231 Target Race Set

ZOWEES (Shell Promo)
Babby Buggy
Beddy Bye
Bumble Seat
Covered Draggin
Desperado
Diablo
Good Knight
Red Lighter

ZOWEES (Retail)
Numb Skull
Goin Fishin
Shifty
Fire Truck
Light My Fire
Home Sweet Home

CHOPCYCLES/SETS
#4932 Riptile
#4933 Ghost Rider
#4936 Triking Viking
#4937 Sourkraut
#4938 Ragecoach
#4934 Truckin' Trike Set
#5642 Great 8 Set

RRRUMBLERS
#4935 Centurian
#6644 Preying Mantis
#6645 Boneshaker
#6675 Rip Code

HOT SHOTS
#6960 Bustin' Bronc
#6961 Thunder Bolt

5880 Double Header

6004 Super Fine Turbine

6971 Street Snorter

6007 Sweet "16"

6974 Sand Witch

6967 Dune Daddy

6975 Double Vision

6968 Alive '55

6977 Xploder

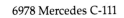

6978 Mercedes C-111

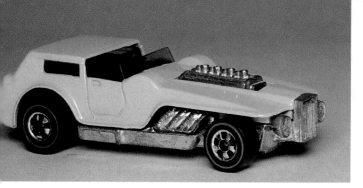

6979 Hiway Robber

#6963 Police Cruiser: same casting as 1974 Police Cruiser
#6964 Red Baron: same casting as 1970 Red Baron
#6965 Prowler: same casting as 1970 The Demon
#6966 Paddy Wagon: same casting as 1970 Paddy Wagon
#6969 Snake: same casting as 1970 Snake/1971 Snake 2
#6970 Mongoose: same casting as 1970 Snake/1971 Snake 2
#6972 Porsche 917: same casting as 1970 Porsche 917

6982 Show-Off

#6973 Ferrari 312P: same casting as 1970 Ferrari 312P
#6975 Double Vision: same casting as 1970 Mantis
#6976 Buzz Off: same casting as 1970 Tri-Baby
#6980 Ice "T": same casting as 1970 Ice "T"
#6981 Odd Job: same casting as 1971 Mutt Mobile
#6982 Mercedes-Benz 280SL: same casting
        as 1969 Mercedes-Benz 280SL

1974

The 24 cars in the 1974 Hot Wheels line were referred to as Flying Colors. A new blisterpack with a Flying Colors design was developed. Again, enamel colors were used, and despite few color variations, imprints added color and design to the cars. One of the most valuable and collectible Hot Wheels items, the Road King Truck, was issued in 1974. This truck, part of the regular Hot Wheels line, was available only in the Mountain Mining Set. This truck is very popular with collectors and is extremely difficult to find today.

SETS AND ACCESSORIES
    #7615 Mountain Mining Set
    #7623 City Police Set
    #7624 Highway Drive-Ins Set
    #7631 Speed Stunter Set
    #7632 Double Dare Set
    #4975 12 Car Collector's Case

6964 Red Baron (rounded spike on helmet)

6963 Police Cruiser

6965 Prowler

6968 Alive '55

6972 Porsche 917

7616 Rash 1

6973 Ferrari 312P

7617 Carabo

6976 Buzz Off

7618 Winnipeg

6978 Mercedes C-111

7619 Heavy Chevy

7615 Road King Truck (cab only)

7620 Volkswagen

24

7621 Funny Money

8259 Rodger Dodger

7622 Grass Hopper

8260 Steam Roller

7630 Top Eliminator

8261 Sir Rodney Roadster

8258 Baja Breaker

8262 Breakaway Bucket

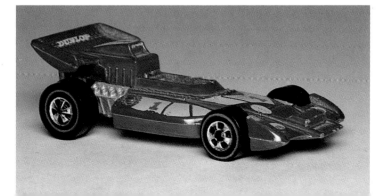

8273 El Ray Special

25

1975

Flying Colors remained the theme as 25 new cars were added in 1975. Motocross I and Street Eater are the only motorcycles that are part of the regular Hot Wheels line. Several military vehicles were introduced during the year. A special series of six-packs was available. Herfy's, a fast food chain, teamed up with Mattel and six special models were produced for a promotion. Many of the related items such as RRRumblers and Sizzlers were discontinued.

SETS AND ACCESSORIES
    #7672 Cutoff Canyon
    #7673 Thundershift 500
    #9084 Country Life Play Set
    #8827 Collector's Race Case

1975 6-PACKS
    #9031 H.E.L.P. Machin
    #9032 Street Machines
    #9033 Fun Machines
    #9034 Streak Machine

6967 Dune Daddy

7644 Mustang Stocker

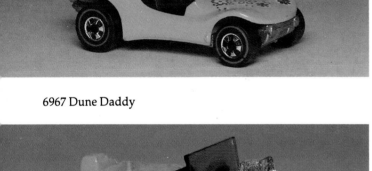

7622 Grass Hopper

7647 Torino Stocker

7648 P-911

7644 Mustang Stocker

7649 Super Van

7649 Super Van

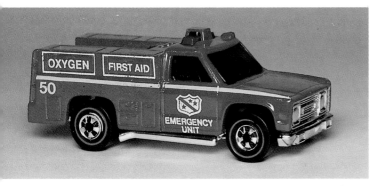

7650 Emergency Squad

7651 Sand Drifter

7652 Gremlin Grinder

7653 Mighty Maverick

7654 Warpath

7660 Monte Carlo Stocker

7661 Paramedic

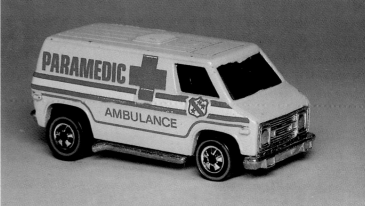

7662 American Victory

7658 Vega Bomb

7664 Gun Slinger

7659 Ramblin' Wrecker

7665 Chief's Special

7666 Ranger Rig

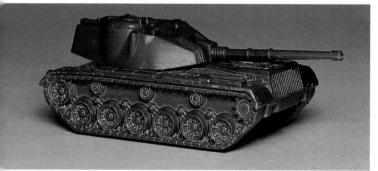

7655 Tough Customer

7668 Motocross 1

7669 Street Eater

7670 Backwoods Bomb

7671 Chevy Monza 2+2

8272 Large Charge

1976

The exciting and popular Flying Colors series continued to be produced in 1976. The year also saw the introduction of a new line of 18 chrome cars called Super Chromes. Several new military vehicles were also produced, the most interesting being the Army Staff Car. This model was sold only as part of the Military Machines 6 Pack and is another extremely rare and collectible vehicle. The first of three Toys-R-Us promotional Hot Wheels cars were sold at the popular toy chain. Sizzlers cars made a return but were chrome-plated and called Sizzlers II.

8235 Jet Threat II

SETS AND ACCESSORIES
    #9245 Super Chrome Stunt Set
    #9274 Double Duel Speedway
    #9275 Loco-Motion
    #4975 12 Car Collector's Case
    #8227 24 Car Collector's Case
    #9530 Super Rally Case

1976 6-PACKS
    #9504 Military Machines
    #9505 Super Chromes Machines

8240 Twin Mill II

SIZZLERS II
    #9378 The Vantom
    #9379 Boss Hoss II
    #9380 Chevy Camaro II
    #9381 Live Wire II
    #9382 Anteater II
    #9383 Side Burn II
    #9276 Silver Circuit Set

9031 Formula P.A.C.K.

9088 Rock Buster

9089 American Tipper

9090 Gun Bucket

9118 American Hauler

9119 Formula 5000

9120 Cool One

9183 Khaki Kooler

9184 Maxi Taxi

9185 Lowndown

9186 Inferno

9240 Poison Pinto

9241 Corvette Stingray

9242 Street Rodder

9243 Aw Shoot

9244 Neet Streeter

9521 Army Staff Car

31

1977

In 1977 Mattel began to phase out the red stripe on the tires which was unique to Hot Wheels cars. In the interim, many cars were available with and without the red-striped wheels. Another 12 new castings were issued that year. Hot Wheels were marketed in Japan in 1977. The models were the same as the U.S. issues but were sold in special red boxes. Motorcycles continued to be popular with Mattel and a new series called Mean Machines was introduced. As with many other related items, these motorcycles were not part of the regular Hot Wheels line. However, they still make a nice addition to any Hot Wheels collection.

SETS
- #9676 Double Scare Speedway
- #9793 Thrill Drivers Corkscrew Race Set
- #9876 Turbo Blast 600 Race Set

1977 6-PACKS
- #9855 Classic Machines
- #9856 Truckin' Machines

MEAN MACHINES
- #9869 Yamaha 400
- #9870 Honda 250
- #9871 Honda 750
- #9872 Honda Superwedge
- #9873 Chopper Cycle
- #9874 Police Cycle

9638 '57 Chevy

9640 Fire Eater

9638 '57 Chevy

9639 Z Whiz

9641 Spoiler Sport

9642 Odd Rod

9643 Letter Getter

9644 Second Wind

9645 GMC Motor Home

9646 Show Hoss II

9647 '56 Hi-Tail Hauler

9648 T-Totaller

9649 '31 Doozie

9793 Thrill Drivers Torino

1978

All of the cars issued in 1978 had black wall tires. The following themes were used to classify the cars: Speedway Specials, Classy Customs, Oldies But Goodies, Rescue Team, Super Streeters, Drag Strippers, and The Heavies. A special cloth patch for each theme could be obtained by mail through an offer on the backs of the blisterpacks. The Night Ridin' Sizzler, a new style of Sizzler featuring working headlights, also appeared in 1978.

SETS
#2011 Stingray Stunt
#2363 Thundershift Roarin' Raceway
#2386 T-Bird Tossup
#2835 Belt Buckle with 3 cars

1978 6-PACKS
#2360 Sprint Machines

NIGHT RIDIN' SIZZLERS
#2353 Dark Shadow
#2354 Moon Ghost
#9863 Lamborghini Countach
#9864 Corvette 4-Rotor
#9865 Short Fuse
#9866 Long Count
#2355 Nightmare Alley Set

2012 Jaguar XJS

2014 Hot Bird

2013 '57 T-Bird (with side window)

2015 Packin' Pacer

2013 '57 T-Bird (no side window)

2016 A-OK

2020 Stagefright

2017 Lickety Six

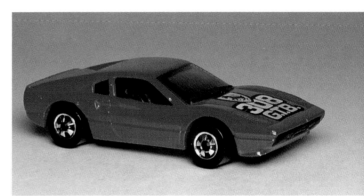

2021 Race Bait 308

2018 Science Friction

2022 Baja Breaker

2019 Highway Patrol

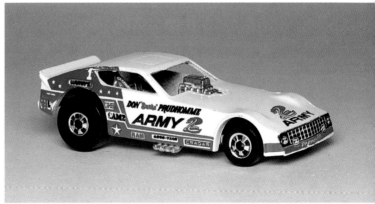

2023 Army Funny Car

1979

In 1979 Mattel continued the seven themes introduced in the previous year. The Heroes were a new group of cars representing famous comic book characters. Scene Machines offered a special picture that could be viewed through a small lens in the back of the vehicle. There was a special 6-pack of gold cars called Golden Machines issued in 1978. Scorchers cars, separate from the regular line, had plastic bodies and spring activated motors.

2501 Royal Flash

SETS AND ACCESSORIES
#1082 Captain America Stunt Set
#1937 The Heroes 2 Pack
#2858 Scene Machines Pack
#2886 Spider-Man's Web of Terror Set
#2945 Criss-Cross Crash Set
#4445 Getaway 12 Car Case

1979 6-PACKS
#2860 Class of 79 Machines
#2861 Golden Machines

SCORCHERS / SETS
#2544 Zappin' Z-28
#2589 Black Bird
#2640 White Thunder
#2641 Magnum XE
#2642 Good Looker
#2643 El Camino Real
#2645 Cool Capri
#2892 Magnum Fever
#2893 Vandemonium
#2894 Chevy Light
#2895 Cookin' Camaro
#2896 Capri Turbo
#1265 Scorchers Photo Finish Set
#1644 Scorchers Spinout Set
#2974 Scorchers Chamber Set

2502 Greased Gremli

2503 Spacer Race

2500 Upfront

2504 Hare Splitter

2504 Hare Splitter

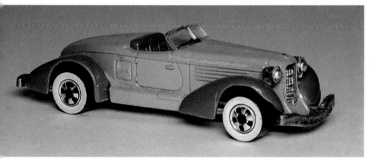

2505 Auburn

2506 Flat Out 442

2507 Dumpin' A

2508 Vetty Funny

2509 Bywayman

2510 Inside Story

2511 Bubble Gunner

2639 Fire Chaser

2851 Captain America (Scene Machines)

2852 Spider-Man (Scene Machines)

2853 Motocross Team (Scene Machines)

2854 S.W.A.T. Van (Scene Machines)

2855 Space Van (Scene Machines)

2877 Spider-Man

2878 The Incredible Hulk

2879 Captain America

2881 Human Torch

2880 Thor

2882 The Thing

1980

The 1980 line was made up of 19 models. Work horses were a new line of construction vehicles. Other new cars, called Hi-Rakers, had special rear wheels that could be raised or lowered.

SETS
    #1349 Hi-Raker 3-Pack
    #1437 The Great American Truck Race
    #1503 Service Center
    #1547 Wipeout Side by Side Raceway

1980 6-PACKS
    #1493 The Heroes
    #1501 Class of 80' Machines

1127 Greyhound MC-8

1125 Turbo Mustang

1129 Super Scraper

1126 Stutz Blackhawk

1130 Tricar X8

1131 40's Woodie

1132 3-Window '34

1134 Turbo Wedge

1135 'Vette Van

1136 Split Window '63

1153 Dodge D-50

1168 CAT Forklift

1169 Peterbilt Cement Mixer

1171 CAT Dump Truck

1173 CAT Wheel Loader

1172 CAT Bulldozer

1174 Hiway Hauler

1981

Twelve new models were introduced in 1981. A series of cars with new gold wheels called Hot Ones was introduced. A very important collector's book was marketed by Mattel. This catalog was included in a special 3-pack and proved to be a great source of information for collectors. The book featured color pictures of every casting produced back to the 1968 model year. Many people were attracted to the vast line of Hot Wheels as the catalog provided information previously unavailable to the average collector. Scene Machines and The Heroes added several new models. Scorchers increased by six models too. A line of trucks called Steering Rigs featured a small plastic steering wheel on the back of each truck.

SETS AND ACCESSORIES
#1495 3-Pack and Collector's Book
#3324 City Sto & Go Set
#3342 Flyin' Bronco Set
#3370 Dixic Challenger Thrill
#3854 Dixie Challenger Getaway Spinout
#4975 12 Car Collector's Case
#8227 24 Car Collector's Case

1981 6-PACKS
#1990 U.S.A. Machines
#2860 Weekend Machines

SCORCHERS
#1505 Time Bender
#1593 Turbo 928
#1594 Firebrand
#1595 Sundrifter
#1596 Britework
#1597 Blue Fever

STEERING RIGS
#1915 Kenworth Van
#1916 Peterbilt Tanker
#1917 GMC Hauler
#1918 Kenworth Tanker
#1919 Peterbilt Hauler
#1920 GMC Van

1689 Peterbilt Tank Truck

1690 Bronco 4-Wheeler

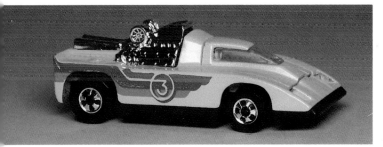

1691 Cannonade

1692 Omni 024

1693 Chevy Citation

1695 Old Number 5

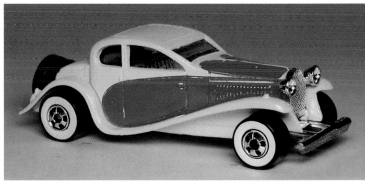

1696 '37 Bugatti

1697 Minitrek

1699 Airport Rescue

1694 Turismo

1700 Mirada Stocker

3300 Silver Surfer

3301 Iron Man

3303 Circus Cats (Scene Machines)

3304 Rescue Squad (Scene Machines)

3305 Racing Team (Scene Machines)

3364 Dixie Challenger

1982

During 1982 the production of Hot Wheels moved from Hong Kong to Malaysia. Another collector's book was available with the purchase of a special Showcase/Display case. This book featured information about Hot Wheels from 1968 through the 1982 model year. McDonald's had a promotion in which Hot Wheels cars were offered. Megaforce vehicles were a separate line of vehicles based on a movie of the same name. Neither the movie nor the cars were around for very long. Several new Steering Rigs were available.

1698 Cadillac Seville

SETS AND ACCESSORIES
#1503 Service Center Sto & Go
#1898 Photo Finish Race Set
#3534 Hot Ones Drag Race Set
#3741 Hot Wheels U.S.A. Deluxe Set
#3808 Inside Track Sto & Go
#3896 Loop & Chute Stunt Set
#5051 Radio Controlled Hauler
#5054 U.S.A. Starter Set 2
#5055 U.S.A. Builder Set
#5086 Hot Ones 3-Pack with Patch
#5324 Megaforce Desert Strike Set
#5360 U.S.A. Starter Set 1

2019 Sheriff Patrol

1982 6-PACKS
#3757 City Machines
#3756 Hot Ones Machines
#1989 Weekend Machines

2023 Pepsi Challenger

MEGAFORCE SERIES
#5268 Megadestroyer 2
#5269 Megadestroyer 1
#5270 Personnel Carrier
#5271 Megaforce Motorcycle - (Prototype)
#5272 Battle Tank
#5273 Tac-Com
#5324 Desert Strike Set

STEERING RIGS
#3430 Ford LTL Cattle Trailer
#3431 Mack Moving Van
#3432 White Grain Trailer
#3433 Ford LTL Moving Van
#3434 Mack Grain Trailer
#5177 Sand and Gravel Playset
#5178 Oil Refinery Playset

3250 Firebird Funny Car

3251 Sunagon

3252 '35 Classic Caddy

3253 Ford Dump Truck

3254 Construction Crane

3255 Datsun 200SX

3256 Rapid Transit / School Bus

3257 Front Runnin' Fairmont

3258 Aries Wagon

3259 Jeep CJ-7

3260 Land Lord

3261 Mercedes 380 SEL

3281 Peugeot 505

3911 Mercedes 540K

3912 Trash Truck

5158 Taxi

5179 '55 Chevy

5180 P-928

5282 Camaro Z-28

9037 Malibu Grand Pr

1983

The year 1983 was the 15th anniversary for Hot Wheels cars. To celebrate, Mattel issued a reproduction of the 1967 Camaro. The car was produced in metal-flake green and was available as part of a 15th Birthday 3-pack. A special 15th Birthday Belt Buckle was also part of the offer. The Real Rider line was introduced, too, and went on to be one of the most popular lines of Hot Wheels cars. Real rubber tires with Goodyear markings made the cars very attractive. Extras were a line of basic vehicles that were packaged with an extra part that could be attached. Another set of trucks called Truck Co. was introduced, but did not stay in production very long. Shift Kickers were similar to Scorchers but were equipped with a large gear shifter on the back of the vehicle. A group of 21 all-plastic cars called Speed Machines were sold. These cars were re-issues of previous castings, had little or no detailing, and sold for less than a regular Hot Wheels car.

SETS AND ACCESSORIES
#2275 U.S.A. Starter Set 2
#4001 Construction Site Sto & Go
#4061 Spiral Speedway
#4062 Jumpmasters
#4223 Play Settings City Set
#4224 Play Settings Camping Set
#4225 Play Settings Firefighters Set
#4490 Flying Firebird Variable Jump
#5323 Cargo Plane
#5563 Dash & Crash Speedway
#5709 Special 15th Birthday Offer

1983 6-PACKS
#3757 City Gift Pack
#5760 60's Teen Gift Pack
#5849 Competition Gift Pack
#5759 Racer Gift Pack

STEERING RIG CABS
#5668/5671 Kenworth Cab - white/red
#5670/5673 GMC Cab - yellow/silver
#5672/5669 Peterbilt Cab - orange/red
#5674/5677 Ford Cab - light blue/yellow

HOT WHEELS TRUCK CO.
#5953 Auto Hauler with Omni
#5955 Race Car Hauler with Formula Fever
#5956 Auto Hauler with Aries Wagon
#5957 Construction Hauler with Wheel Loader
#5958 Race Car Hauler with P-911
#5959 Construction Hauler with Dump Truck

SHIFT KICKERS
#5826 High Frequency
#5827 Wind Sprinter
#5828 Cookin Capri
#5829 Heat Streaker
#5830 TNT Bird
#5831 Torquin T

SPEED MACHINES
American Victory
Bubble Gunner
Dumpin' A
Hare Splitter
Inside Story
Lowdown
Mustang Stocker
Packin' Pacer
Poison Pinto
Rock Buster
Turbo Wedge
Second Wind
Top Eliminator
Spoiler Sport
Show Hoss II
Spacer Racer
Super Van
T-Totaller
Z Whiz
'Vette Van
Vega Bomb

3289 BMW M1

3287 Fiat Ritmo

3288 Ford Escort

3292 Renault LeCar

3768 Long Shot

3916 Rig Wrecker

3913 '67 Camaro

3917 Pontiac J-2000

3914 Turbo Streak

3918 80's Firebird

3915 Formula Fever

3919 40's Ford 2-Door

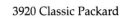

3920 Classic Packard

3923 Classic Cobra

3928 '80s Corvette

3924 Thunder Roller

4017 Peterbilt Dump Truck

3925 '82 Supra

4018 Ford Stake Bed Truck

3927 NASCAR Stocker

4368 Beach Patrol

4370 Jeep Scrambler   Food Service Truck

Airport Security

1984

The popular Real Rider line continued in 1984. A new style of wheels called Ultra Hots was introduced. A special Gold Camaro Z-28 and a chrome 80s Firebird were offered through a mail-in offer. Models produced and sold in Mexico and France started to become available to U.S. collectors as word of these models spread. Not available in stores in the U.S., foreign Hot Wheels featured many different colors and imprints. Crack-Ups were a new line of cars with crash panels and Color Racers changed color with a change in temperature. A line of plastic trains with the Hot Wheels name was available for only a short time and were not very popular with collectors.

SETS AND ACCESSORIES
#7003 Thrill Driver's Corkscrew Set
#7101 Speed Shifter 500
#7226 Cobra Stunt Set
#3464 Showcase Carry Case
#4445 Getaway 12 Car Case
#7001 Racer's Engine Case

1984 4-CAR GIFT PACKS   CRACK-UPS
#7120 Construction Pack   #7065 Crash Patrol
#7121 Military Pack   #7066 Smak Bak
#7122 Collector Series Pack   #7067 Stocker Smasher
#7123 Off Road 4X4 Pack   #7068 Fire Smasher
#7125 City Service Pack   #7070 Sport Crasher
#7127 Racing Series Pack   #7076 Hatch Popper

HOT WHEELS RAILROAD
#2117 Iron Horse Steam Engine Gift Pack
#5590 Santa Fe Locomotive
#5591 Santa Fe Caboose
#5592 Rail Box Boxcar
#5593 Cheesie Locomotive
#5595 Conrail Flatcar
#5758 Freight Yard Sto' N Go
#7113 Freight Master Gift Pack
#7114 Northland Express Gift Pack
#7115 Timberland Express Gift Pack
#7116 Burlington Northern Locomotive
#7117 Burlington Northern Boxcar
#7118 SOO Line Flatcar
#9605 Side Dump Car
#9422 Superrails Station
#9591 Banjo Flats Gift Pack

3290 Rolls-Royce Phantom II

4372 Lightning Gold

5901 Blown Camaro Z-28

4920 Battle Tank

5902 Sol-Aire CX4

4921 Troop Convoy

5903 Dodge Rampage

5900 Thunderbird Stocker

5904 Good Humor Truck

5905 Oshkosh Snow Plow

5906 Phone Truck

5907 Baja Bug

5908 '65 Mustang Convertible

5909 Dream Van XGW

5910 Blazer 4X4

5911 Turbo Heater

7292 Predator

7293 Flame Runner

7296 Wind Splitter

7295 Quik Trik

7299 Speed Seeker

9643 Delivery Van

1985

In 1985 the Hot Wheels line continued to expand. A group of Army vehicles made up the Action Command line. Several 3-packs with an ink stamper featuring special cars from the Real Rider, Hot Ones, and Ultra Hots series were available. Hot Wheels promotions continued as the Kellogg Company offered three special vehicles in a mail-in offer with the purchase of cereal. The Crack-Ups and Color Racer lines expanded with new colors and variations.

SETS
#9176 Dynamite Crossing
#9250 Action Command Sto & Go
#9511 Snake Mountain Challenge

1985 GIFT AND MULTIPACKS
#9255 Crack-Ups Stamper 2-Pack
#9257 Crack-Ups Stamper 2-Pack
#9326 Hot Ones Stamper 3-Pack
#9327 Ultra Hots Stamper 3-Pack
#9328 Real Riders Stamper 3-Pack
#9412 Action Command Battleground Gift Pack
#9416 Ultra Hots 4 Car Gift Pack
#9417 Speed Busters 4 Car Gift Pack

CRACK-UPS
----- Test Vehicle	#7823 Smash Mobile
#7572 Crunch Chief	#7824 Speed Crasher
#7573 Basher	#7827 Super Blaster
#7577 Blind Sider	#9038 Front Ender
#7578 Back Biter	#9155 Hood Basher
#7579 Bang-Up Job	#9329 Sock' N Roll
#7580 Side Banger	#9331 Exploder
#7581 Bumper Thumper	#9333 Ringer
#7582 Top Bopper	#9340 Bash Up
#7821 Smash Hit	

1691 Snake Busters Car

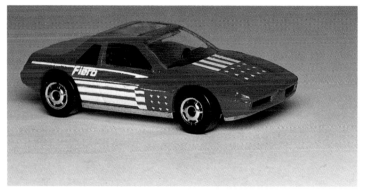

7527 Pontiac Fiero 2M4

7528 Jet Sweep X5

7529 Nissan 300ZX

7530 Tall Ryder

7531 XT-3

7532 Gulch Stepper

9371 Command Tank

9372 Big Bertha

9373 Super Cannon

9374 Tank Gunner

9375 Roll Patrol Jeep

9521 Screamin'

9523 Fat Fendered '40

9531 Mustang S.V.O.

9533 Torino Tornado

9534 Redliner

9538 Street Beast

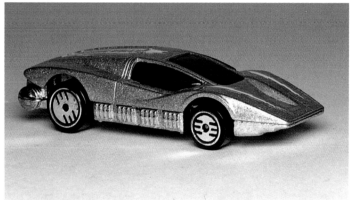

9535 Silver Bullet

9541 Good Ol' Pick-Um-Up

9536 Street Scorcher

9544 **Black** Lightning

9537 Nightstreaker

9545 Thunderstreak

1986

Among the newest member of the Hot Wheels line in 1986 were Speed Demons. These monster-like vehicles came with Ultra Hot Wheels. Four more vehicles made up another promotion with the Kellogg Company. XV Racers were a related line of cars designed for spins and stunts. Flip-Outs had a feature to make the models flip over.

SETS AND ACCESSORIES
#1262 Turbotrax Mach 1
#2137 Super Turbotrax 3000
#2148 Turbotrax
#2159 Turbotrax Straight Trax
#2160 Turbotrax Curved Trax
#2161 Turbotrax Crossroads Trax
#2162 Turbotrax Columns

2057 Double Demon

1986 GIFT AND MULTIPACKS
#1156 Classic 5 Car Gift Pack
#1158 Ultra Hots 5 Car Gift Pack
#1159 Racers 5 Car Gift Pack
#1161 Super Sportscar 5 Car Gift Pack
#2817 Smash & Tow Gift Pack
#2848 Real Rider Off Road 4X4
#2849 Racers

2058 Cargoyle

FLIP-OUTS
#2280 Road Flipper
#2281 Flipper Snapper
#2283 Vaultin' Van
#2284 Capsider
#2286 Flipbuster
#2287 Fliproarin'
#2289 Flippin Frenzy
#2290 Drag Flip

2059 Fangster

XV RACERS
#2564 Ultimator
#2565 Mach 7
#2566 Proformer
#2567 Gyracer
#2568 Ultra-Sonix
#2569 Hyper Twister
#2570 Stunt Racer
#2571 Speed Spinner

2060 Vampyra

2061 Turboa

2520 Race Ace

2062 Eevil Weevil

2522 Stock Rocket

2518 Shell Shocker

2534 Path Beater

2519 Combat Medic

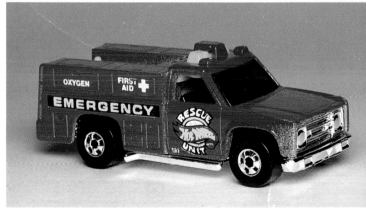

2537 Rescue Ranger

2538 Power Plower

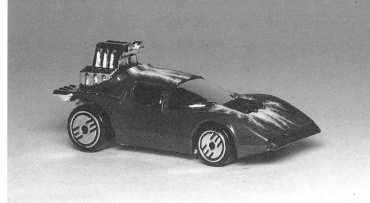

2544 Back Burner

1987

By 1987 Mattel discontinued the Real Rider line of cars. The original Real Riders had grey wheels, but before production ended, many cars were available with white rims. These tires were more expensive to produce and collectors were disappointed when the decision was made to discontinue the wheel style. XV Racers and Crack-Ups had new additions in 1987. Stunt-Ratz were off road vehicles with gyro-type motors. Hyper Cycles, a set of motorcycles, also featured gyro-type motors.

SETS AND ACCESSORIES
#1142 Fix & Fill Center Sto & Go
#1673 CarGo Carrier
#2063 Leapin' Demons Chase Set
#3051 Speed Trigger
#3243 Turbotrax Turboglo Jump Set
#3342 Car Wash & Service Station Sto & Go
#9980 Turbotrax Turbo Drive Power Booster

MULTIPACKS
#2164 Body Swappers Pack

XV RACERS
#1653 Excelerator
#1654 Velocitor
#2802 XV Challenger Set

CRACK-UPS
#1730 Wreckin' Rig
#1731 Deformula
#1802 Cab Cruncher
#1803 Indentor

STUNT-RATZ
#3006 Desert Rat
#3007 Sand Runner
#3008 Scatterat
#3009 Dirt Rat
#3010 Road Rat
#3011 Off Rodent
#3017 Rat-A-Pult - (accessory)

HYPER CYCLES
#4157 Dirt Rover
#4158 Moto-Crossed
#4159 Street Wheeler
#4160 Street Feat
#3771 Stunt Drome Thrill Set

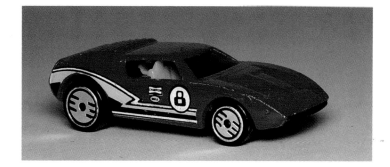

1500 Road Torch

1456 Thunderburner

1897 Ferrari Testarossa

3209 Suzuki Quadracer

3716 Monster 'Vette

3286 Sharkruiser

3851 Phantomachine

3338 Assault Crawler

3852 Zombot

3715 CAT Earth Mover

3853 CAT Road Roller

4059 Tail Gunner

1988

Production of Hot Wheels was moved from Hong Kong to Malaysia in 1988. This year was also the 20th anniversary of Hot Wheels. Special gold and silver chrome cars cast with a 20th anniversary logo were produced. These cars were sold in 3-packs with two regular cars.

SETS AND ACCESSORIES
#4451 Alpine Mountain Adventure Sto & Go
#4513 Dinosaur Mud Pit Set
#5190 Sight & Smash Booster Set
#5463 Building Site Sto & Go
#5464 Mini-Market Sto & Go
#5465 Drive & Eat Sto & Go

20TH ANNIVERSARY 3-PACKS
(gold or gold chrome cars)
#4590 with Firebird Funny Car
#4591 with Firebird Funny Car
#4592 with Ferrari Testarossa
#4594 with Ferrari Testarossa

4384 Lamborghini Countach

4292 Nissan Hardbody

4389 Rodzilla

#4600 with Tall Ryder
#4601 with Tall Ryder
#4602 with Mercedes 540K
#4603 with Mercedes 540K
#4604 with Monster Vette
#4605 with Monster Vette
#4606 with Combat Medic
#4607 with Combat Medic

MULTIPACKS
#1629 Classics 5 Car Gift Pack
#1631 Racers 5 Car Gift Pack
#1634 Super Sportcar 5 Car Gift Pack
#3870 Action Command Gift Pack
#3871 Workhorses Gift Pack
#3872 Trailbusters Gift Pack

61

4631 Porsche 959

4699 Shadow Jet

4741 Talbot Lago

5026 Alien

5022 Radar Ranger

5025 Sting Rod

5027 Flame Stopper

5028 Ratmobile

9380 Rocketank

1989

In 1989 Mattel issued a new collector's handbook. As of this writing, it is the last catalog of this type. The new Park'n Plates series featured regular Hot Wheels cars packaged with a small plastic display case. Micro Park'n Plates and Micro Color Racers were miniature versions of the regular series. A set of four cars was produced for a promotion with Getty Oil Co. In this fall promotion, the special Hot Wheels cars were given to consumers of gasoline at Getty Gas Stations.

SETS AND ACCESSORIES
#1684 G-Force Stunt Set
#1673 Cargo Carrier
#1903 Emergency Station Sto & Go
#2642 Sprint & Spin Speed Trigger
#2683 Fire Fighter Sto & Go
#2756 Pop n' Play School House
#2757 Pop n' Play Construction Co.
#2759 Pop n' Play Police Station
#3254 Double Barrel Stunt Set
#3277 Light Speeders Racing Set
#3495 Hot Wheels Track Pak
#3496 Hot Wheels Loop Pak
#3497 Hot Wheels Launch Pak
#3498 Hot Wheels Curve Pak
#3464 Showcase Carry Case
#5790 Color Racers Auto Paint Factory

MULTIPACKS
#3268 Emergency 5 Car Gift Pack

1468 Ferrari F40

MICRO PARK 'N PLATES
#9717 Camaro
#9783 Blazer
#9785 '57 Chevy
#9786 Baja Bug
#9803 Cobra
#9773 Countach
#9774 Corvette
#9778 Ferrari
#9782 Iroc Z
#9784 Stingray
#9787 Firebird
#9789 Mustang

1469 Peugeot 205 Rallye

MICRO COLOR RACERS 4-PACKS / SETS
#3226 Race Pack
#3227 Street Pack
#3228 Off Road Pack
#3229 Classic Pack
#3601 Speed Blaster
#3989 Highway Hauler Transport
#3994 Loop 'n Splash Set

CHROME MICRO RACERS
#4975 Vette Pack
#4982 Collection I
#4983 Collection II
#4984 Collection III

MICRO RACE 'N SHOW PLAY PACKS
#9804 Corner Spin Out
#9806 Finish Line
#9807 Pit Stop
#9808 Repair Garage
#9809 Gas Station
#9811 Drive-In Burger Joint

1470 Street Roader

1792 Ambulance

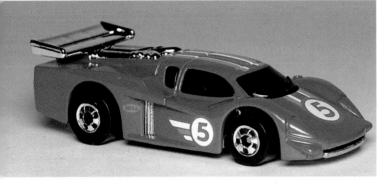

1789 GT Racer

1795 School Bus

1790 Big Rig

1791 Chevy Stocker

1796 Pontiac Banshe

2808 Delivery Van

7672 '32 Ford Delivery

7670 Custom Corvette

7671 VW Bug

7673 T-Bucket

1990

Mattel issued several cars as part of an international line in 1990. These cars, issued in special packaging, were not available in the United States. California Customs featured bright colors, imprints, and special custom wheels. A collector's button was also issued with each California Custom car. A line of unique vehicles based on the animated television show The Simpsons was produced. A promotion with Ralston Purina featured Hot Wheels Cereal and several unique cars. A special Hot Wheels car was included in each box of cereal. A Ziplock Thunderstreak was available through a mail-in promotion. Cadbury Schweppes had an offer available in Europe which included two Cadbury Hot Wheels cars. The Getty Oil promotion continued in the fall of 1990, as four more cars with Getty imprints were produced.

SETS AND ACCESSORIES
 #2758 Pop 'n Play Drive-In-Bank
 #4980 California Custom Freeway
 #5469 Mini Market Sto & Go - (Getty Promo)
 #7554 Custom Car Center
 #9093 Wildwave Stunt
 #9938 Round-Up Ranch Sto & Go

MULTIPACKS
 #3871 Construction Crew 5 Car Gift Pack
 #3872 Trailbusters 5 Car Gift Pack

2099 Minitruck

2102 Corvette Funny Car

2104 Firebird

2173 Passion

4005 Fire Chief

7608 Probe Funny Car

7609 Nissan 300ZX

9112 Propper Chopper

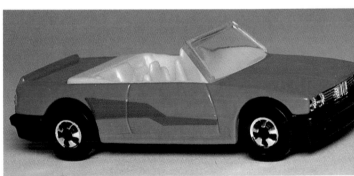

9726 BMW 323

9738 Range Rover

1991

Only 23 years after their introduction, the one billionth Hot Wheels vehicle was produced by Mattel in 1991. To commemorate this achievement, 4 gold-plated corvettes were available with special trophy display stands. Promotions involving Hot Wheels were in full gear. Special vehicles were produced for McDonald's, Kool-Aid, Chuck E. Cheese, Eco-Lab, Claforan, Getty, Wal-Mart, and Rose's Department Stores. Hot Wheels cartoon videos, packaged with a special car, were available at select stores. The Park n' Plates series was discontinued and California Customs were replaced with a line called Super Cal Customs. Convertables changed shape and color with a change in temperature.

2920 Mazda MX-5 Miata

SETS AND ACCESSORIES
 #2680 Dash 'N Crash
 #2756 Starter City School
 #2758 Starter City Police Station
 #3285 Wal-Mart Playset
 #7493 Jumpbuster Stunt Set
 #7552 Starter City Bank
 #9511 Starter City Hospital
 #9512 Starter City Burger Stand
 #9515 Starter City Mini Market
 #9568 City Wash 'n Wax
 #9576 City Highway Builder
 #9577 City Airport
 #9578 City Race Center
 #9579 City Construction Co.
 #9650 Turbo Tube Raceway

MULTIPACKS
 #7456 Funny Car Gift Pack

BILLIONTH CAR COLLECTION
 '63 Split Window Corvette
 '68 Corvette Stingray
 '80's Corvette Hardtop
 Custom Corvette Convertible

CONVERTABLES
 #3935 Fab Cab
 #3936 Crunch Chief
 #3938 Pick-Up Trick
 #3941 Shift Kicker
 #3942 Vary Cool
 #3944 Engine-Air
 #3945 Double Duty
 #3946 Shiftin' 50's

2097 '59 Caddy

4695 Ford Aerostar

5343 Ramp Truck

5348 Surf Patrol

5665 Ferrari 250

5636 Trailbuster

5637 Street Beast

5666 Ferrari 348

5638 Limozeen

5640 Speed Shark

5667 BMW 85

5669 Toyota MR2 Rally

5674 Zender Fact 4

5670 Peugeot 405

7607 Porsche 930

5672 Lamborghini Diablo

9258 Buick Stocker

5673 Mercedes-Benz Unimog

9557 VW Golf

9713 Holden Commodore

9749 Renault 5 Turbo

9770 Mercedes Benz SL

1992

The Gleam Team, a new series of cars featuring metallic paint hit the market in 1992. Pro Circuit cars were introduced and were very popular with collectors because they were very detailed and were based on actual race cars. This line of cars was manufactured in China and each car came with a numbered trading card. A unique Mall 2 Pack which contained special Hot Wheels was given away at some shopping malls during the Christmas seasons. This was the last year of the Getty / Hot Wheels promotions.

SETS AND ACCESSORIES
#2114 Pro Circuit Speedway Set
#5736 Quick-Fire Crash Curve

PRO-CIRCUIT CARS
#2115 Jack Baldwin Chevrolet Camaro
#2565 Mark Martin Thunderbird Stock Car
#2567 Brett Bodine Thunderbird Stock Car
#2568 Morgan Shepherd Thunderbird Stock Car
#2623 Richard Petty Pontiac Stock Car
#2628 Kyle Petty Pontiac Stock Car
#2630 Rusty Wallace Pontiac Stock Car
#2638 Michael Andretti Ford Lola Indy Car
#2677 Mario Andretti Ford Lola Indy Car
#2690 Al Unser Jr. Chevrolet Indy Car
#2692 Rick Mears Penske Chevrolet
#2692 Emerson Fittipaldi Penske Chevrolet
#2696 Roberto Guerrero Lola Indy Car
#2738 Scott Sharp Chevrolet Camaro
#2739 Greg Pickett Chevrolet Camaro
#2743 John Force Oldsmobile Funny Car
#2841 Kenny Berstein Buick Funny Car

773 Hummer

1384 Goodyear Blimp

1781 Aeroflash

2029 '56 Flashsider

2076 Tank Truck

2073 Recycling Truck

3021 1993 Camaro

2074 Oshkosh Cement Mixer

3156 Flashfire

2075 Tractor

3164 Shock Factor

3765 Bulldozer

3782 Hiway Hauler

5675 Chevy Lumina

1993

1993 marked the 25th Anniversary of Mattel's Hot Wheels vehicles. To celebrate, eight replica cars were produced and marketed, like the originals, in blisterpacks with plastic collector buttons. Six of the cars were available in twelve different spectraflame colors. Each car had the famous red stripe on the tires and the 25th Anniversary logo cast on the base. The cars in this series retailed for about $2.00 and were extremely popular with collectors. The Revealers line was unique as the cars were wrapped in paper bags numbered 1 through 12 then sealed in blisterpacks. The cars were available in 3 different bright color variations and consumers did not know which car they had until after purchase. Lucky collectors could find a special token wrapped with the car which would be redeemed for a special set of Revealers or a Hot Wheels bike and a special gold-plated Lamborghini Countach. Tattoo Machines were vehicles made in China with unusual colors and imprints and were sold with matching stick-on tattoos. A line of vehicles based on the motion picture "Demolition Man" were available for a short time during the year. The Color FX series featured cars that changed color with temperature. In 1993 The Museum of American Heritage in Palo Alto, California had a complete collection of Hot Wheels on display and a special model was produced for this event. Hot Wheels promotions in 1993 included four cars for Shell Gas Stations, a group of cars as part of an Aqua Fresh Toothpaste promotion, a new Chuck E. Cheese vehicle, several Kool-Aid models, and a set of cars for McDonalds.

MISCELLANEOUS HOT WHEELS ITEMS
#1864 G Force Set
#2585 Engine Car Case
#3254 Double Barrel Set
#7904 Crashpile
#7976 Criss Cross Crash Set
#8180 Mighty Rigs -
   (Champion Hauler or Shell Tanker)

25TH ANNIVERSARY PACKS
Ford 5 Pack
Chevy 5 Pack
Dream Car 5 Pack
Exotic Racers 5 Pack
All American 16 Car Set

TATTOO MACHINES
#3479 Spiderider
#3488 Dragon Wagon
#3489 Road Pirate
#3490 Open Wide
#3491 Street Beast
#3492 Skull rider
#3493 Eye-Gor
#3494 Hot Wheels
#3501 Street Dog
#3502 Bus Boys
#3510 Light Storm
#3527 Ammo

DEMOLITION MAN
#11082 Olds 442
#11083 Ultralite Police Car
#11084 GM Lean Machine
#11085 Corvette Sting Ray III
#11086 Oldsmobile Aurora
#11087 Pontiac Salsa
#11088 Pontiac Banshee
#11089 Buick Wildcat
#11090 Chevrolet ACC Camaro

COLOR FX - 2 PACKS
#11042 Hummer / Big Bertha
#11043 Command Tank / Roll Patrol
#11044 Camaro Racer / GT Racer
#11045 T-Bird / Funny Car
#11046 Baja Bug / Aeroflash
#11047 Vampyra / Ferrari Testarossa
#11048 Tanker / Camaro
#11049 Hiway Hauler / Lamborghini Countach

COLOR FX SETS
#11388 Paintworks
#11889 Loop and Splash

1993 McDONALDS CARS
(these cars were not manufactured by Mattel)
T-Bird Stocker, Quaker State
T-Bird Stocker, McDonalds
1993 Camaro, Duracell
1993 Camaro, Hot Wheels
Dragster, Hot Wheels
Dragster, McDonalds
Funny Car, Hot Wheels
Funny Car, McDonalds

3035 Treadator

3036 Pipe Jammer

1691 Gleamer Patrol

3050 Vector "Avtech" WX-3

3026 Jaguar XJ 220

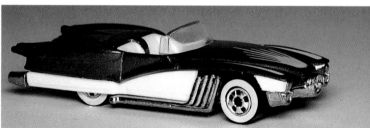

4312 Swingfire

3029 Oscar Mayer Wienermobile

5623 Lexus SC400

73

1994

The 25th Anniversary series name was changed to the Vintage Collection in 1994 and six more models were added to the line. Many color variations were introduced and two of the more popular models included the Custom Mustang and S'Cool Bus. Information about the models and colors available in the 25th Anniversary and Vintage lines can be found in the variation guide. Several new Color FX cars were introduced. Once again Hot Wheels promotions were very popular in 1994 with participation by the following products and companies: Kinkos, Spam, Tony's Pizza, Kraft, Malt-O-Meal, Dinty Moore, Little Debbie, Unocal, Gulf Oil, Shell Oil, and McDonalds. A special World Cup Soccer 5 Pack was available to celebrate the worldwide tournament. A special promotion with FAO Schwarz was available for a very limited time and was extremely popular with collectors. A new line of futuristic racers called Top Speed was available late in the year. Many new models and colors of the regular line were introduced late in the year. A new wheel called Gold Medal Speed was available on some cars. A special Snake and Mongoose set was produced to celebrate the popularity of the original Series.

Collectors can only guess what the coming years will bring to the Hot Wheels line but based on current popularity they can look forward to many new models and unique variations. The hobby will continue to grow as more collectors become involved in searching for the special Hot Wheels vehicle to add to their collection.

MISC HOT WHEELS ITEMS
#11592 Power Loop Set
#11644 Mongoose and Snake Drag Race Set
#65355 Duracell Racing Team Truck and Car
#65602 Sto & Go City Playset
#65603 Sto & Go Parking and Service Garage
#65606 Sto & Go Drag Race Case and Playset
#65669 Super Rally Case
FAO Schwarz 16 Car Set (only 3000 sets produced)

5-PACKS
#1629 Classic Collection
#1631 Racing Team
#3870 Emergency Squad
#3871 Construction Crew
#3872 Off Road Explorers
#11363 Speed Demons
#11364 Blimp and Support Team
#11365 Action Command
World Cup Gift Pack

COLOR FX 2 - PACKS
#12110 Swarmula 1 / Double Demon
#12111 Sting Rod / Off Roadent
#12112 Octo Blimp / Shark Teeth
#12113 Grim Creeper / Skin Shedder
#12115 Killer Copter / Evil Weevil
#12116 Arachnorod / Cargoyle

TOP SPEED 2-PACKS
#12081 Corkscrew / Sting Shot
#12082 Road Vac / Shock Rod
#12511 Road Vac / Shock Rod

TOP SPEED SETS
#12203 Ultra Pipe Fight Set
#12262 Triple Threat Set

1994 McDONALDS CARS
(these cars were not manufactured by Mattel)

Turbine 4-2	2 Cool
X2IJ Cruiser	Gas Hog
Bold Eagle	Black Cat
Flame Rider	Stocker

5200 Avus Quatro

5205 Viper

74

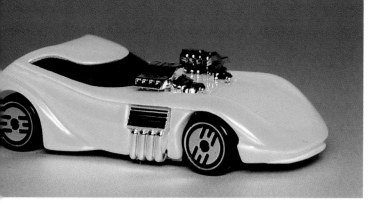

5206 Twin Mill II

5267 Silhouette II

12341 Fuji Blimp

11846 No Fear Race Car

11847 Driven To The Max Dragster

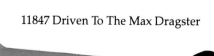

11848 Shadow Jet II

11849 Rigor-Motor

11850 Splittin' Image II

12352 Lumina Minivan

12354 Cyber Cruiser

12356 Mean Green Passion

12360 Olds 442 - W30

12358 Oldsmobile Aurora

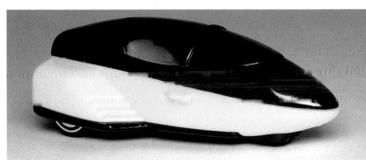

12361 GM Lean Machine

25TH ANNIVERSARY / VINTAGE SERIES

5700 Red Baron - royal blue

5708 Splittin' Image - pink

5709 Twinmill - emerald green

5707 Paddy Wagon - sea green

5714 Beatnik
Bandit - mint

5715 Silhouette - mauve

10496 Mustang - brown

5730 The Demon - violet

10497 Snake - lime

5743 Nomad - metallic dark green

10783 Mongoose - orange

10494 Ford Vicky - magenta

10495 Deora - metallic blue

11522 S'Cool Bus - gold

11523 Whip Creamer - green

Snake - 1994 Drag Race Set

11524 Mutt Mobile - red

Mongoose - 1994 Drag Race Set

PACKAGED CARS

2855 Space Vehicle, 1984

2594 Highway Heat, 1986

2850 Incredible Hulk
(Scene Machines), 1979

4703 Cargo Lift, 1983

3291 Double Deck Bus, 1983

Fireball Torino, 1983

2528 Poppa Vette, 1986

Grand Prix Series Package

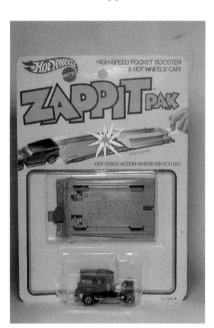

Zappit Pak

1969 Package

The Heavyweights Package

The Spoilers Package

1970 Jack in the Box Promo

1973 Shell Promo - Ferra

1973 Shell Promo - Strip Teaser

1973 Shell Promo - Swingin' Wing

1973 Shell Promo - Twinmill

1973 Shell Promo - Short Order

1976 Herfy's Promo in package

1976 Herfy's Promo

1976 Toys R Us Promo
- Geoffrey's Van

1979 Toys R Us Promo
- Geoffrey's Pickup

1982 Toys R Us Promo - Geoffrey's Bronco

1985 Kelloggs Promos

1986 Kelloggs Promos

1994 Unocal Promo

1994 Kraft Promo

1992 Mall 2-Pack Promo

1993 Chuck E. Cheese's Pizza Promo

1993 Kool-Aid 2-Pack Promo

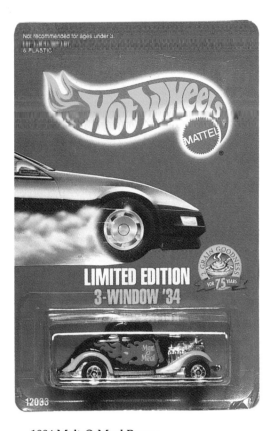

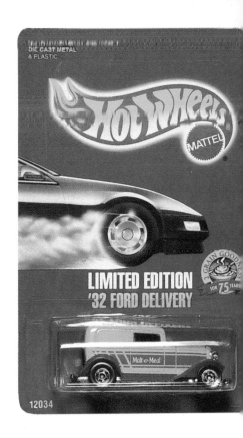

1994 Malt-O-Meal Promo

1994 Little Debbie Promo

1994 Malt-O-Meal Promo

1989 Getty Promo

1990 Getty Promo

1991 Getty Promo

1992 Getty Promo

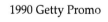

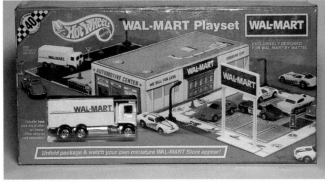

Wal-Mart Promo

1993 Shell Promo

LIMITED EDITION

Tim Flock - 55 Chevy

Elmo Langley Race Car

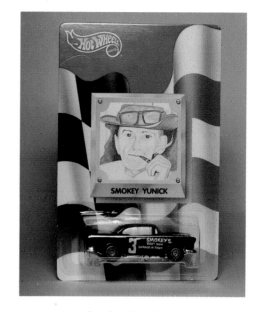

Smokey Yunick

Smokey Yunick

Fireball Roberts - '57 Chevy

'32 Ford Delivery - "Early Times - Temecula"

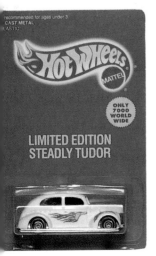

Steadly
Tudor

Old Number 5

Limited Edition
Stock Car

'55 Candy Apple Chevy

'56 Flashsider - "1993 Greater Seattle Toy Show"

Ruby Red Passion

Limited Edition - 40's Woodie

Hot Pink Passion

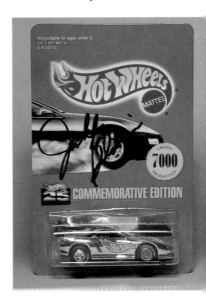

Limited Edition 1993 Camaro

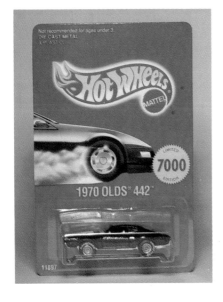

1970 Olds 442 -
"1994 Greater Seattle Toy Show"

Limited Edition - Nomad - white sidewalls

Limited Edition - Nomad - rubber ti

Limited Edition -
Golden '59 Caddy

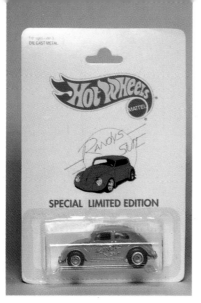

Limited Edition Randy's Stuff Bug

1994 Seatle Toy Show Car

Limited Edition Fat
Fendered '40

MISCELLANEOUS

3256 Rapid Transit - rear window variations

80's Firedbird Camaro Z-28 1984 mail-in offer

3209 Suzuki QuadRacer - pre-production colors

2014 Hot Bird - color variations

3927 NASCAR Stocker - 3 color variations

6219 Hot Heap - U.S.A. and Hong Kong

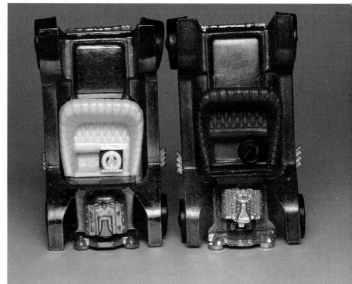

5270 MegaForce Personnel Carrier

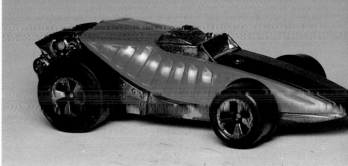

Fat Daddy Sizzler - 4944 Needle Nose

Steering Rigs - 1920 GMC Van

Fat Daddy Sizzler - 4947 Red Baron

Steering Rigs - 3420 Ford LTL Cattle Trailer

Fat Daddy Sizzler - 4943 Fire Works

Steering Rigs - 3432 White Grain Trailer

Fat Daddy Sizzler - 4946 Hiway Hauler

Steering Rigs - 1915 Kenworth Van

Fat Daddy Sizzler - 4948 Law Mill

Steering Rigs - 1918 Kenworth Tanker

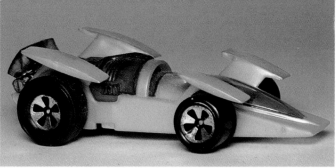

Fat Daddy Sizzler - 4945 Ram Rocket

Steering Rigs - 3433 Ford LTL Moving Van

1970 Sizzlers - Hot Head

Steering Rigs - 3434 Mack Citrus Trailer

1971 Sizzlers - 6526 Backfire

Steering Rigs - 3431 Mack Moving Van

1971 Sizzlers - #6520 Spoil Sport

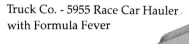

Steering Rigs - 1919 Peterbilt Hauler

1971 Sizzlers - 6532 Indy Eagle

Truck Co. - 5955 Race Car Hauler
with Formula Fever

Steering Rigs - 1917 GMC Hauler

Steering Rigs - 1916 Peterbilt Tanker

Steering Rigs - 3435 White Cattle Trailer

Gran Toros - #6603 T'rantula

Dragsters - Drag Strip Duel Set

Scorcher

1971 Sizzlers - 5884 Up Roar

1972 Sizzlers - 6538 Ferrari 512s

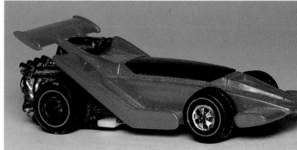

1971 Sizzlers

RRRumbler 6011 Hi-Tailer

Crack-Ups Crash Test Vehicle

Hot Wheels Watch

Hot Wheels Stop Watch

Real Rider 3-Pack with stamper

Hot Shots - #5876 Purple Rage

15th Birthday 3-Pack

Ultra Hots 3-Pack with stamper

1981 Collector's Book 3-Pack

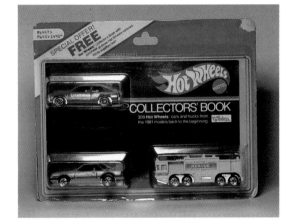

Speed Machines - Mustang Stocker

Revers - #6988 Haulin' Horses

Hot Ones 3-Pack with stamper

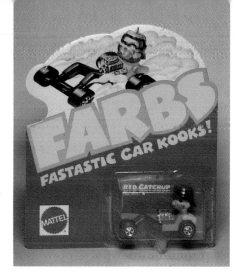

Farbs - #5853 Red Catchup

SPAWN Comic Car

20th Anniversary 3-Pack

Gold Passion 1992 Toy Fair

Prototype - T-Bird Stocker

Rare - Fuji Race Car

Mattel Toy Club Car

Museum of American Heritage Cadillac

Gold Lamborghini - Revealers Prize

1994 Hot Wheels Convention C

Gold P-911 (given to top Mattel salespeop
in 1975)

1994 Toy Fair Car

90

Rare T-Bird Stocker

Pink Spoiler Sport - Mexico

Micro Color Racers

Pontiac J-2000 - Mexico

Datsun 200 SX - Canada

Pro Circuit

California Customs

Convertables

The Simpsons

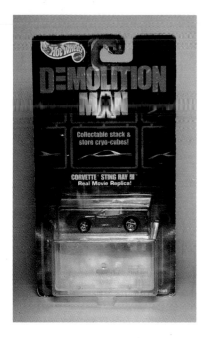

Demolition Man

Stunt Ratz

Flip-Outs

X-V Racers

Super California Customs

Hot Wheels Video with car

Classic Collection 5-Pack

Park'n Plates

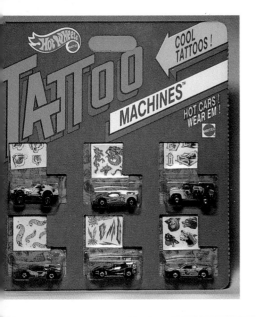

Tattoo Machines

City Burger Stand

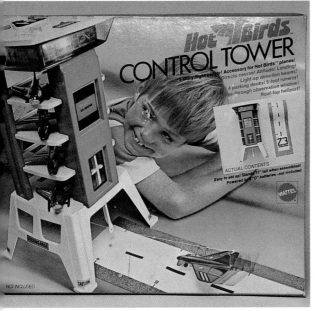

Hot Birds
Control Tower

Scorchers

Gran Toros

Chopcycles

1994 Mongoose and Snake Drag Race Set

Accessory Pak - Jump Ramp

Pop-Up House and Car Port

Accessory -
Super Charger

Rally Case

Billionth Car Trophy Display Stand

HOT WHEELS VARIATION GUIDE

1968-1972

Spectraflame paint colors were used on most of the Hot Wheels cars produced between 1968-1972. There are 21 recognized shades of colors which are listed below. Not all of the colors were used at the same time and not all were used on all cars. Some models were produced in enamel colors.

There are six interior color variations including: black, grey, brown, blue, red, and white. There are interior shade variations which vary from year to year. Not all interior colors were available on all cars.

All of the vehicles produced between 1968 and 1972 were manufactured in the U.S.A. or Hong Kong. All of the U.S.A. vehicles have clear windows. All of the Hong Kong vehicles have blue tinted windows. In most cases when a model was produced in both countries there are minor casting variations.

There are four different types of red stripe wheels which vary from car to car.

1968 - 1972 Spectraflame Colors

Metallic Orange
Metallic Green
Metallic Lime Green
Metallic Olive Green
Metallic Emerald Green
Metallic Red
Metallic Rose Red
Metallic Pale Brown
Metallic Dark Brown
Metallic Purple
Metallic Magenta
Metallic Pink
Metallic Hot Pink
Metallic Salmon Pink
Metallic Yellow
Metallic Lime Yellow
Metallic Gold
Metallic Blue
Metallic Pale Blue
Metallic Ice Blue
Metallic Aqua

1968
MODEL#

6205 Custom Cougar, $60
Hood opens. Available with or without black painted roof. U.S.A. has dashboard; Hong Kong has no dashboard.

6206 Custom Mustang, $60
hood opens. Available with or without louvered rear window. Some Hong Kong versions have open hood scoop. U.S.A.: small steering wheel; Hong Kong: large steering wheel.

6207 Custom T-Bird, $50
Hood opens. Available with or without black painted roof. U.S.A. has dashboard; Hong Kong has no dashboard.

6208 Custom Camaro, $60
Hood opens. Available with or without black painted roof. U.S.A.: small steering wheel; Hong Kong: large steering wheel. Also available in white enamel.

6209 Silhouette, $20
U.S.A.: small steering wheel; Hong Kong: large steering wheel

6210 Deora, $50.00
U.S.A. has dashboard; Hong Kong has no dashboard.

6211 Custom Barracuda, $60.
Hood opens. U.S.A.: small steering wheel; Hong Kong: large steering wheel

6212 Custom Firebird, $45.00
Hood opens. U.S.A.: small steering wheel; Hong Kong: large steering wheel

6213 Custom Fleetside, $45
U.S.A.: small steering wheel; Hong Kong: large steering wheel

6214 Ford J-Car, $20.00
Rear hood opens. U.S.A.: small steering wheel (also available in white enamel); Hong Kong: large steering wheel (only in white enamel).

6215 Custom Corvette, $50.00
Hood opens. U.S.A.: small steering wheel; Hong Kong: large steering wheel

6216 Python, $25.00
U.S.A. has dashboard; Hong Kong: no dashboard. Cheetah was original name.

6217 Beatnik Bandit, $20
U.S.A.: steering rod; Hong Kong: large steering wheel.

6218 Custom Eldorado, $45.00
Hood opens. U.S.A.: small steering wheel; Hong Kong: large steering wheel

6219 Hot Heap, $25.00
U.S.A.: small steering wheel; Hong Kong: large steering wheel

6220 Custom Volkswagen, $40.00
Opening sun roof. U.S.A has dashboard; Hong Kong has no dashboard. Some Hong Kong have no sun roof. Also available in white enamel and magenta enamel.

1969

6250 Classic '32 Ford Vicky, $30.00
Available with smooth or rough roof. U.S.A. only.

6251 Classic '31 Ford Woody, $30
Available with smooth or rough roof. U.S.A. only.

6252 Classic '57 T-Bird, $30
Hood opens. U.S.A. only

6253 Classic '36 Ford Coupe, $25.00
Opening rumble seat. U.S.A. only.

6254 Lola GT70 (Gr. Prix Se), $20
Rear hood opens. U.S.A. and Hong Kong. Also available in dark green enamel.

6255 McLaren M6A (Gr.Prix Ser.), $25
Rear hood opens. U.S.A. and Hong Kong. Also available in orange enamel.

6256 Chaparral 2G (Gr. Prix Ser.), $30
Rear hood opens. U.S.A. and Hong Kong. Also available in white enamel.

6257 Ford Mark IV (Gr. Prix Ser.), $20
Rear hood opens. U.S.A. and Hong Kong. Also available in red enamel.

6258 Twinmill, $20
U.S.A. only.

6259 Turbofire, $20
Rear hood opens. U.S.A. only.

6260 Torero, $25.00
Hood opens. U.S.A. only.

6261 Splittin' Image, $25
U.S.A. only.

6262 Lotus Turbine (Grand Prix Series), $20.00
Hong Kong only.

6263 Indy Eagle (Grand Prix Series), $20.00
Hong Kong Only. Also available in gold chrome.

6264 Brabham-Repco F1 (Grand Prix Series), $20.00
Hong Kong only. Also available in dark green enamel.

6265 Shelby Turbine (Grand Prix Series), $20.00
Hong Kong only.

6266 Custom Continental Mark III, $30
Hood opens. U.S.A. only.

6267 Custom AMX, $45.00
Hood opens. U.S.A. only.

6268 Custom Charger, $60
Hood opens. U.S.A. only.

6269 Custom Police Cruiser, $50
Available with opaque or transparent red dome light. U.S.A. only. Available in white only.

6274 Volkswagen Beach Bomb, $45
Most models have side mounted surfboards. Very rare models have surfboards through the rear window. Hong Kong only.

6275 Mercedes-Benz 280SL, $30
Hood opens. Available with or without black painted roof. Hong Kong only.

6276 Rolls-Royce Silver Shadow, $40
Hood opens. Available with or without black painted roof. Hong Kong only. Also available in grey enamel.

6277 Maserati Mistral, $45
Hood opens. Available with or without black painted roof. Hong Kong only.

1970

6400 Red Baron, $20
Hong Kong only. Available in red only.

6401 The Demon, $25
Hong Kong only.

6402 Paddy Wagon, $20
Police in silver or gold. U.S.A. only. Available in dark blue only.

6403 Sand Crab, $25
U.S.A. only.

6404 Classic Nomad, $45
Hood opens. U.S.A. only.

6405 Nitty Gritty Kitty (The Spoilers), $45
Available with 1 to 9 on doors. Hong Kong only.

6407 TNT-Bird (The Spoilers), $45
Available with 1 to 9 on doors. Hong Kong only.

6408 Heavy Chevy (The Spoilers), $45
Available with 1 to 9 on doors. Hong Kong only. #6189 - chrome - only in club kit.

6409 Snake, $75
U.S.A. and Hong Kong. Available in yellow only.

6410 Mongoose, $75
U.S.A. and Hong Kong. Available in red only.

6411 King Kuda (The Spoilers), $45
Available with 1 to 9 on doors. Hong Kong only. #6190 - chrome - only in club kit.

6412 Light My Firebird (The Spoilers), $45
Available with 1 to 9 on doors. Hong Kong only.

6413 Seasider, $60
Plastic boat - red top white bottom or white bottom red top. U.S.A. only.

6414 Mighty Maverick, $50
Hood opens. Available with white or black stripes. U.S.A.: thick stripe on roof; Hong Kong: thin stripe on roof.

6416 Porsche 917 (Grand Prix Series), $40
Rear hood opens. U.S.A. and Hong Kong. Also available in grey enamel.

6417 Ferrari 312P (Grand Prix Series), $35
Rear hood opens. U.S.A. and Hong Kong. Also available in red enamel.

6419 Peepin' Bomb, $25
Available with silver or chrome headlights. U.S.A. only.

6420 Carabo, $30
Doors open. U.S.A. and Hong Kong.

6421 "Jack Rabbit Special", $20
U.S.A. only. Available in white enamel only.

6422 Swingin' Wing, $25
U.S.A. and Hong Kong.

6423 Mantis, $25
U.S.A. and Hong Kong.

6424 Tri Baby, $30
U.S.A. and Hong Kong.

6436 Sky Show Fleetside, $500
U.S.A. only. Also same # Sky Show Deora.

6450 Tow Truck (The Heavyweights), $30
Hong Kong only.

6451 Ambulance (The Heavyweights), $45
Hong Kong only. Also available in white enamel.

6452 Cement Mixer (The Heavyweights), $30
Available with brown or orange truck bed. Hong Kong only. Also available in white enamel.

6453 Dump Truck (The Heavyweights), $30
Available with brown or orange truck bed. Available with yellow or orange dumper. Hong Kong only.

6454 Fire Engine (The Heavyweights), $45
Hong Kong only. Available in red and red enamel only.

6455 Moving Van (The Heavyweights), $40
Available with white or grey trailer with smooth or ridged doors. Hong Kong only.

6456 Mod Quad, $25
Canopy opens. U.S.A. and Hong Kong.

6457 Whip Creamer, $25
U.S.A. and Hong Kong.

6459 Power Pad, $35
U.S.A. only.
6469 Fire Chief Cruiser, $25
U.S.A. only. Available in red or
dark red only.
6499 Boss Hoss (The Spoilers), $15
Available with 1 to 9 on doors.
Hong Kong Only. Available in
chrome only - only in club kit.

1971.

5178 Bugeye, $40
U.S.A. and Hong Kong.
5951 Snake Dragster, $100
U.S.A. only. Black rear wheels;
available with clear or black
front wheels. Available in white
enamel only.
5952 Mongoose Dragster, $100
U.S.A. only. Black rear wheels;
available with clear or black
front wheels. Available in metallic blue only.
5953 Snake 2, $150
U.S.A. and Hong Kong. Available in white enamel only.
5954 Mongoose 2, $150
U.S.A. and Hong Kong. Avail-

able in metallic blue only.
6000 Noodle Head, $50
Hood opens. U.S.A. and Hong
Kong.
6001 What-4, $75
Hong Kong only.
6003 Six Shooter, $60
Hong Kong only.
6006 Special Delivery, $60
Hong Kong only. Available in
metallic blue and metallic light
blue only.
6018 Fuel Tanker (The Heavyweights), $60
Hong Kong only. Available in
white enamel only.
6019 Team Trailer (The Heavyweights), $75
Hong Kong only. Available in
metallic red and white enamel
only.
6020 Snorkel (The Heavyweights),
$60
Hong Kong only. Also available
in white enamel.
6175 The Hood, $45
Available with or without black
painted roof. U.S.A. and Hong
Kong.

6176 Short Order, $45
Hong Kong only.
6177 T-4-2, $50
Hong Kong only.
6179 Jet Threat, $45
Hong Kong only.
6183 Pit Crew Car, $70
trunk opens. Hong Kong only.
Available in white enamel only.
6184 Ice T, $45
Hong Kong only. Available in
yellow only.
6185 Mutt Mobile, $65
Hong Kong only.
6186 Rocket-Bye-Baby, $50
Hong Kong only.
6187 Bye-Focal, $75
Hong Kong only.
6188 Strip Teaser, $55
Hong Kong only.
6192 Waste Wagon (The Heavyweights), $80
Hong Kong only.
6193 Scooper (The Heavyweights),
$80
Hong Kong only.
6194 Racer Rig (The Heavyweights),
$75
Hong Kong only. Available in

metallic red and white enamel
only.
6407 Boss Hoss (The Spoilers), $45
Available with 1 to 9 on doors.
Available with or without black
painted roof. Hong Kong only.
6418 Sugar Caddy (The Spoilers),
$45
Hood opens. Available with 1 to
9 on doors. Hong Kong only.
6458 Hairy Hauler, $40
canopy opens. U.S.A. only.
6460 AMX/2, $35
U.S.A. only.
6461 Grass Hopper, $45
Hong Kong only.
6466 Cockney Cab, $40
U.S.A. and Hong Kong.
6467 Olds 442, $200
Hood opens. U.S.A. only.
6468 S'Cool Bus (The Heavyweights), $200
Hong Kong only. Available in
yellow enamel only.
6471 Evil Weevil (The Spoilers), $40
Available with 1 to 9 on doors.
Hong Kong only.
6472 Classic Cord, $175
Hood opens. Hong Kong only.

1972.

5699 Rear Engine Mongoose, $
Available with clear or b
front wheels. Hong Kong
Available in blue only.
5856 Rear Engine Snake, $200
Available with clear or b
front wheels. Hong Kong
Available in yellow only.
5881 Open Fire, $150
Hong Kong only.
6005 Funny Money, $75
Hong Kong only. Availab
grey only.
6021 Ferrari 512S, $100
Canopy opens. Hong K
only.
6022 Side Kick, $100
Side opens out. Hong K
only.
6169 Mercedes-Benz C-111, $8
Doors open. Hong Kong

1973-1994

ABBREVIATIONS USED IN THE CHARTS

In the different categories that follow abbreviations have
been used in the interest of space. They are listed below

CATEGORY

Ann. = Anniversary
Aq.fresh = Aquafresh
Cal Cus. = Cal Custom
Co. Rcr. = Color Racer
Demo Man = Demolition Man
Gold Ser. = Gold Series
HW Conv. = HW Convention
LE = Limited Edition
McD's = McDonald's
Pre-Pro = Pre-production
RL Conv. = RL Convention
SE = Special Edition
Super Chr. = Super Chrome

CASTING

CSFS = Closed spoiler with flush
struts
CSRS = Closed spoiler with recess
struts
CWng = Closed wing
DRA = Double rear axle
fdrs. = Fenders
lg.r.wndw. = Large rear window
lgr. = Larger
lgr.sunroof = Larger sunroof
LUFV = Lip under front valance
No PBH = No power bulge on hood
No struts, no hole, short fdrs. = No
struts, no hole, short fenders No
EXPS = No exhaust pipes
NWA = Narrow wheel arches
OSFS = Open spoiler with flush struts
OSRS = Open spoiler with recess
struts
OWng = Open wing

PBH = Power bulge on hood
Plst. = Plastic
Plst. w/etched pattern = Plastic with
etched pattern
Pr.Eng. = Protuding Engine
RES = Recessed exhaust stacks
sm.r.wndw. = Small rear window
smr.sunroof = Smaller sunroof
WWA = Wide wheel arches

COLOR

Aq. = Aqua
Blk. = Black
Blu. = Blue
Br. = Bright
Bro. = Brown
Brg. = Burgundy
Cmflg. = Camouflage
Chr. = Chrome
D. = Dark
Des. Scrub = Desert Scrub
Flr. = Flourescent
Glt. = Glitter
Gr. = Green
Khk. = Khaki
MF = Metalflake
M. = Metallic
N.Blz. = Neon Blaze
N. = Neon
Or. = Orange
Pnk. = Pink
Prp. = Purple
Wht. = White
Yl. = Yellow

COUNTRY

CHN = China
FRA = France
HK = Hong Kong
IND = India
MAL = Malaysia
MEX = Mexico

WINDOW

Blk. = Black
BluT = Blue tinted
BluCW = Blue clear windshield
Chr. = Chrome
CF = Clear frame
CL = Clear
DTW = Dark tinted windshield
DTBluT = Dark blue tinted
DT = Dark tint
DC = Dark cockpit
GT = Grey tinted
LC = Light cockpit
LT = Light tint
NW = No windshield
PT = Pale tint
rf. = Roof
Sil. = Silver
TNT = Tinted
WF = White frame
wshld. = Windshield
YT = Yellow tint
Yl. = Yellow

BASE

Clr. sticker = Clear sticker on base
cstg. = Casting

Inv. = Inverted
LgTP = Long tail pipe
N&N = Name & number
NOB = Name on base
RAF & no SIS = Rivet at front & no
step in sump
RAF & SIS = Rivet at front & step in
sump
RAF = Rivet at front
RBCO = Raised bar cast over...
ROA = Rivet over axle
Rsd = Raised
RWJU = Rear wheels jack up
ShTP = Short tail pipe
Sm. = Small
SqH = Square hole

INTERIOR -- SEE COLOR

col. = Column
strg. = Steering
TB = Toolboxes

WHEELS

Dsh-Chr. = Dished-Chrome
HO = Hot Ones
LHb = Large hub
P-C-Chr. = Pro-Circuit-Chrome
Reg = Regular
RL = Red Line
RR = Real Rider
Rtr = Rotor
SHb =Small hub
SS = Six Spoke
UH = Ultra Hot
Uniq. = Unique
WW = White Wall

PAINT

fdrs. = Fenders
geo. = Geometric
Mgta. = Magenta
rf. = Roof
shps. = Shapes
tr.= Trim
wd = Wood
Wdgr pnls = Woodgrain panels

LOGO

HW = Hot Wheels

OTHER

Air Fra = Air France
bmps = Bumpers
FAOSc = FAO Schwartz
FCGP = Funny Car Gift Pack
FWs = Front wheels
GEng = Gold engine
Grl. = Grill
RB = Rollover bar
RRR = Removable roof rack
RWs = Rear wheels
SI = Strut inside

Name	#	Category	Casting	Ctry.	Color	Win.	Base	Interior	Wheels	Paint	Logo	Other	S
1993 Camaro		25th Ann.		MAL	Chr.	Blk.	LgTP	Red	UH				5
1993 Camaro		Barbie		MAL	Pnk.				Dsh - Chr.				50
Chevrolet ACC Camaro	11090	Demo Man		MAL	Red/Blk.	DT		Blk.	P-C - Chr.				6
1993 Camaro		LE		MAL	Gold	CL		Blk.	Dsh - Red front, Gold rear		HW # 1		15
1993 Camaro		Pre-Pro		MAL	N. Pnk.				P-C - Chr.				
1993 Camaro		Pre-Pro		MAL	Grey	TNT	LgTP	Tan	UH				
1993 Camaro		Revealer		MAL	N. Gr.	DT	ShTP	Wht.	UH			Revealers 10 pack	10
1993 Camaro		Spam		MAL	M. Dk. Blu.	YT	ShTP	Red	Reg		Spam 37		10
1993 Camaro		Toy Fair		MAL	Chr.	Blk.	LgTP	Red	UH				125
1993 Camaro		World Cup		MAL	M. Dk. Red	CL	ShTP	Wht.	UH	Wht., Blk., Bro. & Blu. soccer tr.	World Cup USA 94		5
1993 Camaro	3021			MAL	Prp.	TNT	ShTP	Wht.	UH				4
1993 Camaro	3021			MAL	Prp.	DT	ShTP	Wht.	UH				4
1993 Camaro	3021			MAL	Prp.	TNT	ShTP	Grey	UH				4
1993 Camaro	3021			MAL	Prp.	TNT	LgTP	Grey	UH				3
1993 Camaro	3021			MAL	Prp.	CL	ShTP	Wht.	UH				4
1993 Camaro	11243			MAL	M. Blu./Wht.	CL	ShTP	Wht.	Reg		HW 1		4
1993 Camaro	11243			MAL	M. Blu./Wht.	CL	ShTP	Wht.	UH		HW 1		4
1993 Camaro	11243			MAL	Blu./Wht.	CL	ShTP	Wht.	UH		HW 1		4
1993 Camaro	11243			MAL	Blu./Wht.	CL	LgTP	Wht.	UH		HW 1		4
1993 Camaro	11243			MAL	M. Dk. Blu./Wht.	CL	ShTP	Wht.	Reg		HW 1		4
1993 Camaro	11243			MAL	Blu./Wht.	CL	LgTP	Wht.	Reg		HW 1		4
1993 Camaro	11243			MAL	Blu./Wht.	CL	ShTP	Wht.	Reg				4
1993 Camaro	12355			MAL	Red	CL	ShTP	Wht.	UH				3
1993 Camaro	13583	Gold Medal Speed		MAL	M. Blu./Wht.	CL	ShTP	Wht.	UH - Gold		HW 1		3
2 Cool		McD's		CHN	Prp.				Uniq.				5
31 Doozie	2533			HK	Brg.		31 Doozie & no TM		WW				6
31 Doozie	2533			MAL	Brg.		MAL cast Rsd. & no 31		WW				6
31 Doozie	2533			MAL	Brg.		MAL cast flat & no 31		WW				6
31 Doozie	2533			MAL	Brg.		TM & no 31 Doozie		WW				6
31 Doozie	2533			HK	Brg.		TM & no 31 Doozie		WW				6
31 Doozie	2533			MAL	Brg.		31 Doozie & no TM		WW				6
31 Doozie	9649			MAL	Or.		SqH		RL	Bro. fdrs			25
31 Doozie	9649			MAL	Red		MAL on Rsd. cast		WW	Dk. Bro. fdrs		Removable roof	6
31 Doozie	9649			HK	Red				WW	Dk. Bro. fdrs		Removable roof	6
31 Doozie	9649			HK	Or.		SqH		Reg	Gr. fdrs			50
31 Doozie	9649			HK	Red				WW	Red fdrs		Removable roof	6
31 Doozie	9649			MAL	Red				WW	Red fdrs		Removable roof	6
31 Doozie	9649			MAL	Red				WW	Dk. Bro. fdrs		Removable roof	6
31 Doozie	9649			MAL	Or.		SqH		WW	Bro. fdrs			6
31 Doozie	9649			MAL	Or.		No SqH		WW	Bro. fdrs			6

Name	#	Category	Ctry.	Color	Win.	Base	Interior	Wheels	Paint	Logo	Other	$
31 Doozie	9649		MAL	Red		MAL on Rsd. cast		WW	Red fdrs		Removable roof	15
31 Doozie	9649		HK	Red			Small strg. wheel	WW	Dk. Bro. fdrs		Removable roof	6
31 Doozie	9649		MAL	Red		MAL on Rsd. cast	Small strg. wheel	WW	Dk. Bro. fdrs		Removable roof	6
31 Doozie	9649		HK	Or.		SqH		WW	Bro. fdrs			6
31 Doozie	9649		MAL	Red			Small strg. wheel	WW	Dk. Bro. fdrs		Removable roof	6
31 Doozie	9649		MAL	Gr.		SqH		Reg	Yl. sides			6
31 Doozie	9649		HK	Or.		No SqH		WW	Bro. fdrs			6
31 Doozie	9649		MAL	Or.		SqH		Reg	Bro. fdrs			6
31 Doozie	9649		MAL	Gr.		SqH		Reg	Light Gr. sides			6
31 Doozie	9649		HK	Gr.		SqH & no HK		Reg	Light Gr. sides			6
31 Doozie	9649		HK	Or.		SqH		Reg	Bro. fdrs			6
31 Doozie	9649		HK	Gr.		SqH		Reg	Light Gr. sides			6
31 Doozie	9649		MAL	Or.		SqH		Reg	Gr. fdrs			50
31 Doozie	9649		HK	Gr.		SqH & no HK		Reg	Yl. sides			6
31 Doozie	9649		HK	Gr.		SqH		Reg	Yl. sides			6
32 Ford Delivery	9599		MAL	Wht./Aq.				Reg				3
32 Ford Delivery	7672		MAL	Yl.				Reg	Or., Pnk., Prp. & Blk. tr.	Delivery in Blk.		3
32 Ford Delivery	7672		MAL	Yl.				Reg	Or. Pnk. & Prp. tr.	Delivery in purple		3
32 Ford Delivery		25th Ann.	MAL	Pnk.				Reg				3
32 Ford Delivery		HW Conv.	MAL	Yl.				Reg		HW Convention '91		150
32 Ford Delivery		HW Conv.	MAL	Wht./Aq.				Reg		HW Convention '91		150
32 Ford Delivery		Malt-O-Meal	MAL	Yl./Red				Reg	Red tr.	Malt-O-Meal		15
32 Ford Delivery	9599 LE		MAL	Wht./Prp.				Dsh - Grey	Or. & Blu. tr.	Early Times Car Club		15
32 Ford Delivery	9599 LE		MAL	Wht./Prp.				Dsh - Grey	Or. & Blu. tr.	Early Times Car Club & Temecula		100
35 Classic Caddy		LE	MAL	Wht.				WW	Red fdrs	Museum of American Heritage		20
35 Classic Caddy		LE	MAL	Wht.				WW	Blu. fdrs	Museum of American Heritage		20
35 Classic Caddy		Pre-Pro	MAL	Wht.				Reg	Wht. fdrs	HW 25th Ann.		6
35 Classic Caddy	1543		MAL	Silver/Pnk.				WW				6
35 Classic Caddy	1543		HK	Silver/Prp.				WW				6
35 Classic Caddy	1543		MAL	Silver/Prp.				WW				6
35 Classic Caddy	2529		HK	M. Blu.				WW	Dk. Blu. fdrs			6
35 Classic Caddy	2529		MAL	M. Blu.				WW	Dk. Blu. fdrs			6
35 Classic Caddy	3252		MAL	Brg.				Reg				6
35 Classic Caddy	3252		MAL	Tan				Reg				6
35 Classic Caddy	3252		HK	Brg.				WW				6
35 Classic Caddy	3252		HK	Tan				Reg				6
35 Classic Caddy	3252		MAL	Brg.				WW				6
35 Classic Caddy	3252		HK	Brg.				Reg				6
35 Classic Caddy	3371	Cal Cus.	MAL	Gold/Navy Blu.				WW				6
35 Classic Caddy	3371	Cal Cus.	MAL	Gold				WW				6
37 Bugatti		Gold Ser.	MAL	Yl.				SS - Gold			FAOSc	25
37 Bugatti		Pre-Pro	MAL	Yl.				SS - Gold	Blk. tr.			0
37 Bugatti	1696		HK	Blk.				Reg	Red tr. on hood & sides			5
37 Bugatti	1696		HK	Blk.				Reg	Red tr. on sides only			5
37 Bugatti	1696		MAL	Blk.				Reg	Red tr. on hood & sides			5

Name	#	Category	Casting	Ctry.	Color	Win.	Base	Interior	Wheels	Paint	Logo	Other	S
37 Bugatti	1696			HK	Blk.				WW	Red tr. on hood & sides			5
37 Bugatti	1696			MAL	Blk.				WW	Red tr. on hood & sides			5
37 Bugatti	1696			HK	Blk.				Reg	Red tr. on sides only			5
37 Bugatti	2195			HK	Blu.				WW	Blu. fdrs & grey tr.			5
37 Bugatti	2195			HK	Blu.				WW	Yl. fdrs & grey tr.			5
37 Bugatti	2195			MAL	Blu.				WW	Yl. fdrs & grey tr.			5
37 Bugatti	2195			MAL	Blu.				WW	Blu. fdrs & grey tr.			5
37 Bugatti	2526			MAL	Yl.				Reg				5
37 Bugatti	2526		Plst. fdrs.	MAL	Yl.				WW				5
37 Bugatti	2526		Plst. fdrs.	MAL	Yl.				WW				5
37 Bugatti	2526		Plst. fdrs.	HK	Yl.				Reg				5
37 Bugatti	2526		Plst. fdrs.	HK	Yl.				WW				5
37 Bugatti	2526			HK	Yl.				WW				5
37 Bugatti	2526			HK	Yl.				Reg				5
37 Bugatti	2526			MAL	Yl.				WW				5
3-Window '34	2334			MAL	Wht./Prp.		Two rivets		Reg	Prp., Or. & Blk. tr.			3
3-Window '34	2334			MAL	Wht./Prp.		One rivet		Reg	Prp., Or. & Blk. tr.			3
3-Window '34	2334			MAL	Wht./Pnk.		One rivet		Reg	Pnk., Or. & Blk. tr.			6
3-Window '34		25th Ann.		MAL	Gr./Prp.				Reg	Or. & Blu. tr.	Pro Street 34		5
3-Window '34	1299	Cal Cus.		MAL	N. Yl./Blu.				Rtr - Chr.	Neon Or. tr.	Pro Street 34		7
3-Window '34	1299	Cal Cus.		MAL	N. Yl./Blu.				RR - Grey	Neon Or. tr.	Pro Street 34		7
3-Window '34	1299	Cal Cus.		MAL	M. Blu.				RR - Grey	Neon Gr. & neon Pnk. tr.	Pro Street 34		7
3-Window '34		Malt-O-Meal		MAL	Blk./Yl.				Reg	Red flames	Malt-O-Meal		15
3-Window '34	2225	Park'n Plate		MAL	M. Blu.				Reg	Red & Yl. flames		Small RWs	5
3-Window '34	2225	Park'n Plate		MAL	M. Blu.				Reg	Red & Yl. flames		Large RWs	5
3-Window '34	1132	Hiraker		HK	Red		RWJU		Reg	Wht. flames			10
3-Window '34	1132	Hiraker		MAL	Red		RWJU		Reg	Wht. flames			10
3-Window '34	1132	Hiraker		HK	Red		RWJU		Reg	Yl. flames			10
3-Window '34	1132	Hiraker		MAL	Red		RWJU		Reg	Yl. flames			10
3-Window '34	1473			MAL	Red		One rivet		Reg	Yl. & Wht. flames			7
3-Window '34	1473			MAL	Prp.		One rivet		Reg	Red, Blu. & Gr. tr.	34	Larger RWs	7
3-Window '34	1473			MAL	Red		One rivet		Reg	Yl. & Wht. flames		Larger RWs	7
3-Window '34	1473			MAL	Red		One rivet		Reg	Yl., Blk. & Wht. tr.			7
3-Window '34	4352	Hiraker		HK	Red MF.		RWJU & bar cast over MAL		RR - Grey				15
3-Window '34	4352	Hiraker		HK	Red MF.		RWJU		RR - Grey				15
3-Window '34	4352	Hiraker		MAL	Blk.		RWJU		RR - Grey				15
3-Window '34	4352	Hiraker		MAL	Red MF.		RWJU & Rsd. HK		RR - Wht.				20
3-Window '34	4352	Hiraker		HK	Red MF.		RWJU		Reg				10
3-Window '34	4352	Hiraker		MAL	Blk.		RWJU		RR - Wht.				20
3-Window '34	4352	Hiraker		MAL	Blk.		RWJU		Reg				10
3-Window '34	4352	Hiraker		MAL	Red MF.		RWJU & Rsd. HK		RR - Grey				15
3-Window '34	4352	Hiraker		HK	Red MF.		RWJU & bar cast over MAL		RR - Wht.				20
3-Window '34	4352	Hiraker		MAL	Red MF.		RWJU & bar cast over MAL		Reg				10
3-Window '34	4352	Hiraker		MAL	Red MF.		RWJU		Reg				10
3-Window '34	4352	Hiraker		HK	Red MF.		RWJU		RR - Wht.				20
3-Window '34	4352	Hiraker		MAL	Red MF.		RWJU		RR - Wht.				20

Name	#	Category	Casting	Ctry.	Color	Win.	Base	Interior	Wheels	Paint	Logo	Other	$
3-Window '34	4352	Hiraker		MAL	Red MF.		RWJU		RR - Grey				15
3-Window '34	4352	Hiraker		HK	Red MF.		RWJU & Rsd. HK		Reg				10
40s Ford 2 Door		25th Ann.		MAL	Chr.				Reg				5
40s Ford 2 Door		HW Conv.		MAL	Blk.				Reg	Red, Yl. & Wht. flames	First HW Convention 1987		150
40s Ford 2 Door	4367			MAL	Blk.				Reg				6
40s Ford 2 Door	4367			HK	Blk.				RR - Grey				15
40s Ford 2 Door	4367			HK	Blk.				RR - Wht.				15
40s Ford 2 Door	4367			HK	Blk.				Reg				6
40s Ford 2 Door	4367			MAL	Blk.				RR - Wht.				15
40s Ford 2 Door	4367			MAL	Blk.				RR - Grey				15
40s Woodie	4367	LE		MAL	N. Blz.				Dsh - Grey		Early times 94 hot rods to Hemet		15
40s Woodie	4316			MAL	Blk./Turquoise				Reg				3
40s Woodie	1229	Cal Cus.		MAL	Aq./N. Pnk.				Reg - Yl.				6
40s Woodie	1229	Cal Cus.		MAL	N. Or./Bro./Blk.				RR - N. Blaze				6
40s Woodie	9226	Park'n Plate		MAL	M. Red				WW				8
40s Woodie	1131	Hiraker		HK	Blu.		RWJU		Reg	Wdgr pnls			8
40s Woodie	1131	Hiraker		HK	Or.		RWJU		Reg	Bro. wd pnls			8
40s Woodie	1131	Hiraker		HK	Or.		RWJU		Reg	Wdgr pnls & Blu. rf.			8
40s Woodie	1131	Hiraker		MAL	Blu.		RWJU		Reg	Wdgr pnls			10
40s Woodie	1131	Hiraker		HK	Or.		RWJU		Reg	Wdgr pnls & Blu. rf.			15
40s Woodie	1131	Hiraker		MAL	Or.		RWJU		Reg	Wdgr pnls			10
40s Woodie	1131	Hiraker		MAL	Or.		RWJU		Reg	Wdgr pnls			10
40s Woodie	1131	Hiraker		MAL	Or.		RWJU		Reg	Bro. wd pnls			10
40s Woodie	2530			MAL	Yl.				Reg				6
40s Woodie	2530			HK	Yl.				Reg				6
40s Woodie	2530	Hiraker		HK	Yl.		RWJU		Reg	Dk. wd pnls			6
40s Woodie	2530	Hiraker		HK	Yl.		RWJU		Reg	Pale wd pnls			6
40s Woodie	2530	Hiraker		MAL	Yl.		RWJU		Reg	Dk. wd pnls			6
40s Woodie	2530	Hiraker		MAL	Yl.		RWJU		Reg	Pale wd pnls			6
40s Woodie	4351	Hiraker		MAL	Dk. Blu. MF.		RWJU		RR - Grey				10
40s Woodie	4351	Hiraker		HK	Dk. Blu. MF.		RWJU		RR - Wht.				10
40s Woodie	4351	Hiraker		MAL	Dk. Blu. MF.		RWJU		RR - Wht.				10
40s Woodie	4351	Hiraker		HK	Dk. Blu. MF.		RWJU		Reg				10
40s Woodie	4351	Hiraker		HK	Dk. Blu. MF.		RWJU		RR - Grey				10
40s Woodie	4351	Hiraker		MAL	Dk. Blu. MF.		RWJU		Reg				10
40s Woodie	9093	Cal Cus.		MAL	Yl.				Reg - Yl.			with 2 surfbo=ds - Wildwave Set	6
55 Candy Apple Red Chevy		LE	No opening in hood	MAL	Red/Wht.				Dsh - Grey				15
55 Chevy	1467			MAL	Yl.		Grey plstc.		Reg	Blu., Or. & Prp. tr			5
55 Chevy	1467			MAL	Wht.		Grey plstc.		Reg	Prp., Yl. & Red wave tr.			5
55 Chevy		Club Car		MAL	Yl.		Grey plstc.		Reg	Blu., Or. & Prp. tr	North West	Tampo not d==e by Mattel	15
55 Chevy		Gold Ser.		MAL	M. Prp.				P-C - Gold			FAOS;	25
55 Chevy		LE	No opening in hood	MAL	Blk.				RR - Grey	Wht. tr.	Smokey 3 & Paul Goldsmith		15
55 Chevy		LE	No opening in hood	MAL	Blk.				Reg - Blk.	Or. & Wht. tr.	Smokey 3 & Tim Fock		15

Name	#	Category	Casting	Ctry.	Color	Win.	Base	Interior	Wheels	Paint	Logo	Other	S
55 Chevy		LE	No opening in hood	MAL	Pale Blu.				RR - Grey		Smokey 92		15
55 Chevy		Ralston		MAL	Brg.		Logo		HO - Gold	Blu. & Wht. flames & Yl. tr.	55 Chevy		20
55 Chevy		Ralston		MAL	Brg.		Logo		HO - Gold	Blu. & Wht. flames & Or. tr.	55 Chevy		10
55 Chevy	2523			MAL	Red/Wht.		55 Chevy		HO - Gold				6
55 Chevy	2523			MAL	Red/Wht.		No 55 Chevy		HO - Gold				6
55 Chevy		Co. Rcr.		MAL	to		RBCO MAL		Reg				5
55 Chevy	5179			HK	Red		RBCO HK		HO - Gold	Yl. & Or. flames	55 Chevy Fever		5
55 Chevy	5179			MAL	Red		RBCO MAL		HO - Gold	Yl. & Or. flames	55 Chevy Fever		5
55 Chevy	5179			MAL	Red				HO - Gold	Yl. & Or. flames	55 Chevy Fever		5
55 Chevy	5179			HK	Red				HO - Gold	Yl. & Or. flames	55 Chevy Fever		5
55 Nomad	2098 Cal Cus.		Hood does not open	MAL	N. Blz.				Rtr - N. Or.				6
56 Flashsider	2029			MAL	Aq.				HO - Silver				15
56 Flashsider	2029			MAL	Aq.				UH				4
56 Flashsider		HW Conv.		MAL	Blk.				WW		Ronald McDonald Children's Charities		50
56 Flashsider		LE		MAL	Blk.				WW				15
56 Flashsider		Toy Show		MAL	Blk.				WW		Seattle Toy Show 1993		15
56 Hi Tail Hauler	4341			MAL	Blu. MF.				Reg	Red & Yl. flames on hood		Yl. motorcycles	7
56 Hi Tail Hauler	4341			HK	Blu. MF.				Reg	Red & Yl. flames on hood		Yl. motorcycles	7
56 Hi Tail Hauler	4341 Extras			HK	Blu. MF.				Reg	Blu. & Yl. flames on rf. & hood		Yl. motorcycles and top	7
56 Hi Tail Hauler	4341 Extras			MAL	Blu. MF.				Reg	Red & Yl. flames on hood		Yl. motorcycles and top	7
56 Hi Tail Hauler	9647			HK	Or.				Reg	Blu. & Yl. flames on hood		Blk. motorcycles	12
56 Hi Tail Hauler	9647			HK	Blu.				Reg	Red & Yl. flames on hood		Blk. motorcycles	12
56 Hi Tail Hauler	9647			HK	Or.				RL	Blu. & Yl. flames on rf. & hood		Blk. motorcycles	25
56 Hi Tail Hauler	9647			HK	Blu.				Reg	Red & Yl. flames on hood		Yl. motorcycles	12
56 Hi Tail Hauler	9647			HK	Or.				Reg	Blu. & Yl. flames on hood		Blk. motorcycles	12
57 Chevy	1297 Cal Cus.		Pr.Eng.	MAL	N. Or.				Rtr - Chr.	Neon Pnk., Blu., mauve & Wht. tr.	57		6
57 Chevy		Co. Rcr.	Pr.Eng.	MAL	Prp. to Pnk.				Reg				6
57 Chevy		HW Conv.		MAL	Wht.				Dsh - Grey	Blu., Red & Blu. tr.	HW 8th Annual Convention		150
57 Chevy		HW Newsletter	Pr.Eng.	MAL	Aq.				UH	Yl., Blk., Or. & Red tr.	HW Newsletter		100
57 Chevy		McD's	Plst.	MAL	Gr.				Other	Blk. crocodile tr.			5
57 Chevy	2178 Park'n Plate		Pr.Eng.	MAL	M. Red				HO - Gold	Yl., Wht. & Blk. tr.	No 57 Chevy		6
57 Chevy	2178 Park'n Plate		Pr.Eng.	MAL	M. Red				HO - Gold	Yl., Wht. & Blk. tr.	57 Chevy		6
57 Chevy		Pre-Pro		MAL	Bro.				Reg	Wht. & Yl. tr.	57 Chevy		
57 Chevy		Pre-Pro		MAL	Blu.				Dsh - Grey	Yl., Wht. & Red tr.	Fireball 22		
57 Chevy		World Cup	Pr.Eng.	MAL	Red				UH	Wht., Blk., Bro. & Blu. soccer tr.	World Cup USA 94		5
57 Chevy	1538		Pr.Eng.	MAL	Aq.				UH	Yl., Red & Blk. tr.	No 57 Chevy		3
57 Chevy	1538		Pr.Eng.	MAL	M. Blu.				HO - Gold	Yl., Wht. & Blk. tr.			6
57 Chevy	1538		Pr.Eng.	MAL	Aq.				HO - Gold	Yl., Red & Blk. tr.	No 57 Chevy		6

Name	#	Category	Casting	Ctry.	Color	Win.	Interior	Base	Wheels	Paint	Logo	Other	$
57 Chevy	1538		Pr.Eng.	MAL	Aq.				HO - Gold	Yl., Red & Blk. tr.	No 57 Chevy		6
57 Chevy	1538		Pr.Eng.	MAL	Aq.				UH	Yl., Red & Blk. tr.	No 57 Chevy		3
57 Chevy	1538		Pr.Eng.	MAL	Aq.				HO - Gold	Yl., Red & Blk. tr.	57 Chevy		6
57 Chevy	1538		Pr.Eng.	MAL	Aq.				HO - Gold	Yl., Red & Blk. tr.	57 Chevy		6
57 Chevy	1538		Pr.Eng.	MAL	M. Blu.				UH	Yl., Wht. & Blk. tr.			3
57 Chevy	1538		Pr.Eng.	MAL	M. Blu.				UH	Yl., Wht. & Blk. tr.			3
57 Chevy	1538		Pr.Eng.	MAL	M. Blu.				HO - Gold	Yl., Wht. & Blk. tr.	57 Chevy		7
57 Chevy	1538		Pr.Eng.	MAL	M. Blu.				HO - Gold	Yl., Wht. & Blk. tr.			7
57 Chevy	1538		Pr.Eng.	MAL	M. Blu.				HO - Gold	Yl., Wht. & Blk. tr.	57 Chevy		7
57 Chevy		25th Ann.	Pr.Eng.	MAL	Mauve				UH	Pnk., Prp. & Wht. tr.	Chevrolet cross & zigzag on doors		5
57 Chevy	4311		Pr.Eng.	MAL	Turquoise				UH	Or., Yl. & Prp. tr.			5
57 Chevy	4311		Pr.Eng.	MAL	Turquoise				UH	Or., Yl. & Prp. tr.	Chevrolet cross & zigzag on doors		5
57 Chevy	9638			HK	Blk.				HO - Gold	Wht. & Yl. tr.			15
57 Chevy	9638		Pr.Eng.	MAL	Yl.			Logo & no name	Reg	Red flames	57 Chevy		6
57 Chevy	9638			HK	Blk.				Reg	Wht. & Yl. tr.	57 Chevy		15
57 Chevy	9638		Pr.Eng.	MAL	Yl.			HW & name	HO - Silver	Red flames			6
57 Chevy	9638			MAL	Wht.				Dsh - Grey	Blk., Red & Blu. tr.	22		6
57 Chevy	9638		Pr.Eng.	MAL	Yl.			HW & name	Reg	Red flames			6
57 Chevy	9638			MAL	Red MF.			HW & name	HO - Gold	Wht. & Yl. tr.			6
57 Chevy	9638		Pr.Eng.	MAL	Yl.			Logo & no name	HO - Gold	Red flames			6
57 Chevy	9638			HK	Red				Reg	Wht. & Yl. tr.	57 Chevy		6
57 Chevy	9638			HK	Red MF.			HW & name	HO - Gold	Wht. & Yl. tr.			6
57 Chevy	9638		Pr.Eng.	MAL	Yl.			Logo & no name	HO - Silver	Red flames			6
57 Chevy	9638		Pr.Eng.	MAL	Yl.			Logo & no name	UH	Red flames			6
57 Chevy	9638		Pr.Eng.	MAL	Yl.			HW & name	UH	Red flames			6
57 Chevy	9638		Pr.Eng.	MAL	Yl.			HW & name	HO - Gold	Red flames			6
57 Chevy	9638			HK	Red				RL	Wht. & Yl. tr.	57 Chevy		30
57 Chevy	13586		Pr.Eng.	MAL	Turquoise				UH - Gold	Or., Yl. & Prp. tr.			3
57 T-Bird	2072			MAL	Crimson			Grey Plst.	Reg	Pnk., Gr. & Blu. tr.			5
57 T-Bird	2072			MAL	Aq.			Grey Plst.	Reg	Yl. & Prp. tr.			5
57 T-Bird		25th Ann.		MAL	Chr.				Reg				15
57 T-Bird		Co. Rcr.		MAL	Gr. to Yl.				Reg	Dk. Gr., Yl. & Red tr.	T Bird		5
57 T-Bird		Co. Rcr.		MAL	Red to Yl.				Reg	Yl., Bro. & Prp. tr.	T Bird		5
57 T-Bird		Gold Ser.		MAL	Blk.				P-C - Gold			FAOSc	25
57 T-Bird		Gulf		MAL	Aq.			Grey Plst.	Reg	Or., Wht. & Blk. tr.	Gulf		5
57 T-Bird	2072	Park'n Plate		MAL	Aq.				WW	Mgta. Yl. & Blu. tr.	T Bird		6
57 T-Bird	2072	Park'n Plate		MAL	Aq.				Reg	Mgta. Yl. & Blu. tr.	T Bird		20
57 T-Bird	2072	Park'n Plate		MAL	Aq.				WW	Or., Yl. & Blu. tr.	T Bird		6
57 T-Bird	1760	Gleamer		MAL	Pale Gold				Reg				3
57 T-Bird	1760	Gleamer		MAL	Gold				Reg				3
57 T-Bird	2013			HK	Red MF.				Reg				8
57 T-Bird	2013		Round rear side windows	HK	Red MF.				Reg				8
57 T-Bird	2013			MAL	Red MF.				Reg				8

Name	#	Category	Casting	Ctry.	Color	Win.	Base	Interior	Wheels	Paint	Logo	Other	S
57 T-Brd	2013		Round rear side windows	HK	Wht.				Reg	Red, Blu. & Blk. tr.	Thunderbird		5
57 T-Bird	2013		Round rear side windows	HK	Yl.				Reg	Red, Blu. & Blk. tr.	Thunderbird		5
57 T-Bird	2013			HK	Yl.				Reg	Red, Blu. & Blk. tr.	Thunderbird		5
57 T-Bird	2536			HK	Blk.				Reg	Prp., Red & Blu. tr.	T Bird		10
57 T-Bird	2536			MAL	Blk.				RR - Grey	Prp., Red & Blu. tr.	T Bird		15
57 T-Bird	2536			HK	Blk.				RR - Grey	Prp., Red & Blu. tr.	T Bird		15
57 T-Bird	2536			HK	Blk.				RR - Wht.	Prp., Red & Blu. tr.	T Bird		25
57 T-Bird	2536			MAL	Blk.				Reg	Prp., Red & Blu. tr.	T Bird		10
57 T-Bird	2536			MAL	Blk.				RR - Wht.	Prp., Red & Blu. tr.	T Bird		25
57 T-Bird	3992			MAL	Aq.				Reg	Prp. & Red tr.			4
57 T-Bird	3992			HK	Aq.				Reg	Prp. & Red tr.			4
57 T-Bird	3993			HK	Wht.				Reg	Blu. & Red tr.			4
57 T-Bird	3993			MAL	Wht.				Reg	Blu. & Red tr.			4
57 T-Bird	4357			MAL	Red MF.		MAL cast flat & a Rsd. bar		RR - Grey				15
57 T-Bird	4357			MAL	Red MF.		MAL cast flat & a Rsd. bar		RR - Wht.				20
57 T-Bird	4357			HK	Red MF.				RR - Grey				15
57 T-Bird	4357			HK	Red MF				RR - Wht.				20
57 T-Bird	4357			MAL	Red MF.				RR - Wht.				20
57 T-Bird	4357			MAL	Red MF.		Rsd. HK		RR - Grey				15
57 T-Bird	9522			MAL	Red				Reg	Blu., Yl. & Mgta. tr.	T Bird		10
59 Caddy	4694			MAL	Ivory				WW				3
59 Caddy	12359			MAL	Mauve				WW				3
59 Caddy	2097	Cal Cus.		MAL	N. Pnk.				WW				20
59 Caddy	7220 LE	HW Newsletter		MAL	Ivory				WW		HW Newsletter		100
59 Caddy	7220 LE			MAL	Gold plate			Wht.	WW				15
59 Caddy	7218 LE			MAL	Gold plate			Red	WW				15
62KGW Radio Van	9134	Herfy's		HK	Blu.	BluT			RL	Or. tr	62KGW		100
62KGW Radio Van	9134	Herfy's		HK	Blk.	BluT			RL	Yl. tr.	62KGW		100
62KGW Radio Van	9134	Herfy's		HK	Blk.	BluT			RL	Or. tr.	62KGW		100
65 Mustang Convertible	5908			MAL	Br. Red			Tan	WW	Yl. tr.	Mustang		5
65 Mustang Convertible	420			MAL	Red			Tan	WW	Yl. tr.	Mustang		3
65 Mustang Convertible	420			MAL	Red			Cream	WW	Yl. tr.	Mustang		3
65 Mustang Convertible		25th Ann.		MAL	Gr.				WW				5
65 Mustang Convertible	1241	Cal Cus.		MAL	N. Or./Blu.			N. Pnk.	Rtr - Blu.	Blu. & Wht. tr.		Freeway Frenzy Set	6
65 Mustang Convertible		HW Newsletter		MAL	Aq.			Tan	WW	Blk. & Red tr.	HW Newsletter	Tampo not done by Mattel	100
65 Mustang Convertible	2194	Park'n Plate		MAL	Wht.			Tan	WW	Red tr.	Mustang		6
65 Mustang Convertible	2194	Park'n Plate		MAL	Wht.			Red	WW	Red tr.	Mustang		6
65 Mustang Convertible		Revealer		MAL	N. Yl.				WW			Revealers 10 pack	10

Name	#	Category	Casting	Cry.	Color	Win.	Base	Interior	Wheels	Paint	Logo	Other	S
65 Mustang Convertible		RL Conv.		MAL	M. Blu.			Tan	WW	Wht. tr.	Red Line Convention 02	Tampo not done by Mattel	50
65 Mustang Convertible		RL Newsletter		MAL	M. Blu.			Tan	WW	Wht. tr.	Red Line 1991	Tampo not done by Mattel	50
65 Mustang Convertible		Set		MAL	M. Prp.				Serrated	Yl. tr.	Mustang	Double Barrel Set	10
65 Mustang Convertible	1241	Cal Cus.		MAL	N. Gr./Blu.			Blu.	RR - N. Yl.	Dk. Blu., Wht. & Blu. tr.			6
65 Mustang Convertible	1241	Cal Cus.		MAL	N. Gr./Blu.			Blu.	Rtr - N. Yl.	Blu., Wht. & Dk. Blu. tr.			6
65 Mustang Convertible	1542			HK	Aq.			Blk.	WW	Blk. tr.	Mustang		10
65 Mustang Convertible	1542			MAL	Aq.			Blk.	WW	Blk. tr.	Mustang		10
65 Mustang Convertible	1542			MAL	Blk.			Tan	WW	Wht. tr.	Mustang		25
65 Mustang Convertible	1542			MAL	Aq.		Rsd. MAL	Tan	WW	Blk. tr.	Mustang		7
65 Mustang Convertible	1542			MAL	Aq.		Flat MAL	Tan	WW	Blk. tr.	Mustang		7
65 Mustang Convertible	2197			MAL	M. Blu.			Tan	WW	Wht. tr.	Mustang		5
65 Mustang Convertible	5908			MAL	Br. Red			Tan	WW				6
65 Mustang Convertible	5908			HK	Br. Red			Tan	WW				6
67 Camaro	2103	Cal Cus.		MAL	M. Blu.				Rtr - Chr.	Wht., neon Red & neon Gr. tr.			25
67 Camaro		LE		MAL	M. Pale Blu.				RR - RL	Wht. tr.			20
67 Camaro	3913			MAL	Red				Reg				15
67 Camaro	3913			HK	Red				Reg				15
67 Camaro	3913	15th Ann.		HK	Pale M. Gr.				Reg				20
80s Corvette	9250	Billionth Car		MAL	Gold	Chr.		Blk. bag	HO - Gold				10
80s Corvette		HW Conv.		MAL	Gold	Chr.		Blk. bag	HO - Gold	Wht. flames			150
80s Corvette	2170	Park'n Plate		MAL	Red			Blk. bag	HO - Gold				10
80s Corvette	2170	Park'n Plate		MAL	Red			Red bag	HO - Gold				6
80s Corvette	1098			HK	Wht.			Or. bag	HO - Gold	Red & Or. tr.	Corvette	Turbotrax Race	10
80s Corvette	1457			MAL	Blk.			Red bag in rear	HO - Gold				10
80s Corvette	1457			MAL	Blk.			Tan bag in rear	HO - Gold				10
80s Corvette	1457			MAL	Blk.			Red bag in rear	HO - Gold				10
80s Corvette	3928			MAL	Blu.			Tan bag in rear	HO - Gold	Red & Wht. tr.	No tampo on hood		5
80s Corvette	3928			MAL	Blu.			Red bag in rear	HO - Gold	Red & Wht. tr.			10
80s Corvette	3928			MAL	Blu.			Tan bag in rear	HO - Gold	Red & Whi. tr.			10
80s Corvette	3928			MAL	Blu.			Red bag in rear	HO - Gold	Red & Wht. tr.	No tampo on hood		5
80s Corvette	3928			HK	Grey			Red bag in rear	HO - Gold				15
80s Corvette	3928			HK	Red			Bro. bag	HO - Gold				5
80s Corvette	3928			MAL	Silver			Red bag in rear	HO - Gold				5
80s Firebird	3854			MAL	Yl.			Grey	Reg	Blu. bird			10
80s Firebird	3918			FRA	Red			Tan	HO - Gold	Wht. tr.			10
80s Firebird		Chuck E Cheese		MAL	Wht.				Reg	Red & Blk. stripes	Chuck E Cheese		10

Name	#	Category	Casting	Ctry.	Color	Win.	Base	Interior	Wheels	Paint	Logo	Other	S
80s Firebird		Co.rcr.	Tail lights not part of casting	MAL	Prp. to Yl.				Reg				6
80s Firebird		Mall	Tail lights part of casting	MAL	N. Pnk.				Reg				10
	2170	Park'n Plate											7
80s Firebird		Pre-Pro		MAL	M. Red				Reg				10
80s Firebird		Set		MAL	M. Red			Grey	HO - Gold		Firebird	Sight and Smash	10
80s Firebird		Set		MAL	Blk.			Red	HO - Gold	Yl. tr.	Firebird	Sight and Smash	10
80s Firebird				HK	Blk.			Red	HO - Gold	Yl. tr.			10
80s Firebird	3918	Video Car		MAL	Wht.				Reg				10
80s Firebird		445	Tail lights part of casting	MAL	N. Or.				Reg	Pnk. & Prp. tr.			4
80s Firebird		445	Tail lights part of casting	MAL	N. Or.				Reg	Pnk. & Prp. tr. w/ bolt over rear wheels			4
80s Firebird		1452	Tail lights part of casting	MAL	Yl.			Red	Reg	Gr. bird & Red tr.	30		4
80s Firebird		1452	Tail lights not part of casting	MAL	Yl.			Red	Reg	Gr. bird & Red tr.	30		4
80s Firebird	3848			MAL	M. Red			Grey	Reg				10
80s Firebird	3848			MAL	M. Red			Tan	Reg				10
80s Firebird	3918			HK	Blu.				Reg				5
80s Firebird	3918			HK	Blk.				HO - Gold				5
80s Firebird	3918			MAL	Blk.				HO - Gold				5
80s Firebird	3918			MAL	Blu.				Reg				5
80s Firebird	3971			MAL	M. Blu.			Tan	HO - Gold	Grey eagle			5
80s Firebird	3971			HK	M. Blu.		Rsd. HK	Tan	Reg	Grey eagle			5
80s Firebird	3971			HK	M. Blu.		Rsd. HK	Blk.	Reg	Grey eagle			5
80s Firebird	3971			HK	M. Blu.		Rsd. HK	Red	Reg	Grey eagle			5
80s Firebird	3971			HK	M. Blu.		Rsd. HK	Blk.	Reg - Gold	Grey eagle			5
80s Firebird	3971			MAL	M. Blu.			Tan	Reg	Grey eagle			5
80s Firebird	3971			HK	M. Blu.			Blk.	Reg	Grey eagle			5
80s Firebird	3971			HK	M. Blu.		Rsd. HK	Tan	HO - Gold	Grey eagle			5
80s Firebird	3971			HK	M. Blu.			Blk.	Reg - Gold	Grey eagle			5
80s Firebird	3971			MAL	M. Blu.			Tan	HO - Gold	Grey eagle			5
80s Firebird	3971			MAL	M. Blu.			Blk.	Reg - Gold	Grey eagle			5
80s Firebird	3971			MAL	M. Blu.			Blk.	Reg	Grey eagle			5
80s Firebird	3971			HK	M. Blu.			Red	Reg	Grey eagle			5
80s Firebird	3972			HK	Blk.				Reg	Yl. eagle	Formula		5
80s Firebird	3972			HK	Blk.		Rsd. HK		Reg	Yl. eagle	Formula		5
80s Firebird	3972		Tail lights not part of casting	MAL	Blk.				Reg	Yl. eagle	Formula		5
80s Firebird	3972		Tail lights part of casting	MAL	Blk.				Reg	Yl. eagle	Formula		5
80s Firebird	5128			MAL	Blk.			Red	Reg	Yl. tr.	Firebird & Formula		5
80s Firebird	5128			MAL	Blk.			Tan	Reg	Yl. tr.	Firebird		5
80s Firebird	5128			HK	Blk.			Tan	HO - Gold	Yl. tr.	Firebird		5
80s Firebird	5128			HK	Blk.			Red	Reg	Yl. tr.	Firebird & Formula		5
80s Firebird	5128			HK	Blk.			Red	Reg - Gold	Yl. tr.	Firebird & Formula		5
80s Firebird	5128			HK	Blk.			Tan	Reg	Yl. tr.	Firebird		5
80s Firebird	5128			MAL	Blk.			Tan	HO - Gold	Yl. tr.	Firebird		5

Name	#	Category	Casting	Ctry.	Color	Win.	Base	Interior	Wheels	Paint	Logo	Other	$
80s Firebird	5128			MAL	Blk.			Red	Reg - Gold	Yl. tr.	Firebird & Formula		5
80s Firebird	5892 SE			HK	Chr.			Dk. Red	HO - Gold				15
80s Firebird	5892 SE			MAL	Chr.			Dk. Red	HO - Gold				15
80s Firebird	9341			HK	Red			Tan	HO - Gold				5
80s Firebird	9341			MAL	Dk. Red				Reg				10
80s Firebird	9341			MAL	Red			Tan	HO - Gold				5
80s Firebird	9341			HK	Dk. Red				Reg				10
82 Supra		Set		CHN	Gr.				Reg			Sto & Go	10
82 Supra		Set		CHN	Red				Reg			Sto & Go	10
82 Supra	3925			MAL	Red				HO - Gold	Yl., Blu. & Blk. tr.			5
82 Supra	3925			HK	Blk.		Rsd. HK	Tan	HO - Gold		Toyota		5
82 Supra	3925			MEX	Blk.				HO - Gold				25
82 Supra	3925			HK	Blk.			Tan	HO - Gold				5
82 Supra	3925			HK	Blk.		Rsd. HK	Wht.	HO - Gold				5
82 Supra	3925			HK	Blk.			Wht.	HO - Gold				5
82 Supra	3925 Color Changer			MAL	Prp. to Wht.				Reg				5
Aeroflash		Pre-Pro	Plst.	MAL	Wht.				UH				
Aeroflash	1781 Gleamer		Plst. w/ etched pattern	MAL	Flat Mauve				UH				3
Aeroflash	1781 Gleamer		Plst. w/ etched pattern	MAL	Rich Mauve				UH				3
Aggressor - Wind Splitter	7296 Ultra Hot			MAL	M. Gr.				UH				7
Aggressor - Wind Splitter	7296 Ultra Hot			HK	M. Gr.				UH				7
Air Cargo	4703			FRA	Yl./Wht.				Reg				25
Airport Rescue	1699			HK	Yl.				Reg	Or. & Blk. tr.			5
Airport Rescue	1699			HK	Yl.				Reg	Red & Blk. tr.			5
Airport Rescue	1699			MAL	Yl.				Reg	Red & Blk. tr.			5
Airport Rescue	1699			MAL	Yl.				Reg	Or. & Blk. tr.			5
Airport Rescue	1699			MAL	Yl.		Inv. MAL cstg.		Reg	Or. & Blk. tr.			5
Airport Rescue	1699			MAL	Yl.		Inv. MAL cstg.		Reg	Red & Blk. tr.			5
Airport Rescue	1699			MEX	Yl.				Reg	Or. & Blk. tr.			15
Airport Rescue	4897			FRA	Red				Reg				30
Airport Security Car	4709			FRA	Blu.				Reg	Yl.	Airport Security 301		30
Airport Security Car	4709			FRA	Blu.				Reg	Yl. & grey	Airport Security 301 & Club De		50
Airport Transportation	4708			FRA	Wht.				Reg				30
Alien		25th Ann.		MAL	Gr./Blk.				UH				5
Alien		Pre-Pro		MAL	Prp./Blu.				UH				
Alien		Revealer		MAL	Red/Blu.				UH			Revealers 10 pack	10
Alien	5026			MAL	Red		Logo on the right		UH				7
Alien	5026			MAL	Blu.		Logo in the middle		UH				10
Alien	5026			MAL	Red		Logo in the middle		UH				7
Alien	5026			MAL	Blu.		Logo on the right		UH				10
Alive 55	9210	Hood opens		FRA	Gr.				Reg	Blu., Gr., & Yl. flames	Chevrolet		30

Name	#	Category	Casting	Ctry.	Color	Win.	Base	Interior	Wheels	Paint	Logo	Other	S
Alive 55	9210		Hood opens	FRA	Gr.				Reg	Gr. & Yl. flames	Chevrolet		30
Alive 55	9210		Hood opens	FRA	Gr.				Reg	Blu. & Yl. flames	Chevrolet		30
Alive 55		Pre-Pro	Hood opens	HK	Dk. Blu.			Blk.	RL	Gr. & Yl. flames	Chevrolet	Tampo only on left side	30
Alive 55	6968		Hood opens	HK	Red			Grey	RL				80
Alive 55	6968		Hood opens	HK	Or.			Blk.	RL				80
Alive 55	6968		Hood opens	HK	Pale Yl.			Wht.	RL				80
Alive 55	6968		Hood opens	HK	Or.			Grey	RL				80
Alive 55	6968		Hood opens	HK	Gr.			Wht.	RL				80
Alive 55	6968		Hood opens	HK	Plum			Grey	RL				80
Alive 55	6968		Hood opens	HK	Dk. Blu.			Blk.	RL				80
Alive 55	6968		Hood opens	HK	Gr.			Blk.	RL				80
Alive 55	6968		Hood opens	HK	Red			Blk.	RL				80
Alive 55	6968		Hood opens	HK	Or.			Wht.	RL				80
Alive 55	6968		Hood opens	HK	Pale Gr.			Grey	RL				80
Alive 55	6968		Hood opens	HK	Flr. Lime			Blk.	RL				80
Alive 55	6968		Hood opens	HK	Flr. Lime			Grey	RL				80
Alive 55	6968		Hood opens	HK	Pale Gr.			Blk.	RL				80
Alive 55	6968		Hood opens	HK	Dk. Yl.			Wht.	RL				80
Alive 55	6968		Hood opens	HK	Pale Yl.			Grey	RL				80
Alive 55	6968		Hood opens	HK	Dk. Blu.			Grey	RL				80
Alive 55	6968		Hood opens	HK	Pale Gr.			Wht.	RL				80
Alive 55	6968		Hood opens	HK	Pale Blu.			Grey	RL				80
Alive 55	6968		Hood opens	HK	Pnk.			Blk.	RL				80
Alive 55	6968		Hood opens	HK	Pale Yl.			Blk.	RL				80
Alive 55	6968		Hood opens	HK	Pale Blu.			Wht.	RL				80
Alive 55	6968		Hood opens	HK	Flr. Lime			Wht.	RL				80
Alive 55	6968		Hood opens	HK	Pnk.			Blk.	RL				80
Alive 55	6968		Hood opens	HK	Gr.			Grey	RL				80
Alive 55	6968		Hood opens	HK	Dk. Blu.			Wht.	RL				80
Alive 55	6968		Hood opens	HK	Plum			Blk.	RL				80
Alive 55	6968		Hood opens	HK	Pale Blu.			Grey	RL				80
Alive 55	6968		Hood opens	HK	Plum			Wht.	RL				80
Alive 55	6968		Hood opens	HK	Dk. Yl.			Blk.	RL				80
Alive 55	6968		Hood opens	HK	Pale Blu.				RL	Gr. & Yl. flames	Chevrolet		100
Alive 55	6968		Hood opens	HK	Red			Wht.	RL				80
Alive 55	6968		Hood opens	HK	Dk. Gr.				RL	Red & Yl. devil & flames	Chevrolet		75
Alive 55	6968		Hood opens	HK	Pnk.			Wht.	RL				90
Alive 55	6968		Hood opens	HK	Pale Blu.				RL	Red & Yl. devil & flames	Chevrolet		100
Alive 55	6968		Hood opens	HK	Dk. Yl.			Grey	RL				80
Alive 55	9210 Super Chr.		Hood opens	HK	Chr.				RL				50
Alive 55	9210 Super Chr.		Hood does not open	HK	Chr.				RL	Yl., Gr. & Blu. flames	Chevrolet		18
Alive 55	9210 Super Chr.		Hood does not open	HK	Chr.				Reg				18
Ambulance		Set		CHN	Wht.		No lights in centre of front bumper		Reg			Sto & Go	4
Ambulance	1792			MAL	Wht.		2 lights in centre of front bumper		Reg				4

Name	#	Category	Casting	Ctry.	Color	Win.	Base	Interior	Wheels	Paint	Logo	Other	$
Ambulance	1792			MAL	Yl.		2 lights in centre of front bumper		Reg	Red & Wht. tr.			25
Ambulance	1792			MAL	Yl.		2 lights in centre of front bumper		Reg	Blu., Red & Blk. tr.			15
American Hauler	9118		Single rear axle	MAL	Blu./Wht.				Reg				20
American Hauler	9118		Single rear axle	HK	Blu./Wht.				RL				25
American Hauler	9118		Single rear axle	HK	Blu./Wht.				Reg				20
American Tipper	9089			HK	Red/Wht.				Reg				20
American Tipper	9089			MAL	Red/Wht.				Reg				20
American Tipper	9089			HK	Red/Wht.				RL				25
American Victory	7662			FRA	Dk. Blu.				Reg				20
American Victory	7662			FRA	Dk. Red				Reg				20
American Victory	7662			FRA	Pale Blu.				Reg				20
American Victory	7662			FRA	Crimson				Reg				20
American Victory	7662			HK	Magenta				Reg				12
American Victory	7662			HK	Blu.				RL				20
American Victory	7662			HK	Blu.				Reg				12
American Victory	7662			MEX	Dk. Blu.				Reg				15
A-OK	2016			HK	Gr.		No A-OK		Reg				12
A-OK	2016			HK	M. Red		Rsd. HK		Reg				6
A-OK	2016			MAL	M. Red		Rsd. MAL		Reg				6
A-OK	2016			MAL	M. Red				Reg				6
A-OK	2016			MAL	Gr.		No A-OK		Reg				12
A-OK	2016			HK	M. Red				Reg				6
A-OK	2016			HK	Gr.				Reg				12
A-OK	2016			MAL	Gr.				Reg				12
A-OK	4367			HK	Red MF.				Reg				6
A-OK	4367			MAL	Red MF.				RR - Grey				75
A-OK	4367			HK	Red MF.				RR - Grey				75
A-OK	4367			MAL	Red MF.				Reg				5
Aries Wagon	3258			HK	Yl.				Reg				5
Aries Wagon	3258			MEX	Yl.				Reg				10
Army Funny Car	2023			HK	Wht.		RAF		Reg				15
Army Funny Car	2023			HK	Wht.		No rivet		Reg				15
Assault Crawler	3338			MAL	Des. Scrub								5
Assault Crawler	3338			MAL	Khk. Cmflg.								5
Auburn 852		Co. Rcr.		MAL	Blu. to Wht.				WW				5
Auburn 852	1540			MAL	Red				WW	Red fdrs			7
Auburn 852	1540			HK	Red				WW	Red fdrs			7
Auburn 852	2505			MAL	Gold MF.				Reg	Dk. Bro. fdrs			7
Auburn 852	2505			HK	Crimson		1978 to the right of HK		Reg	Dk. Bro. fdrs			7
Auburn 852	2505			HK	Wht.				WW	Wht. fdrs			7
Auburn 852	2505			HK	Gold MF.				Reg	Dk. Bro. fdrs			7
Auburn 852	2505			MAL	Gold MF.				WW	Dk. Bro. fdrs			7
Auburn 852	2505			HK	Gold MF.				WW	Dk. Bro. fdrs			7
Auburn 852	2505			MAL	Wht.				WW	Wht. fdrs			7
Auburn 852	2505			HK	Yl.				Reg	Bro. fdrs			7
Auburn 852	2505			MAL	Wht.				Reg	Wht. fdrs			7

Name	#	Category	Casting	Ctry.	Color	Win.	Base	Interior	Wheels	Paint	Logo	Other	S
Auburn 852	2505			MAL	Yl.				Reg	Dk. Bro. fdrs			7
Auburn 852	2505			MAL	Crimson				Reg	Dk. Bro. fdrs			7
Auburn 852	2505			HK	Crimson				Reg	Dk. Bro. fdrs			7
Auburn 852	2505			HK	Wht.				Reg	Wht. fdrs			7
Auburn 852	2505			MAL	Yl.				Reg	Bro. fdrs			7
Auburn 852	2505			HK	Yl.				Reg	Dk. Bro. fdrs			7
Auburn 852	2527			MAL	Light Gr.				WW	Dk. Gr. fdrs			7
Auburn 852	2527			HK	Light Gr.				WW	Dk. Gr. fdrs			7
Auburn 852	4314			MAL	Crimson				WW	Dk. Bro. fdrs			7
Auburn 852	4314			HK	Crimson				WW	Dk. Bro. fdrs			7
Avus Quattro	5260			MAL	Silver				UH				3
Aw Shoot	9243			HK	Khk.				UH	Wht. letters			25
Back Burner	2544	Ultra Hot		MAL	Brg.				UH				8
Backwoods Bomb	7670			HK	Blu.				RL				35
Backwoods Bomb	7670			HK	Gr.				Reg				30
Baja Breaker	1517		Metal hood does not open	MAL	Wht.		Flat MAL & Rsd. 1977		4x4 LHb	Red, Yl. & Blk. tr.	Suzuki ATV Racing Team		4
Baja B'eaker	1517		Metal hood does not open	MAL	Wht.		Flat MAL & Rsd. 1977		4x4 SHb	Red, Or. & Blk. tr.	Suzuki ATV Racing Team		4
Baja Breaker	1517		Metal hood does not open	MAL	Wht.		Flat MAL & 1977		4x4 SHb	Red, Yl. & Blk. tr.	Suzuki ATV Racing Team		4
Baja B'eaker	1517		Metal hood does not open	MAL	Wht.		Flat MAL & Rsd. 1977		4x4 SHb	Red, Yl. & Blk. tr.	Suzuki ATV Racing Team		4
Baja B'eaker	1517		Metal hood does not open	MAL	Wht.		Flat MAL & 1977		4x4 LHb	Red, Yl. & Blk. tr.	Suzuki ATV Racing Team		4
Baja Breaker	1517		Metal hood does not open	MAL	Wht.		Rsd. MAL & flat 1977		4x4 LHb	Red, Yl. & Blk. tr.	Suzuki ATV Racing Team		4
Baja Breaker	1517		Metal hood does not open	MAL	Wht.		Rsd. MAL & flat 1977		4x4 SHb	Red, Or. & Blk. tr.	Suzuki ATV Racing Team		4
Baja B'eaker	1517		Metal hood does not open	MAL	Wht.		Rsd. MAL & 1977		4x4 SHb	Red, Or. & Blk. tr.	Suzuki ATV Racing Team		4
Baja Breaker	1517		Metal hood does not open	MAL	Wht.		Rsd. MAL & flat 1977		4x4 SHb	Red, Yl. & Blk. tr.	Suzuki ATV Racing Team		4
Baja Breaker	1517		Metal hood does not open	MAL	Wht.		Rsd. MAL & flat 1977		Reg	Red, Yl. & Blk. tr.	Suzuki ATV Racing Team		4
Baja Breaker	1517		Metal hood does not open	MAL	Wht.		Flat MAL & 1977		Reg	Red, Yl. & Blk. tr.	Suzuki ATV Racing Team		4
Baja Breaker	1517		Metal hood does not open	MAL	Wht.		Flat MAL & Rsd. 1977		Reg	Red, Yl. & Blk. tr.	Suzuki ATV Racing Team		4
Baja Ereaker	2022		Plst. hood opens	HK	Grey				Reg				8
Baja Ereaker	2022		Plst. hood opens	HK	Gr.				Reg	Blu. & Yl. tr.			8
Baja Ereaker	2022		Plst. hood opens	HK	Gr.				Reg	Olive & Yl. tr.			8
Baja Ereaker	4360		Metal hood does not open	MAL	Blk.		Flat MAL & 1977		4x4 SHb				6
Baja Breaker	4360		Metal hood does not open	MAL	Blk.		Flat MAL & 1977		Reg				6
Baja Breaker	4360		Plst. hood opens	MAL	Blk.		Flat MAL & 1977		RR- Wht.				20
Baja Breaker	4360		Plst. hood opens	MAL	Blk.		Rsd. MAL & flat 1977		RR - Grey				15

Name	#	Category	Casting	Ctry.	Color	Win.	Base	Interior	Wheels	Paint	Logo	Other	$
Baja Breaker	4360		Plst. hood opens	MAL	Blk.		Flat MAL & Rsd. 1977		RR - Grey				15
Baja Breaker	4360		Plst. hood opens	MAL	Blk.		Flat MAL & 1977		RR - Grey				15
Baja Breaker	4360		Plst. hood opens	MAL	Blk.		Rsd. MAL & flat 1977		RR - Wht.				20
Baja Breaker	4360		Plst. hood opens	MAL	Or. MF.		Flat MAL & Rsd. 1977		RR - Grey				15
Baja Breaker	4360		Metal hood does not open	MAL	Blk.				4x4 SHb				6
Baja Breaker	4360		Metal hood does not open	MAL	Blk.		Rsd. MAL & flat 1977		Reg				6
Baja Breaker	4360		Plst. hood opens	MAL	Blk.		Flat MAL & 1977		Reg				6
Baja Breaker	4360		Metal hood does not open	MAL	Blk.		Rsd. MAL & flat 1977		4x4 SHb				6
Baja Breaker	4360		Plst. hood opens	MAL	Blk.		Rsd. MAL & flat 1977		Reg				6
Baja Breaker	4360		Plst. hood opens	MAL	Or. MF.		Rsd. MAL		RR - Grey				7
Baja Breaker	4360		Plst. hood opens	MAL	Or. MF.		Rsd. MAL		Reg				7
Baja Breaker	4360		Plst. hood opens	HK	Or. MF.				Reg				7
Baja Breaker	4360		Metal hood does not open	MAL	Blk.		Flat MAL & Rsd. 1977		Reg				6
Baja Breaker	4360		Plst. hood opens	MAL	Blk.		Flat MAL & Rsd. 1977		RR - Wht.				6
Baja Breaker	4360		Plst. hood opens	MAL	Blk.		Flat MAL & Rsd. 1977		Reg				6
Baja Breaker	4360		Plst. hood opens	MAL	Or. MF.				Reg				7
Baja Bruiser	8258			MAL	Blu.				Reg	Red, Yl. & Wht. tr.	Baja Bruiser, 711 etc		35
Baja Bruiser	8258			HK	Or.		Plst.		RL	Red, Wht. & Blu. tr.	5, Baja etc		40
Baja Bruiser	8258			HK	Or.		Plst.		RL	Red, Wht. & Blu. tr.	5, Baja etc		40
Baja Bruiser	8258			HK	Gr.		Plst.		Reg	Red, Wht. & Blu. tr.			250
Baja Bruiser	8258			HK	Yl.				RL	Red & Prp. tr.	5, Baja etc		200
Baja Bruiser	8258			HK	Blu.				Reg	Red, Yl. & Wht. tr.	Baja Bruiser, 711 etc		35
Baja Bruiser	8258			HK	Blu.				RL	Red, Yl. & Wht. tr.			40
Baja Bruiser	8258			HK	Yl.				RL	Blu. & Red tr.			40
Baja Bruiser	8258			MAL	Wht.				Reg	Red Blu. & Yl. tr.	6		8
Baja Bruiser	8258			HK	Wht.				Reg	Red Blu. & Yl. tr.	6		8
Baja Bug	3876			MAL	Prp.		HW logo	Red	Reg	Yl. & Wht. flames	Blazin' Bug in Red		10
Baja Bug	3876			MAL	Prp.		HW	Red	Reg	Yl. & Wht. flames	Blazin' Bug in Red		10
Baja Bug	8258			MAL	Glt. Red				Reg				5
Baja Bug		Co. Rcr.		MAL	Or. to Wht.		HW	Or.	Reg	Blu. & Yl. flames	Blazin' Bug in Red		5
Baja Bug		Ralston		MAL	Or. to Wht.		HW	Red	Reg	Or. & Yl. flames & Blu. tr.	Blazin' Bug in Blu.		12
Baja Bug		Ralston		MAL	Brg.		HW logo	Red	Reg	Or. & Yl. flames & Blu. tr.	Blazin' Bug in Blu.		12
Baja Bug		1238 Cal Cus.		MAL	Two-tone N. Pnk.		HW		Reg	Blk. Yl. & neon Blu. tr.			6
Baja Bug		1238 Cal Cus.		MAL	Two-tone N. Pnk.		HW logo		RR - N. Yl.	Blk. Yl. & neon Blu. tr.			6
Baja Bug		1238 Cal Cus.		MAL	Two-tone N. Pnk.		HW		RR - N. Yl.	Blk. Yl. & neon Blu. tr.			6
Baja Bug		1238 Cal Cus.		MAL	Two-tone N. Pnk.		HW logo		Reg	Blk. Yl. & neon Blu. tr.			6

Name	#	Category	Casting	Ctry.	Color	Win.	Base	Interior	Wheels	Paint	Logo	Other	S
Baja Bug	2542			MAL	Wht.		HW logo		RR - Wht.	Red & Or. flames & Prp. tr.	Blazin' Bug in purple		15
Baja Bug	2542			MAL	Wht.		HW		Reg	Red & Or. flames & Prp. tr.	Blazin' Bug in purple		5
Baja Bug	2542			MAL	Wht.		HW		RR - Wht.	Red & Or. flames & Prp. tr.	Blazin' Bug in purple		15
Baja Bug	2542			MAL	Wht.		HW logo		Reg	Red & Or. flames & Prp. tr.	Blazin' Bug in purple		5
Baja Bug	5907			HK	Yl.		HW & name		RR - Grey	Pnk. & Prp. tr.	Baja Bug		15
Baja Bug	5907			MAL	Yl.		HW, name & Rsd. MAL		Reg	Pnk. & Prp. tr.	Baja Bug		6
Baja Bug	5907			MAL	Yl.		HW, name & Rsd. MAL		RR - Grey	Pnk. & Prp. tr.	Baja Bug		15
Baja Bug	5907			MAL	Yl.		HW, name & Rsd. MAL		RR - Wht.	Pnk. & Prp. tr.	Baja Bug		15
Baja Bug	9343			MAL	Blk.			Tan	RR - Wht.	Or. & Yl. flames	Blazin' Bug in Wht.		15
Baja Bug	9548			MAL	Red			Red	RR - Wht.	Wht. & Or. flames	Blazin' Bug in Yl.		15
Baja Bug	9548			MAL	Red			Blk.	Reg	Yl. & Wht. flames	Blazin' Bug in Blu.		5
Baja Bug	9548			MAL	Red			Red	RR - Wht.	Yl., Or. & Wht. tr.	Baja Bug		15
Baja Bug	9548			MAL	Red			Blk.	Reg	Yl. & Wht. flames	Blazin' Bug in purple		5
Banshee	11088	Demo Man	No Pontiac on rear	MAL	Red				P-C - Chr.				10
Banshee		Pre-Pro		MAL	Blk.				UH	Blk. rollover bar			
Banshee		Revealer	No Pontiac on rear	MAL	Red	Revealers on wshld.			Reg			Revealers 10 pack	10
Banshee		Video Car	No Pontiac on rear	MAL	Blu.				UH	Yl. tr.			12
Banshee	1303	Cal Cus.	No Pontiac on rear	MAL	Gold/Blk.				RR - N. Yl.	Or. tr.		Neon Or. roll over bar	7
Banshee	1303	Cal Cus.	No Pontiac on rear	MAL	Gold/N. Red				Rtr - Chr.	Or. tr.		Hood is Pnk.er	7
Banshee	1303	Cal Cus.	No Pontiac on rear	MAL	Gold/N. Red				RR - N. Yl.	Or. tr.			7
Banshee	1796		Pontiac on rear	MAL	Red				UH	Red rollover bar			7
Banshee	1796		No Pontiac on rear	MAL	Red				UH	Red rollover bar			7
Banshee	1796		No Pontiac on rear	MAL	Red				UH	Pnk. rollover bar			7
Banshee	1796		No Pontiac on rear	MAL	Red				UH - Gold	Red rollover bar			12
Battle Tank	5272	Mega Force		HK	Khk. Cmflg.								20
Beach Patrol	4368			FRA	Wht.				Reg			Wheels are small	15
Beach Patrol	2101	Cal Cus.		MAL	N. Gr.				Rtr - N. Yl.			Large wheels	6
Beach Patrol	2101	Cal Cus.		MAL	N. Gr.				Rtr - N. Yl.			Small wheels	6
Beach Patrol	4368			HK	Wht.				RR - Grey				6
Beach Patrol	4368			MAL	Wht.				Reg				6
Beach Patrol	4368			HK	Wht.				Reg				6
Beach Patrol	4368			MAL	Wht.				RR - Grey				15

Name	#	Category	Casting	Ctry.	Color	Win.	Base	Interior	Wheels	Paint	Logo	Other	$
Beach Patrol	4368			HK	Wht.				RR - Wht.				15
Beach Patrol	4368			MAL	Wht.		MAL cast flat		RR - Wht.				15
Beach Patrol	4368			MAL	Wht.				RR - Wht.				15
Beach Patrol	4368			MAL	Wht.		MAL cast flat		Reg				6
Beatnik Bandit	5714	25th Ann.		CHN	M. Olive Gr.				RL				4
Beatnik Bandit	5714	25th Ann.		CHN	M. Gr.				RL				4
Beatnik Bandit	5714	25th Ann.		CHN	M. Br. Red				RL				4
Beatnik Bandit	5714	25th Ann.		CHN	M. Violet				RL				4
Beatnik Bandit	5714	25th Ann.		CHN	M. Turquoise				RL				4
Beatnik Bandit	5714	25th Ann.		CHN	Gold				RL				4
Beatnik Bandit	5714	25th Ann.		CHN	M. Or.				RL				4
Beatnik Bandit	5714	25th Ann.		CHN	M. Blu.				RL				4
Beatnik Bandit	5714	25th Ann.		CHN	M. Pnk.				RL				4
Beatnik Bandit	5714	25th Ann.		CHN	M. Red				RL				4
Beatnik Bandit	5714	25th Ann.		CHN	M. Magenta				RL				4
Beatnik Bandit	5714	25th Ann.		CHN	M. Bro.				RL				4
Beatnik Bandit	5714	25th Ann.		CHN	M. Lime				RL				4
Beatnik Bandit	5714	Gold Ser.		CHN	M. Mauve				RL - Gold			GEng - FAOSc	25
Beatnik Bandit	5714	Vintage		CHN	Wht.				RL				4
Beatnik Bandit	5714	Vintage		CHN	M. Royal Blu.				RL				4
Beatnik Bandit	5714	Vintage		CHN	M. Gold				RL				4
Beatnik Bandit	5714	Vintage		CHN	Gunmetal				RL				4
Beatnik Bandit	5714	Vintage		CHN	M. Prp.				RL				4
Beatnik Bandit	5714	Vintage		CHN	Maroon				RL				4
Beatnik Bandit	5714	Vintage		CHN	M. Dk. Gr.				RL				4
Beatnik Bandit	5714	Vintage		CHN	M. Dk. Bro.				RL				4
Beatnik Bandit	5714	Vintage		CHN	M. Pale Pnk.				RL				4
Beatnik Bandit	5714	Vintage		CHN	Meallic Grey				RL				4
Beatnik Bandit	5714	Vintage		CHN	M. Br. Blu.				RL				4
Beatnik Bandit	5714	Vintage		CHN	M. Electric Gr.				RL				4
Beatnik Bandit	5714	Vintage		CHN	Br. Red				RL				4
Big Bertha	400			MAL	Des. Scrub		No Lrg. Rsd. rectangle							4
Big Bertha	400			MAL	Des. Scrub		Lrg. Rsd. rectangle							4
Big Bertha	9372			MAL	Khk. Cmflg.								5
Big Bertha	9372			MAL	Des. Cmflg.		No Lrg. Rsd. rectangle							5
Big Rig	1790		No struts, hole & long fdrs.	MAL	Blk.				Reg	Red, Or. & Blu. tr.			4
Big Rig	1790		Struts, no hole & short fdrs.	MAL	Blk.				Reg	Or., Red & Blu. tr.			4
Big Rig	1790		Struts, no hole & short fdrs.	MAL	Blk.				Reg	Red, Or. & Blu. tr.			4
Big Rig	1790		No struts, no hole & short fdrs.	MAL	Blk.				Reg	Red, Or. & Blu. tr.			4
Bigfoot		Auto Palace		MAL	Wht.				Oversize Wide - Red	Red, Blu. & Blk. tr.	Auto Palace		10
Bigfoot Auto Hauler		Auto Palace		MAL	Red/Wht.				Reg	Blu, Yl. & Blk. tr.	Auto Palace		15
Blk. Cat		McD's	Plst.	CHN	Blk.				Uniq.				5
Blk. Lightning		Aqua Fresh		MAL	M. Sea Gr.				Reg	Red & Wht. lightning tr.	3		6

Name	#	Category	Casting	Ctry.	Color	Win.	Base	Interior	Wheels	Paint	Logo	Other	$
Blk. Lightning	2124			MAL	Yl.				RR - Grey	Red, Wht. & Blu. stripes	20		6
Blk. Lightning	2124			HK	Yl.				RR - Grey	Red, Wht. & Blu. stripes	20		6
Blk. Lightning	2124 Kelloggs			MAL	Yl.				Reg	Red, Wht. & Blu. stripes	20		10
Blk. Lightning	2124 Kelloggs			HK	Yl.				Reg	Red, Wht. & Blu. stripes	20		10
Blk. Lightning	9544			HK	Blk.		HW logo		RR - Grey	Red & Wht. lightning tr.	3		10
Blk. Lightning	9544			HK	Blk.				Reg	Red & Wht. lightning tr.	3		6
Blk. Lightning	9544			MAL	Blk.				Reg	Red & Wht. lightning tr.	3		6
Blk. Lightning	9544			MAL	Blk.		HW logo		RR - Grey	Red & Wht. lightning tr.	3		10
Blk. Lightning	9544			MAL	Blk.				RR - Grey	Red & Wht. lightning tr.	3		10
Blk. Lightning	9544			HK	Blk.		HW logo		Reg	Red & Wht. lightning tr.	3		6
Blk. Lightning	9544			MAL	Blk.		HW logo		Reg	Red & Wht. lightning tr.	3		6
Blk. Lightning	9544			HK	Blk.				RR - Grey	Red & Wht. lightning tr.	3		6
Blazer 4x4	1514			MAL	M. Pale Blu.				4x4 SHb	Blu. & Prp. tr.			5
Blazer 4x4	4324			MAL	Glt. Blu.				4x4 SHb				5
Blazer 4x4		25th Ann.		MAL	Ivory				4x4 SHb	Blu., Bro. & Prp. tr.			5
Blazer 4x4	9231 Park'n Plate			MAL	Pale Gr.				4x4 LHb	Yl., Blu. & Or. tr.	Blazer 4x4		12
Blazer 4x4		World Cup		MAL	Wht.				4x4 SHb	Red, Blk., & Blu. soccer tr.	World Cup USA 94		5
Blazer 4x4	1514			MAL	Blu.				4x4 LHb	Gr., Red & Blk. tr.	Blazer		5
Blazer 4x4	1514			MAL	Blu.				4x4 SHb	Gr., Red & Blk. tr.	Blazer		5
Blazer 4x4	5910			MAL	Blk.		Rsd. name & MAL		4x4 LHb	Red & Yl. tr.	4x4 Blazer		4
Blazer 4x4	5910			HK	Blk.		N&N		4x4 SHb	Red & Yl. tr.	4x4 Blazer		4
Blazer 4x4	5910			HK	Blk.		No name		4x4 SHb	Red & Yl. tr.	4x4 Blazer		4
Blazer 4x4	5910			MAL	Blk.		Name		4x4 SHb	Red & Yl. tr.	4x4 Blazer		4
Blazer 4x4	5910			MAL	Blk.		No name		4x4 SHb	Red & Yl. tr.	4x4 Blazer		4
Blazer 4x4	5910			HK	Blk.		N&N		4x4 SHb	Red & Yl. tr.	4x4 Blazer		4
Blazer 4x4	5910			HK	Blk.		Name		4x4 SHb	Red & Yl. tr.	4x4 Blazer		4
Blown Camaro	1289 Cal Cus.			MAL	Red			Blk.	RR - Grey	Neon Or., neon Blu. & neon Pnk. tr.			30
Blown Camaro	1289 Cal Cus.			MAL	Wht.	TNT		Or.	Rtr - Chr.	Neon Or., neon Blu. & neon Pnk. tr.			7
Blown Camaro	1289 Cal Cus.			MAL	Wht.	CL		Or.	Rtr - Chr.	Neon Or., neon Blu. & neon Pnk. tr.			7
Blown Camaro	1289 Cal Cus.			MAL	Wht.	DTed		Blk.	RR - Grey	Neon Or., neon Blu. & neon Pnk. tr.			7
Blown Camaro	1289 Cal Cus.			MAL	Wht.	TNT		Or.	RR - Grey	Neon Or., neon Blu. & neon Pnk. tr.			7
Blown Camaro		Getty		MAL	Blk.				Reg	Red, Wht. & Yl. tr.	Getty		7
Blown Camaro		Getty		MAL	Blk.				UH	Red, Wht. & Yl. tr.	Getty		7
Blown Camaro	3858 Set			MAL	Blu.				HO - Gold	Luminous flames		Turbotrax Race	15
Blown Camaro	4363			MAL	Brg.	CL	N&N & flat MAL	Tan	UH	Blu., Prp. & Yl. tr.	IROC Camaro		7
Blown Camaro	4363			MAL	Brg.	CL	N&N & flat MAL	Red	Reg	Blu., Prp. & Yl. tr.	IROC Camaro		7
Blown Camaro	4363			MAL	Brg.	CL	N&N	Red	Reg	Blu., Or. & Yl. tr.	IROC Camaro		7
Blown Camaro	4363			MAL	Brg.	CL	N&N & Rsd. MAL	Tan	UH	Blu., Prp. & Yl. tr.	IROC Camaro		7
Blown Camaro	4363			MAL	Brg.	CL	N&N	Red	UH	Blu., Or. & Yl. tr.	IROC Camaro		7
Blown Camaro	4363			MAL	Brg.	TNT	Logo	Grey	UH	Blu., Prp. & Yl. tr.	IROC Camaro		7

Name	#	Category	Casting	Ctry.	Color	Win.	Base	Interior	Wheels	Paint	Logo	Other	S
Blown Camaro	4363			MAL	Brg.	CL	N&N & Rsd. MAL	Red	Reg	Blu., Prp. & Yl. tr.	ROC Camaro		7
Blown Camaro	4363			MAL	Brg.	TNT	N&N & Rsd. MAL	Grey	UH	Blu., Prp. & Yl. tr.	IROC Camaro		7
Blown Camaro	4363			MAL	Brg.	CL	Logo	Red	Reg	Blu., Prp. & Yl. tr.	IROC Camaro		7
Blown Camaro	4363			MAL	Brg.	CL	Logo	Tan	UH	Blu., Prp. & Yl. tr.	iROC Camaro		7
Blown Camaro	4363			MAL	Brg.	TNT	N&N & flat MAL	Grey	UH	Blu., Prp. & Yl. tr.	IROC Camaro		7
Blown Camaro	5138			MAL	Aq.	BluT	N&N	Grey	UH	Blu., Wht. & Yl. tr.	Camaro Z-28	Tampo on hood	5
Blown Camaro	5138			MAL	Aq.	DT / BluT	N&N	Grey	UH	Prp., Wht. & Yl. tr.	Camaro Z-28	Tampo on hood	5
Blown Camaro	5138			MAL	Aq.	DT / BluT	N&N	Grey	HO - Gold	Prp., Wht. & Yl. tr.	Camaro Z-28	Tampo on hood	5
Blown Camaro	5138			MAL	Aq.	DT / BluT	No N&N	Grey	HO - Gold	Prp., Wht. & Yl. tr.	Camaro Z-28	Tampo on hood	5
Blown Camaro	5138			MAL	Aq.	BluT	Logo	Grey	Reg	Blu., Wht. & Yl. tr.	Camaro Z-28	Tampo on hood	5
Blown Camaro	5138			MAL	Aq.	BluT	N&N	Grey	HO - Gold	Blu., Wht. & Yl. tr.	Camaro Z-28	Tampo on hood	5
Blown Camaro	5138			MAL	Aq.	BluT	N&N	Grey	Reg	Blu., Wht. & Yl. tr.	Camaro Z-28	Tampo on hood	5
Blown Camaro	5138			MAL	Aq.	BluT	Logo	Grey	UH	Blu., Wht. & Yl. tr.	Camaro Z-28	Tampo on hood	5
Blown Camaro	5138			MAL	Aq.	BluT	Logo	Grey	HO - Gold	Blu., Wht. & Yl. tr.	Camaro Z-28	Tampo on hood	5
Blown Camaro	5138			MAL	Aq.	BluT	Logo	Grey	UH	Pale Blu., Wht. & Yl. tr.	Camaro Z-28	No tampo on hood	5
Blown Camaro	5138			MAL	Aq.	DT / BluT	No N&N	Grey	UH	Prp., Wht. & Yl. tr.	Camaro Z-28	Tampo on hood	5
Blown Camaro	5138			MAL	Aq.	BluT	N&N & 2 bars under HW	Grey	UH	Blk., Wht. & Yl. tr.	Camaro Z-28	No tampo on hood	5
Blown Camaro	5138			MAL	Aq.	BluT	N&N	Grey	UH	Blk., Wht. & Yl. tr.	Camaro Z-28	No tampo on hood	5
Blown Camaro	5138			MAL	Aq.	BluT	N&N	Grey	HO - Silver	Pale Blu., Wht. & Yl. tr.	Camaro Z-28	No tampo on hood	5
Blown Camaro	5138			MAL	Aq.	BluT	N&N	Grey	UH	Pale Blu., Wht. & Yl. tr.	Camaro Z-28	No tampo on hood	5
Blown Camaro	5138			MAL	Blk.	BluT	Logo	Grey	HO - Gold	Pale Blu., Wht. & Yl. tr.	Camaro Z-28	No tampo on hood	5
Blown Camaro	5901	Set		CHN	Blu.				Reg	Red tr.		Triple Level Garage	10
BMW 323 Cabriolet	2100 Cal Cus.		BMW on rear licence plate	MAL	Wht./N. Blu.				Rtr - Blu.	Red & Yl. tr.			8
BMW 323 Cabriolet	9726			MAL	Blk.				UH		M3		4
BMW 323 Cabriolet	9726			MAL	Blk.				Reg		M3		4
BMW 323 Cabriolet	9726		BMW on rear licence plate	MAL	Blk.				HO - Silver		M3		4
BMW 323 Cabriolet	9726			MAL	Blk.				Reg		M3		4
BMW 323 Cabriolet	9726		BMW on rear licence plate	MAL	Blk.				UH		M3		4
BMW 850		Getty		MAL	Red				Reg		Getty		5
BMW 850	5667			MAL	Blu.				UH				3
BMW 850	5667			MAL	Blu.				Five Spoke - Lime Gr.				3
BMW 850	5667			MAL	Blu.				HO - Silver				3
BMW 850	5667 Pre-Pro			MAL	Blu.				Five Spoke - Yl.				3
BMW 850	12348			MAL	M. Dk. Blu.				UH				3
BMW M1	3289			FRA	Red				Reg	Or., Wht. & Blk. tr.			20
BMW M1	3289			FRA	Red				Reg	Yl., Wht. & Blk. tr.			20
BMW M1	3487 Co. Rcr.			MAL	Red to Pnk.				Reg				5
BMW M1	4364			HK	Red				Reg				10

Name	#	Category	Casting	Ctry.	Color	Win.	Base	Interior	Wheels	Paint	Logo	Other	$
BMW M1	4364			HK	Red				RR - Grey				18
BMW M1	4364			MAL	Red				RR - Grey				18
BMW M1	4364			MAL	Red				Reg				10
Bob's Big Boy Truck		Big Boy	DRA	HK	Wht.				Reg		Great in any weather		100
Bold Eagle		McD's	Plst.	CHN	Yl.				Uniq.				5
Breakeaway Bucket	8282			HK	Blu.				RL				55
Breakeaway Bucket	8282	Pre-Pro		HK	Blu.				RL				
Broncc 4-whlr	1520			HK	Wht.	TNT	Rivet close to front axle		Reg	Red flames, Blu. tr. w/no lower Blu. stripe			5
Broncc 4-whlr	1520			HK	Wht.		Rivet close to front axle		4x4 SHb	Red flames, Blu. tr. w/no lower Blu. stripe			5
Broncc 4-whlr	1520			MAL	Wht.	TNT			Reg	Red flames, Blu. tr. w/ lower Blu. stripe			5
Broncc 4-whlr	1520			MAL	Wht.	TNT	Rivet close to front axle		Reg	Red flames, Blu. tr. w/ lower Blu. stripe			5
Broncc 4-whlr	1520			MAL	Wht.	CL			Reg	Red flames, Blu. tr. w/ lower Blu. stripe			5
Broncc 4-whlr	1520			MAL	Wht.				4x4 SHb	Red flames, Blu. tr. w/no lower Blu. stripe			5
Broncc 4-whlr	1520			MAL	Wht.	CL	Rivet close to front axle		Reg	Red flames, Blu. tr. w/ lower Blu. stripe			5
Broncc 4-whlr	1520			MAL	Wht.	TNT			Reg	Red flames, Blu. tr. w/no lower Blu. stripe			5
Broncc 4-whlr	1690			HK	Blk.	BluT			Reg				7
Broncc 4-whlr	1690			MAL	Bk.	BluT			Reg				7
Broncc 4-whlr	1690			HK	Blk.	CL			Reg				7
Broncc 4-whlr	4355			MAL	Red/Blk.				RR - Grey				15
Broncc 4-whlr	4355			HK	Red/Wht.				Reg				7
Broncc 4-whlr	4355			MAL	Red/Wht.				Reg				7
Broncc 4-whlr	4355			MAL	Red/Wht.		Rsd. 1980		Reg				7
Broncc 4-whlr	4355			MAL	Red/Blk.				Reg				7
Broncc 4-whlr	4355			HK	Red/Blk.				Reg				7
Broncc 4-whlr	4355			MAL	Aq.	TNT	Rivet close to front axle		4x4 SHb	Red & Wht. tr.	Ford Bronco		5
Broncc 4-whlr	4355			HK	Red/Wht.	CL			RR - Wht.				15
Broncc 4-whlr	4355			MAL	Red/Wht.	TNT			RR - Wht.				15
Broncc 4-whlr	4355			HK	Red/Wht.				RR - Grey				15
Broncc 4-whlr	4355			HK	Red/Wht.		Rsd. 1980		Reg				7
Broncc 4-whlr	4355			HK	Red/Blk.				RR - Grey				15
Broncc 4-whlr	4355			MAL	Red/Wht.				RR - Grey				15
Broncc 4-whlr	4355			MAL	Red/Wht.	CL			RR - Wht.				15
Broncc 4-whlr	4355			HK	Red/Wht.	TNT			RR - Wht.				15
Bubble Gunner	2511			MAL	Gr.				Reg				7
Bubble Gunner	2511			HK	Gr.				Reg				7
Bubble Gunner	2511			HK	Magenta				Reg				7
Buick Funny Car		Pro-Circuit		CHN	Red	PT			P-C - Chr.	Wht., Gr. & Blu. tr.	King Kenny	Strut inside & 4 headlights	5
Buick Funny Car		Pro-Circuit		CHN	Red	PT			P-C - Chr.	Wht., Gr. & Blu. tr.	King Kenny	Strut inside & 3 headlights	5
Buick Stocker		Video Car		MAL	Yl.				Reg	Red tr.	3		10

Name	#	Category	Casting	Ctry.	Color	Win.	Base	Interior	Wheels	Paint	Logo	Other	$
Buick Stocker	2172	Pre-Pro		MAL	Gr.				Reg	Wht. tr.	Quaker State & 26		
Buick Stocker	9258	Roses		MAL	Blu.				Reg	Red & Wht. tr.	Roses & 6		8
Buick Stocker	9258	Roses		MAL	Blu.				Reg	Red & Wht. tr.	Roses & stylized 6		8
Buick Wildcat	11089	Demo Man		MAL	Red				Reg				10
Buzz Off	6976			HK	Dk. Blu.		Plst.		RL	Yl. pin-stripe tr.			90
Buzz Off	6976			HK	Pale Blu.			Grey	RL				90
Buzz Off	6976			HK	Gold plated				RL	Red, Or. & Blk. tr.	The Gold One		25
Buzz Off	6976			HK	Gr.			Dk. Bro.	RL				90
Buzz Off	6976			HK	Red			Grey	RL				90
Buzz Off	6976			HK	Or.			Blk.	RL				90
Buzz Off	6976			HK	Dk. Yl.			Blk.	RL				90
Buzz Off	6976			HK	Gr.			Grey	RL				90
Buzz Off	6976			HK	Pale Yl.			Grey	RL				90
Buzz Off	6976			HK	Or.			Grey	RL				90
Buzz Off	6976			HK	Flr. Lime			Grey	RL				90
Buzz Off	6976			HK	Dk. Blu.			Blk.	RL				90
Buzz Off	6976			HK	Plum			Dk. Bro.	RL				90
Buzz Off	6976			HK	Pale Blu.			Blk.	RL				90
Buzz Off	6976			HK	Pale Yl.			Blk.	RL				90
Buzz Off	6976			HK	Pnk.			Dk. Bro.	RL				90
Buzz Off	6976			HK	Pnk.			Blk.	RL				90
Buzz Off	6976			HK	Gold plated				Reg	Red, Or. & Blk. tr.	The Gold One		15
Buzz Off	6976			HK	Pnk.			Grey	RL				95
Buzz Off	6976			HK	Or.			Dk. Bro.	RL				90
Buzz Off	6976			HK	Pale Gr.			Dk. Bro.	RL				90
Buzz Off	6976			HK	Pale Yl.			Dk. Bro.	RL				90
Buzz Off	6976			HK	Plum			Blk.	RL				90
Buzz Off	6976			HK	Pale Gr.			Grey	RL				90
Buzz Off	6976			HK	Dk. Blu.		Plst.		Reg	Yl. pin-stripe tr.			50
Buzz Off	6976			HK	Blu.				RL	Yl. pin-stripe tr.			50
Buzz Off	6976			HK	Red			Dk. Bro.	RL				90
Buzz Off	6976			HK	Flr. Lime			Blk.	RL				90
Buzz Off	6976			HK	Dk. Yl.			Dk. Bro.	RL				90
Buzz Off	6976			HK	Gr.			Blk.	RL				90
Buzz Off	6976			HK	Pale Gr.			Blk.	RL				90
Buzz Off	6976			HK	Red			Blk.	RL				90
Buzz Off	6976			HK	Dk. Blu.			Dk. Bro.	RL				90
Buzz Off	6976			HK	Dk. Blu.			Grey	RL				90
Buzz Off	6976			HK	Pale Blu.			Dk. Bro.	RL				90
Buzz Off	6976			HK	Dk. Yl.			Grey	RL				90
Buzz Off	6976			HK	Flr. Lime			Dk. Bro.	RL	Yl. pin-stripe tr.			90
Buzz Off	6976			HK	Dk. Blu.				RL				90
Buzz Off	6976			HK	Plum			Grey	RL	Yl. & Gr. tr.			90
Buzz Off	6976			HK	Dk. Blu.		Plst.		RL				100
Bywayman		Getty		MAL	Yl.				4x4 SHb	Red, Wht. & Prp. tr.	Getty		4
Bywayman		Shell		MAL	Blk.			Bright Yl.	4x4 SHb	Red, Yl. & Wht. tr.			4
Bywayman		Shell		MAL	Blk.			Mustard Yl.	4x4 SHb	Red, Yl. & Wht. tr.			4
Bywayman		Shell		MAL	Blk.				4x4 SHb	Red, Yl. & Wht. tr.	Truck Guard		4
Bywayman	1518			MAL	Brg.		Rsd. 1977		4x4 SHb	Yl. & Wht. eagle tr.			6
Bywayman	1518			HK	Brg.		Flat 1977		Reg	Yl. & Wht. eagle tr.			6
Bywayman	1518			HK	Brg.		Rsd. 1977		4x4 SHb	Yl. & Wht. eagle tr.			6

Name	#	Category	Casting	Ctry.	Color	Win.	Base	Interior	Wheels	Paint	Logo	Other	$
Bywayman	1518			MAL	Brg.		Flat 1977		Reg	Yl. & Wht. eagle tr.			6
Bywayman	1518			MAL	Brg.		Rsd. 1977		Reg	Yl. & Wht. eagle tr.			6
Bywayman	1518			HK	Brg.		Rsd. 1977		Reg	Yl. & Wht. eagle tr.			6
Bywayman	1518			MAL	Brg.		Flat 1977		4x4 SHb	Yl. & Wht. eagle tr.			6
Bywayman	1518			HK	Brg.		Flat 1977		4x4 SHb	Yl. & Wht. eagle tr.			6
Bywayman	2196			HK	Blk.				4x4 SHb	Blu., Yl. & Wht. eagle tr.			5
Bywayman	2196			HK	Blk.				Reg	Blu. & Wht. eagle tr.			5
Bywayman	2196			MAL	Blk.				Reg	Blu. & Wht. eagle tr.			5
Bywayman	2196			MAL	Blk.				4x4 SHb	Blu., Yl. & Wht. eagle tr.			5
Bywayman	2509			MAL	Blu.			No TB	Reg				10
Bywayman	2509			MAL	Gr.				Reg				10
Bywayman	2509			HK	Blu.			No TB	Reg				10
Bywayman	2509			HK	Gr.				Reg				10
Bywayman	4321			MAL	Ivory				4x4 SHb	Pnk. & Bro. speckle tr.			10
Bywayman	4361			MAL	Blu. MF.			TB	RR - Grey				15
Bywayman	4361			HK	Blu. MF.			TB	Reg				10
Bywayman	4361			MAL	Blu. MF.		1977 Rsd. & MAL cast flat	No TB	RR - Grey				15
Bywayman	4361			MAL	Blu. MF.			TB	RR - Wht.				15
Bywayman	4361			HK	Blu. MF.			TB	RR - Wht.				15
Bywayman	4361			MAL	Blu. MF.			TB	Reg				10
Bywayman	4361			MAL	Blu. MF.		1982 & MAL cast flat	No TB	RR - Grey				15
Bywayman	4361			MAL	Blu. MF.		1977 Rsd. & MAL cast flat	TB	RR - Wht.				15
Bywayman	4361			HK	Blu. MF.			TB	RR - Grey				15
Bywayman	4361			HK	Blu. MF.			No TB	Reg				10
Bywayman	4361			MAL	Blu. MF.		1977 Rsd. & MAL cast flat	No TB	Reg				10
Bywayman	4361			MAL	Blu. MF.		1982 & MAL cast flat	No TB	Reg				10
Bywayman	4361			MAL	Blu. MF.		1977 Rsd. & MAL cast flat	TB	RR - Grey				15
Bywayman	4361			MAL	Blu. MF.		1982 & MAL cast flat	TB	RR - Wht.				15
Bywayman	4361			MAL	Blu. MF.		1977 Rsd. & MAL cast flat	No TB	4x4 SHb				15
Bywayman	4361			MAL	Blu. MF.		1982 & MAL cast flat	TB	Reg				10
Bywayman	4361			MAL	Blu. MF.		1982 & MAL cast flat	No TB	4x4 SHb				10
Bywayman	4361			MAL	Blu. MF.			No TB	Reg				10
Bywayman	4361			MAL	Blu. MF.		1982 & MAL cast flat	TB	RR - Grey				15
Bywayman	4361			HK	Blu. MF.		1977 Rsd. & MAL cast flat	No TB	RR - Grey				15
Bywayman	4361			MAL	Blu. MF.		1982 & MAL cast flat	TB	Reg				10
Bywayman	4361			MAL	Blu. MF.		1982 & MAL cast flat	TB	4x4 SHb				10
Bywayman	4361			MAL	Blu. MF.			No TB	RR - Grey				15

Name	#	Category	Casting	Ctry.	Color	Win.	Base	Interior	Wheels	Paint	Logo	Other	$
Bywayman	9349			MAL	Yl.		1977 Rsd. & MAL cast flat	No TB	Reg				10
Bywayman	9349			MAL	Yl.		1977 Rsd. & MAL cast flat	TB	Reg				10
Bywayman	9349			MAL	Yl.		1977 Rsd. & MAL cast flat	No TB	RR - Wht.				15
Bywayman	9349			MAL	Yl.		1977 cast flat & MAL Rsd.	TB	Reg				10
Bywayman	9349			MAL	Yl.		1977 Rsd. & MAL cast flat	TB	RR - Wht.				15
Bywayman	9349			MAL	Yl.		1977 cast flat & MAL Rsd.	TB	RR - Wht.				15
Bywayman	9349			MAL	Yl.		1977 cast flat & MAL Rsd.	No TB	RR - Wht.				15
Bywayman	9349			MAL	Yl.		1977 cast flat & MAL Rsd.	No TB	Reg				10
Cadillac Seville	1698			FRA	Grey				RR - Grey	Blu. tr. on hood			40
Cadillac Seville	1698			FRA	Grey				RR - Grey	Yl. tr. on hood			40
Cadillac Seville	1698			FRA	Grey				RR - Grey				40
Cadillac Seville	1698			FRA	Grey				Reg				20
Cadillac Seville	1698			FRA	Gold MF.				Reg				20
Cadillac Seville	1698			MEX	Tan				Reg				40
Cadillac Seville	1698			MAL	Grey				Reg	Mgta. sides			7
Cadillac Seville	1698			HK	Grey				Reg	Mgta. sides			7
Cadillac Seville	4356			HK	Gold MF.				Reg	Mgta. sides			50
Cadillac Seville	4356			HK	Gold MF.				RR - Grey				20
Cadillac Seville	4356			MEX	Gold MF.				RR - Grey				20
Cadillac Seville	4356			MEX	Gold MF.				Reg				50
Cadillac Seville	4356			MAL	Gold MF.				Reg	Mgta. sides			40
Cadillac Seville	4356			MEX	Gold MF.				WW				50
Cadillac Seville	4356			HK	Gold MF.				Reg				7
Camaro Stocker		McD's		CHN	Yl.	CL			Uniq.	Blk. & Wht. tr.	Duracell # 88		5
Camaro Stocker		McD's		CHN	Blu./Wht.	CL			Uniq.	Red tr.	HW # 1		5
Camaro Z-28	9532			MAL	Or.		Blk. Plst.		UH	Blu., Prp. & Yl. tr.	Camaro Z-28		6
Camaro Z-28	9532			MAL	Or.		Logo & flat MAL		UH	Blu., Prp. & Yl. tr.	Camaro Z-28		6
Camaro Z-28	9532			MAL	Prp.		Blk. Plst.		Reg	Yl., Or. & Gr. geo. tr.			6
Camaro Z-28		Co. Rcr.		MAL	Prp. to Pnk.				Reg				5
Camaro Z-28		Getty		MAL	Wht.		Name & Rsd. MAL		HO - Gold	Red, Yl. & Blu. tr.	Getty		8
Camaro Z-28	2179 Park'n Plate			MAL	Or.		Name & Rsd. MAL		HO - Gold	Blu., Prp. & Yl. tr.	Camaro Z-28		7
Camaro Z-28	5282 Ralston			MAL	Prp.		Name & Rsd. MAL		HO - Gold	Gr., Wht. & Yl. tr.	Camaro Z-28		6
Camaro Z-28		Set		MAL	Wht.				HO - Gold	Or., Blu. & Blk. stripes		Double Barrel Stunt Set	10
Camaro Z-28		Set		MAL	Blu.				UH	Yl., Red & Pnk. block tr.			10
Camaro Z-28	2179			MAL	Or.		Blk. Plst.		UH	Prp., Blu. & Yl. tr.			7
Camaro Z-28	2179			MAL	Or.		Blk. Plst.		Reg	Prp., Blu. & Yl. tr.			7
Camaro Z-28	5182			MAL	Dk. Red MF.				HO - Gold	Blu., Wht. & Yl. tr.	Z-28		7
Camaro Z-28	5182			HK	Wht.		Camaro		HO - Gold	Red, Prp. & Yl. stripes	Z-28		7

Name	Category	#	Casting	Ctry.	Color	Win.	Base	Interior	Wheels	Paint	Logo	Other	S
Camaro Z-28	5182			HK	Grey				HO - Gold	Or. stripe	Z-28		7
Camaro Z-28	5182			HK	Wht.		Camaro		HO - Gold	Red, Prp. & Yl. stripes	Z-28		7
Camaro Z-28	5182			HK	Dk. Red MF.				HO - Gold	Blu., Wht. & Yl. tr.	Z-28		7
Camaro Z-28	5894 SE			MAL	Gold				HO - Gold				15
Camaro Z-28	9344			MAL	Silver MF.				HO - Gold	Or. stripe	Z-28		15
Camaro Z-28	9344			HK	Wht.				HO - Gold	Red, Yl. & Blk. tr.	Camaro Z-28		7
Camaro Z-28	9344			MAL	Wht.				HO - Gold	Red, Yl. & Blk. tr.	Camaro Z-28		7
Camaro Z-28	9344			HK	Silver MF.				HO - Gold	Or. stripe	Z-28		7
Camaro Z-28	9532			MAL	Red		Blk. Plst.		UH	Blu., Yl. & Blk. tr.			7
Camaro Z-28	9532			MAL	Red		Logo & flat MAL		UH	Blu., Yl. & Blk. tr.			7
Camaro Z-28	9532			MAL	Red		Name & Rsd. MAL		HO - Gold	Blu., Yl. & Blk. tr.			7
Camaro Z-28	9532			MAL	Red		Blk. Plst.		Reg	Blu., Yl. & Blk. tr.			7
Cannonade	1691			HK	Yl.				HO - Gold				5
Cannonade	1691			HK	Yl.				Reg				5
Cannonade	1691			MAL	Red				HO - Gold				5
Cannonade	1691			MEX	Maroon				HO - Gold				25
Cannonade	1691			MEX	Yl.				HO - Gold				15
Captain America	2851 Scene Machine			HK	Wht.				Reg				30
Captain America	2879 Heroes			MAL	Wht.				Reg				15
Captain America	2879 Heroes			MAL	Wht.				HO - Gold				15
Carabo	7617			HK	Gr.				RL	Or. & Blu. tr.			35
Carabo	7617			HK	Yl.				RL	Or. & Blu. tr.			300
Cargoyle	2058 Speed Demon			HK	Or.		Logo		UH	Blk. markings on back			4
Cargoyle	2058 Speed Demon			MAL	Or.		Logo		UH	Blk. markings on back			4
Cargoyle	2058 Speed Demon			HK	Yl.				UH	Blk. markings on back		Leapin' Demons Chase	4
Cargoyle	2058 Speed Demon			MAL	Or.				UH	Prp. markings on back			4
Cargoyle	2058 Speed Demon			MAL	Or.		N&N		UH	Blk. markings on back			4
Cargoyle	2058 Speed Demon			HK	Or.		N&N		UH	Blk. markings on back			4
Cargoyle	2058 Speed Demon			MAL	Or.		Rsd. MAL		UH	Blk. markings on back			4
CAT Bulldozer	1172 Workhorse			MAL	Yl.				4x4 SHb - Yl.				5
CAT Bulldozer	1172 Workhorse			HK	Yl.				4x4 SHb - Yl.				5
Bulldozer	3765			MAL	Yl.								4
CAT Dump Truck	1171 Workhorse	No CAT casting	HK	Yl.				4x4 SHb - Yl.				5
CAT Dump Truck	1171 Workhorse	CAT cast over	MAL	Yl.				4x4 SHb - Gold				5
CAT Dump Truck	1171 Workhorse	CAT cast over	HK	Yl.				4x4 SHb - Yl.				5
CAT Dump Truck	1171 Workhorse	No CAT casting	MAL	Yl.				4x4 SHb - Yl.				5
CAT Dump Truck	1171 Workhorse		HK	Yl.				4x4 SHb - Yl.		CAT tampo to right of driver's door		5
CAT Dump Truck	1171 Workhorse	CAT cast over	MAL	Yl.				4x4 SHb - Yl.				5
CAT Dump Truck	1171 Workhorse		MAL	Yl.				4x4 SHb - Yl.		CAT tampo to right of driver's door		5
CAT Dump Truck	1171 Workhorse	CAT cast over	HK	Yl.				4x4 SHb - Gold				15
CAT Dump Truck	1171 Workhorse	CAT cast to right of driver's door	MAL	Yl.				4x4 SHb - Yl.				5
CAT Dump Truck	1171 Workhorse	CAT cast to right of driver's door	HK	Yl.				4x4 SHb - Yl.				5

Name	#	Category	Casting	Ctry.	Color	Win.	Base	Interior	Wheels	Paint	Logo	Other	$
CAT Earth Mover	3715			MAL	Yl.				4x4 SHb - Gold	No tr.	No CAT		5
CAT Earth Mover	3715			MAL	Yl.		N&N		4x4 SHb - Yl.	No tr.	No CAT		5
CAT Earth Mover	3715			MAL	Yl.				4x4 SHb - Yl.	No tr.	No CAT		5
CAT Earth Mover	3715			MAL	Yl.				4x4 SHb - Gold	Blk. & Wht. tr.	CAT		15
CAT Forklift	1168			MEX	Yl.				Reg				12
CAT Forklift	1168 Workhorse			MAL	Yl.				Reg				12
CAT Forklift	1168 Workhorse			MAL	Gr.				Reg				30
CAT Forklift	1168 Workhorse			HK	Yl.				Reg				12
CAT Road Roller	3853		5 windshield struts	MAL	Yl.					Blk. stripe	Caterpillar		18
CAT Road Roller	3853		3 windshield struts	MAL	Yl.					Blk. stripe	Caterpillar		18
CAT Road Roller	3853		3 windshield struts	MAL	Yl.		N&N						7
CAT Road Roller	3853		3 windshield struts	MAL	Yl.								7
CAT Road Roller	3853		3 windshield struts	MAL	Yl.								7
CAT Wheel Loader	1173 Workhorse			IND	Yl.		MAL scraped off		4x4 SHb - Yl.				6
CAT Wheel Loader	1173 Workhorse			HK	Yl.				4x4 SHb - Gold				18
CAT Wheel Loader	1173 Workhorse		lgr. opening round HK air filter		Yl.				4x4 LHb - Yl.				6
CAT Wheel Loader	1173 Workhorse			HK	Yl.				4x4 SHb - Yl.				6
CAT Wheel Loader	1173 Workhorse		lgr. opening round MAL air filter		Yl.				4x4 SHb - Yl.				6
CAT Wheel Loader	1173 Workhorse		lgr. opening round HK air filter		Yl.				4x4 SHb - Yl.				6
CAT Wheel Loader	1173 Workhorse			MAL	Yl.				4x4 SHb - Yl.				6
CAT Wheel Loader	1173 Workhorse		lgr. opening - air filter no CAT	HK	Yl.				4x4 SHb - Yl.				6
CAT Wheel Loader	1173 Workhorse			MAL	Yl.				4x4 SHb - Gold				18
CAT Wheel Loader	1173 Workhorse		lgr. opening - air filter no CAT	MAL	Yl.				4x4 SHb - Yl.				6
CAT Wheel Loader	1173 Workhorse		lgr. opening round MAL air filter		Yl.				4x4 LHb - Yl.				6
CAT Wheel Loader	1173 Workhorse			HK	Yl.		Rsd. HK		4x4 SHb - Yl.				6
Chevrolet Camaro		Pre-Pro		CHN	Blu./Wht.				P-C - Chr.	Red & Blk. tr.	74		12
Chevrolet Camaro	2115 Pro-Circuit			CHN	Blu./Wht.				P-C - Red	Red & Yl. tr.	HW logo	Dk. Red logo on roof	12
Chevrolet Camaro	2115 Pro-Circuit			CHN	Blu./Wht.				P-C - Red front, Wht. rear	Red & Yl. tr.	HW logo	Bright Red logo on roof	5
Chevrolet Camaro		Pro-Circuit		CHN	Wht.				P-C - Chr.	Gr., neon Pnk., Blu. & Blk. tr.	Cytomax 3		20
Chevrolet Camaro	2738 Pro-Circuit			CHN	Or.				P-C - Chr.	Blk., Red & Wht. tr.	Duracell		5
Chevrolet Lumina	5675			MAL	Red				Reg			Small wheels	4
Chevrolet Lumina	5675			MAL	Red				Reg			Large wheels	4
Chevrolet Lumina Taxi	12352			MAL	Yl.				Reg	Blk. tr.	Taxi		3
Chevy Citation	1693			FRA	Bro. MF.			Red	HO - Gold	Red, Wht. & Blk. tr.	Citation X-II		20
Chevy Citation	1693			FRA	Wht.			Blk.	Reg	Red & Blk. tr.			20
Chevy Citation	1693			FRA	Wht.			Red	Reg	Red & Blk. tr.			20
Chevy Citation	1693			FRA	Bro. MF.			Red	Reg	Red, Wht. & Blk. tr.	Citation X-II		20

Name	#	Category	Casting	Ctry.	Color	Win.	Base	Interior	Wheels	Paint	Logo	Other	S
Chevy Citation	1693			FRA	Blu.			Red	Reg	Wht. tr.			20
Chevy Citation				IND	Gr.			Wht.	Reg	Yl. & Wht. tr.			10
Chevy Citation				IND	Red			Tan	Reg	Blk. & Wht. tr.			10
Chevy Citation		Pre-Pro		MAL	Gr.			Red	HO - Gold	Red, Wht. & Blk. tr.	Citation X-II		5
Chevy Citation	1693			MAL	Yl.			Red	HO - Gold	Red & Blk. tr.			5
Chevy Citation	1693			HK	Wht.				HO - Gold				5
Chevy Citation	1693			MAL	Red			Tan	Reg	Yl., Wht. & Blk. tr.	Citation X-II		10
Chevy Citation	1693			HK	Red			Tan	Reg	Yl., Wht. & Blk. tr.	Citation X-II		10
Chevy Citation	1693			HK	Wht.			Red	HO - Gold	Red & Blk. tr.			5
Chevy Citation	1693			HK	Yl.			Red	HO - Gold	Or., Wht. & Blk. tr.	Citation X-II		5
Chevy Citation				HK	Bro. MF.				HO - Gold				5
Chevy Citation	3362			MEX	Bro. MF.				Reg		Citation X-II		15
Chevy Citation	3362			MAL	Bro. MF.				HO - Gold				5
Chevy Citation	3362			MEX	Bro. MF.				Reg				15
Chevy Citation	3362			IND					Reg				10
Chevy Monza 2+2	7671			IND	Prp.				Reg	Wht., Yl. & Blk.	442		20
Chevy Monza 2+2	9202			FRA	Or.	TNT			Reg	Blk. tr.	Monza		10
Chevy Monza 2+2	7671			IND	Light Blu.				Reg	Wht. & Blu. tr.	442		20
Chevy Monza 2+2	9202			FRA	Or.	CL			Reg	Blk. tr.	Monza		10
Chevy Monza 2+2	7671			IND	Blk.				Reg	Wht. & Yl. tr.	442		20
Chevy Monza 2+2	9202			FRA	Or.	CL			Reg	Blk. & Wht. tr.	Monza, & BP on roof		20
Chevy Monza 2+2	9202			FRA	Or.	TNT			Reg	Blk. & Wht. tr.	Monza, & BP on roof		25
Chevy Monza 2+2	9202			MEX	Or.	Yl. TNT	Fra		Reg	Blk. & Wht. tr.	Monza		25
Chevy Monza 2+2	9202			MEX	Pale Or.	GT	Fra		Reg	Blk. & Wht. tr.	Monza		300
Chevy Monza 2+2	7671			HK	Gr.				RL				25
Chevy Monza 2+2	9202			MEX	Or.	GT	Fra		RL	Blk. & Wht. tr.	Monza		40
Chevy Monza 2+2	7671			HK	Or.				RL	Blk. tr.	Monza		25
Chevy Monza 2+2	9202			MEX	Or.	Yl. TNT	Fra		WW				25
Chevy Monza 2+2	9202			MEX	Pale Or.	GT	Fra		Reg				25
Chevy Monza 2+2	9202			MEX	Or.	GT	Fra		Reg	Blk. & Yl. tr.	Monza		25
Chevy Monza 2+2	9202			MEX	Or.	Yl. TNT	Fra		Reg				25
Chevy Monza 2+2	9202			MEX	Or.	CL	Fra		WW				25
Chevy Monza 2+2	9202	Super Chr.		HK	Chr.	GT	Fra		Reg				25
Chevy Monza 2+2	9202	Super Chr.		HK	Chr.				RL				25
Chevy Nomad	3360		Opening hood	MAL	Red			Yl.	Reg				20
Chevy Stocker		Ralston		MAL	Aq.				Reg	Red, Wht., & Yl. tr.	3		8
Chevy Stocker	452			MAL	Glt. N. Or.				Reg				3
Chevy Stocker	1791			MAL	Blk.				Reg	Red, Wht., & Yl. tr.	3	4 tampos behind FW	6
Chevy Stocker	1791			MAL	Blk.				Reg	Red, Wht., & Yl. tr.	3	2 tampos behind FW	6
Chief's Special	7665		Metal roof light & hood do not open	HK	Red				Reg				30
Chief's Special	7665		Hood does not open	HK	Red				RL				35
Chief's Special	9117	Herfy's	Metal roof light & hood do not open	HK	Red				RL		Herfy's		100
Circus Cats	3303	Scene Machine		MAL	Wht.				Reg				40
Claforan 500		Park'n Plate	Short rear wing	MAL	Wht.				Reg		Claforan 500		35
Classic '32 Ford Vicky	10494	Vintage		CHN	M. Bro.				RL			Smooth roof	4

Name	#	Category	Casting	Ctry.	Color	Win.	Base	Interior	Wheels	Paint	Logo	Other	$
Classic '32 Ford Vicky	10494	Vintage		CHN	M. Red				RL			Smooth roof	4
Classic '32 Ford Vicky	10494	Vintage		CHN	M. Electric Gr.				RL			Smooth roof	4
Classic '32 Ford Vicky	10494	Vintage		CHN	Gold				RL			Smooth roof	4
Classic '32 Ford Vicky	10494	Vintage		CHN	Br. Red				RL			Smooth roof	4
Classic '32 Ford Vicky	10494	Vintage		CHN	M. Magenta				RL			Smooth roof	4
Classic '32 Ford Vicky	10494	Vintage		CHN	Wht.				RL			Smooth roof	4
Classic '32 Ford Vicky	10494	Vintage		CHN	M. Turquoise				RL			Smooth roof	4
Classic '32 Ford Vicky	10494	Vintage		CHN	Maroon				RL			Smooth roof	4
Classic '32 Ford Vicky	10494	Vintage		CHN	M. Dk. Bro.				RL			Smooth roof	4
Classic '32 Ford Vicky	10494	Vintage		CHN	M. Pnk.				RL			Smooth roof	4
Classic '32 Ford Vicky	10494	Vintage		CHN	M. Lime				RL			Smooth roof	4
Classic '32 Ford Vicky	10494	Vintage		CHN	Gunmetal				RL			Smooth roof	4
Classic '32 Ford Vicky	10494	Vintage		CHN	M. Or.				RL			Smooth roof	4
Classic '32 Ford Vicky	10494	Vintage		CHN	M. Oiive Gr.				RL			Smooth roof	4
Classic '32 Ford Vicky	10494	Vintage		CHN	M. Pale Pnk.				RL			Smooth roof	4
Classic '32 Ford Vicky	10494	Vintage		CHN	M. Br. Blu.				RL			Smooth roof	4
Classic '32 Ford Vicky	10494	Vintage		CHN	M. Violet				RL			Smooth roof	4
Classic '32 Ford Vicky	10494	Vintage		CHN	M. Gold				RL			Smooth roof	4
Classic '32 Ford Vicky	10494	Vintage		CHN	M. Dk. Gr.				RL			Smooth roof	4
Classic '32 Ford Vicky	10494	Vintage		CHN	M. Prp.				RL			Smooth roof	4
Classic '32 Ford Vicky	10494	Vintage		CHN	M. Blu.				RL			Smooth roof	4
Classic '32 Ford Vicky	10494	Vintage		CHN	M. Gr.				RL			Smooth roof	4
Classic '32 Ford Vicky	10494	Vintage		CHN	M. Royal Blu.				RL			Smooth roof	4
Classic Cobra		25th Ann.		MAL	Pale Blu.				Reg				5
Classic Cobra	1296	Cal Cus.		MAL	N. Yl.				Reg				8
Classic Cobra	1296	Cal Cus.		MAL	Wht.				RR - Grey				8
Classic Cobra		Gold Ser.		MAL	Red				P-C - Gold			FAOSc	25
Classic Cobra	2055	Park'n Plate		MAL	Blk.				Reg				7
Classic Cobra		Revealer		MAL	Ivory				Reg			Revealers 10 pack	10
Classic Cobra		Revealer		MAL	Wht.				Reg			Revealers 10 pack	10
Classic Cobra	2535			MAL	Red				RR - Grey		No 427 on hood		15
Classic Cobra	2535			MAL	Red				Reg	Wht. stripes	No 427 on hood		10
Classic Cobra	2535			MAL	Red				Reg		427 on hood		10
Classic Cobra	2535			HK	Red				Reg		No 427 on hood		10
Classic Cobra	2535			HK	Red				RR - Grey		No 427 on hood		15
Classic Cobra	2535			MAL	Red				RR - Grey		427 on hood		15
Classic Cobra	2535			HK	Red				Reg		427 on hood		10
Classic Cobra	4369			HK	Blu.				RR - Wht.	Wht. stripes			20
Classic Cobra	4369			MAL	Blu.				RR - Wht.	Wht. stripes			20
Classic Cobra	4369			MAL	Blu.				Reg				12
Classic Cobra	4369			HK	Blu.	Yl. TNT			RR - Grey	Wht. stripes			15
Classic Cobra	4369			HK	Blu.				RR - Grey	Wht. stripes			15
Classic Cobra	4369			MEX	Blu.				RR - Grey	Wht. stripes			15
Classic Cobra	4369			HK	Blu.				Reg				12
Classic Cobra	4369			MEX	Blu.				Reg	Yl. stripes			50
Classic Cobra	4369			MAL	Blu.				RR - Grey	Wht. stripes			15
Classic Cobra	4369			MEX	Blu.				RR - Grey	Yl. stripes		Smaller wheels	50

Name	#	Category	Casting	Ctry.	Color	Win.	Base	Interior	Wheels	Paint	Logo	Other	S
Classic Ferrari	5665			MAL	Yl.		Chr.		Reg				4
Classic Ferrari	5665			MAL	Yl.		Yl.		Reg				4
Classic Nomad		Pre-Pro	Hood opens	CHN	Blk./Wht.				RL				5
Classic Nomad	5743	25th Ann.	Hood opens	CHN	M. Turquoise				RL				5
Classic Nomad	5743	25th Ann.	Hood opens	CHN	M. Olive Gr.				RL				5
Classic Nomad	5743	25th Ann.	Hood opens	CHN	M. Red				RL				5
Classic Nomad	5743	25th Ann.	Hood opens	CHN	M. Or.				RL				5
Classic Nomad	5743	25th Ann.	Hood opens	CHN	M. Violet				RL				5
Classic Nomad	5743	25th Ann.	Hood opens	CHN	M. Blu.				RL				5
Classic Nomad	5743	25th Ann.	Hood opens	CHN	Navy Blu.				RL				5
Classic Nomad	5743	25th Ann.	Hood opens	CHN	M. Lime				RL				5
Classic Nomad	5743	25th Ann.	Hood opens	CHN	M. Bro.				RL				5
Classic Nomad	5743	25th Ann.	Hood opens	CHN	M. Magenta				RL				5
Classic Nomad	5743	25th Ann.	Hood opens	CHN	M. Pnk.				RL				5
Classic Nomad	5743	25th Ann.	Hood opens	CHN	Gold				RL				5
Classic Nomad	5743	25th Ann.	Hood opens	CHN	M. Gr.				RL				5
Classic Nomad	5743	Gold Ser.	Hood opens	CHN	M. Sky Blu.				RL - Gold			FAOSc	25
Classic Nomad	5743	Vintage	Hood opens	CHN	M. Prp.				RL				5
Classic Nomad	5743	Vintage	Hood opens	CHN	M. Pale Pnk.				RL				5
Classic Nomad	5743	Vintage	Hood opens	CHN	M. Br. Blu.				RL				5
Classic Nomad	5743	Vintage	Hood opens	CHN	M. Electric Gr.				RL				5
Classic Nomad	5743	Vintage	Hood opens	CHN	M. Gold				RL				5
Classic Nomad	5743	Vintage	Hood opens	CHN	M. Dk. Bro.				RL				5
Classic Nomad	5743	Vintage	Hood opens	CHN	Br. Red				RL				5
Classic Nomad	5743	Vintage	Hood opens	CHN	M. Royal Blu.				RL				5
Classic Nomad	5743	Vintage	Hood opens	CHN	M. Prp.				RL				5
Classic Nomad	5743	Vintage	Hood opens	CHN	Maroon				RL				5
Classic Nomad	5743	Vintage	Hood opens	CHN	Gunmetal				RL				5
Classic Nomad	5743	Vintage	Hood opens	CHN	Wht.				RL				5
Classic Nomad	5743	Vintage	Hood opens	CHN	M. Dk. Gr.				RL				5
Classic Nomad	13523	Toy Show	Hood opens	CHN	Blk./Wht.				Wht. Line - Gold			Seattle Toy Show 1994	15
Classic Packard	3920			HK	Blk.				WW				7
Classic Packard	3920			MEX	Blk.				WW				15
Classic Packard	3920			MAL	Blk.				WW				7
Combat Medic	2519			MAL	Des. Scrub				Reg - Blk.				6
Combat Medic	2519			HK	Des. Cmflg.				Reg				6
Combat Medic	2519			MAL	Khk. Cmflg.				Reg - Blk.				6
Combat Medic	2519			HK	Khk. Cmflg.				Reg - Blk.				6
Combat Medic	2519			MAL	Des. Scrub				Reg				6
Command Tank	9371			MAL	Des. Scrub								6
Command Tank	9371			HK	Des. Scrub								6
Command Tank	9371			MAL	Arctic Cmflg.								6
Command Tank	9371			MAL	Jungle Cmflg.								6
Command Tank	9371		Plst.	MAL	Gr. Cmflg.								6
Command Tank	9371			MAL	Khk. Cmflg.		Name						6
Command Tank	9371			MAL	Khk. Cmflg.		No name						6
Command Tank	9371			MAL	Des. Cmflg.								6
Construction Crane	3254			HK	Yl.				Reg				10
Construction Crane	3254			MAL	Yl.				Reg				10
Cool One	9120			HK	Plum				RL	Wht. & Yl. tr.	Cool One & zap	Blk. FWs	40

Name	#	Category	Casting	Ctry.	Color	Win.	Base	Interior	Wheels	Paint	Logo	Other	$
Cool One	9120			HK	Gr.				Reg	Red & Yl. arrows	Cool One	Clear FWs	30
Cool One	9120			HK	Gr.				Reg	Red & Yl. arrows	Cool One	Blk. FWs	30
Corvette Funny Car		2102 Cal Cus.		MAL	Wht.		ROA		Reg	Neon Pnk. & pale Blu. flames			7
Corvette Funny Car		2102 Cal Cus.		MAL	Wht.		RAF & SIS		Reg	Neon Pnk. & Blu. flames			7
Corvette Funny Car		2102 Cal Cus.		MAL	Wht.		RAF & SIS		Reg	Neon Pnk. & pale Blu. flames			7
Corvette Funny Car		2102 Cal Cus.		MAL	Wht.		ROA		Reg	Neon Pnk. & Blu. flames			7
Corvette Funny Car		2102 Cal Cus.		MAL	Wht.		RAF & no SIS		Reg	Neon Pnk. & Blu. flames			7
Corvette Funny Car		2102 Cal Cus.		MAL	Wht.		RAF & no SIS		Reg	Neon Pnk. & pale Blu. flames			7
Corvette Stingray	9206			HK	Red				HO - Gold	Red, Yl. & Or. tr.	Corvette		7
Corvette Stingray	9252	Billionth Car		MAL	Gold				Reg				6
Corvette Stingray		Co. Rcr.		MAL	Dk. Blu. to Pale Blu.				Reg				5
Corvette Stingray		Co. Rcr.		MAL	Prp. to Wht.				Reg				5
Corvette Stingray		Co. Rcr.		MAL	Bro. to Yl. MF.				Reg				5
Corvette Stingray	1793	Gleamer	Plst. w/ etched pattern	MAL	Gr.				Reg				10
Corvette Stingray		HW Conv.		MAL	Gold				Reg		HW 6th Annual Convention		150
Corvette Stingray		NPS		MAL	Wht.				Reg	Blk. tr.	NPS		30
Corvette Stingray		NPS		MAL	Red				Reg	Wht. tr.	NPS		30
Corvette Stingray		Ralston		MAL	Or.		Lrg. letters		Reg	Blu. stripes	Corvette		7
Corvette Stingray		Ralston		MAL	Or.		Sm. letters		Reg	Blu. stripes	Corvette		7
Corvette Stingray	1448			MAL	Grey MF.		HW		Reg	Or., Yl. & Blk. tr.			5
Corvette Stingray	1448			MAL	Grey MF.		HW		Reg	Or., Yl. & Prp. tr.			5
Corvette Stingray	1448			MAL	Grey MF.		Logo & no name		Reg	Or., Yl. & Blk. tr.			5
Corvette Stingray	1448			MAL	Grey MF.		Logo & name		Reg	Or., Yl. & Blk. tr.			5
Corvette Stingray	1448			MAL	Grey MF.		Logo & name		Reg	Or., Yl. & Prp. tr.			5
Corvette Stingray	1448			MAL	Grey MF.		Logo & no name		Reg	Or., Yl. & Prp. tr.			5
Corvette Stingray	1793	Gleamer	Plst. w/ etched pattern	MAL	Silver				Reg				4
Corvette Stingray	2123	Kelloggs		MAL	Red				Reg	Blu., Yl. & Wht. stripes			20
Corvette Stingray	3974			MAL	Yl.		No name		Reg	Or., Prp. & Blu. tr.	Stingray		5
Corvette Stingray	3974			MAL	Yl.		Name		Reg	Or., Prp. & Blu. tr.	Stingray		5
Corvette Stingray	5084			HK	Red MF.				HO - Gold	Red, Yl. & Blk. tr.	Corvette		7
Corvette Stingray	5084			MAL	Red MF.				HO - Gold	Red, Yl. & Or. tr.	Corvette		7
Corvette Stingray	9241			HK	Or.				HO - Gold	Yl., Mgta. & Blk. ribbon tr.			10
Corvette Stingray	9241			HK	Or.				HO - Gold	Yl., Mgta. & Blk. ribbon tr.			10
Corvette Stingray	9241			HK	Blk.				HO - Gold	Red, Yl. & Or. tr.	Corvette	Hot Ones 3 Pack	15
Corvette Stingray	9241			HK	Grey				Reg	Blk., Wht. & Red ribbon tr.			10
Corvette Stingray	9241			HK	Yl.				Reg	Red, Blk. & Wht. ribbon tr.			10
Corvette Stingray	9241			HK	Red				Reg	Yl., Blu. & Wht. ribbon tr.			10
Corvette Stingray	9241			HK	Red				RL	Yl., Blu. & Wht. ribbon tr.			10
Corvette Stingray	9241			MAL	Yl.				HO - Gold	Blu., Or. & Mgta. tr.	Stingray		10
Corvette Stingray	9241			HK	Yl.				HO - Gold	Blu., Or. & Mgta. tr.	Stingray		10
Corvette Stingray	9506			HK	Gold				Reg	Red, Wht. & Blu. ribbon tr.		Golden Machines Six Pack	25

Casting	Number	Country	Color	Name	Window	Wheels	Tampo	Logo	Qty
Corvette Stingray	9506 Super Chr.	HK	Chr.			RL	Blu., Wht. & Yl. ribbon tr.		50
Corvette Stingray	9506 Super Chr.	HK	Chr.			Reg	Blu., Wht. & Yl. ribbon tr.		50
Corvette Stingray	9525	MAL	Wht.	Name		Reg	Red, Blu. & Blk. tr.		10
Corvette Stingray	9525	MAL	Wht.	Name		HO - Gold	Red, Blu. & Blk. tr.		10
Corvette Stingray	9525	MAL	Wht.	No name		HO - Gold	Red, Blu. & Blk. tr.		10
Corvette Stingray	9525	MAL	Wht.	No name		Reg	Red, Blu. & Blk. tr.		10
Corvette Stingray III	11065 Demo Man	MAL	Dk. Red			P-C - Chr.			10
Custom Corvette	2898	MAL	Ivory		CL	UH	Red, Yl. & Blk. tr.	Corvette	3
Custom Corvette	25th Ann.	MAL	M. Bro.		TNT	UH	Gr., Prp. & Blu. tr.	Corvette	5
Custom Corvette	9246 Billionth Car	MAL	Gold		CL	UH			8
Custom Corvette	1301 Cal Cus.	MAL	N. Or.		CL	Rtr - Chr.	Pnk., Wht. & Yl. tr.	Corvette	7
Custom Corvette	1301 Cal Cus.	MAL	Blu. Chr.		CL	RR - N. Yl.	Pnk., Wht. & Yl. tr.	Corvette	7
Custom Corvette	Co. Rcr.	MAL	Prp. to Blu.			Reg			5
Custom Corvette	Getty	MAL	Blk.		TNT	UH	Red flames & Yl., Red & Wht. tr.	Getty	15
Custom Corvette	Ralston	MAL	Wht.		TNT	UH	Dk. Red & Blu. stripes		6
Custom Corvette	Ralston	MAL	Wht.		TNT	UH	Red & Blu. stripes		6
Custom Corvette	Revealer	MAL	Gunmetal			UH - N. Yl.	Red, Yl. & Wht. fireworks		5
Custom Corvette	Revealer	MAL	Ivory			UH - N. Pnk.	Red, Yl. & Wht. fireworks		5
Custom Corvette	Revealer	MAL	M. Blu.			UH - N. Or.	Red, Yl. & Wht. fireworks		5
Custom Corvette	World Cup	MAL	Ivory		CL	UH	Blk., Red & Blu. soccer tr.	World Cup USA 94	5
Custom Corvette	7670	MAL	Brg.		TNT	UH		ZR1 on hood	7
Custom Corvette	7670	MAL	Brg.		CL	UH		ZR1 on hood	10
Custom Corvette	7670	MAL	Brg.		TNT	UH		No ZR1 on hood	7
Custom Mustang	10496 Vintage	CHN	Wht.			RL			5
Custom Mustang	10496 Vintage	CHN	M. Pale Pnk.			RL			5
Custom Mustang	10496 Vintage	CHN	M. Pnk.			RL			5
Custom Mustang	10496 Vintage	CHN	M. Violet			RL			5
Custom Mustang	10496 Vintage	CHN	M. Blu.			RL			5
Custom Mustang	10496 Vintage	CHN	M. Or.			RL			5
Custom Mustang	10496 Vintage	CHN	Gold			RL			5
Custom Mustang	10496 Vintage	CHN	Br. Red			RL			5
Custom Mustang	10496 Vintage	CHN	M. Dk. Bro.			RL			5
Custom Mustang	10496 Vintage	CHN	M. Magenta			RL			5
Custom Mustang	10496 Vintage	CHN	M. Turquoise			RL			5
Custom Mustang	10496 Vintage	CHN	Gunmetal			RL			5
Custom Mustang	10496 Vintage	CHN	M. Olive Gr.			RL			5
Custom Mustang	10496 Vintage	CHN	M. Electric Gr.			RL			5
Custom Mustang	10496 Vintage	CHN	M. Dk. Gr.			RL			5
Custom Mustang	10496 Vintage	CHN	Maroon			RL			5
Custom Mustang	10496 Vintage	CHN	M. Gold			RL			5
Custom Mustang	10496 Vintage	CHN	M. Gr.			RL			5
Custom Mustang	10496 Vintage	CHN	M. Br. Blu.			RL			5
Custom Mustang	10496 Vintage	CHN	M. Lime			RL			5
Custom Mustang	10496 Vintage	CHN	M. Royal Blu.			RL			5
Custom Mustang	10496 Vintage	CHN	M. Prp.			RL			5
Custom Mustang	10496 Vintage	CHN	M. Bro.			RL			5
Custom Mustang	10496 Vintage	CHN	M. Red			RL			5
Custom Nissan Z	Revealer	MAL	Yl.			UH - N. Or.	Gr., Wht. & Or. burning money tr.		5

Name	#	Category	Casting	Ctry.	Color	Win.	Base	Interior	Wheels	Paint	Logo	Other	S
Custom Nissan Z		Revealer		MAL	Prp.				UH - N. Yl.	Gr., Wht. & Or. burning money tr.			5
Custom Nissan Z		Revealer		MAL	Blk.				UH - N. Pnk.	Gr., Wht. & Or. burning money tr.			5
Custom Nissan Z	4628			MAL	M. Prp.				UH	Yl. tr.	300ZX		5
Custom Nissan Z	7609			MAL	Brg.				UH - Gold	Yl. tr.	300ZX		5
Custom Nissan Z	7609			MAL	Brg.				UH	Yl. tr.	300ZX		5
Custom Nissan Z	7609			MAL	Brg.				HO - Silver	Yl. tr.	300ZX		5
Custom Nissan Z	13584 Gold Medal Speed			MAL	M. Prp.				UH - Gold	Yl. tr.	300ZX		3
Cyber Cruiser	12354			MAL	Prp. MF.				UH				3
Datsun 200SX	3255			IND	Blu.				Reg	Blk. & Wht. tr.	Chase Taxi Service		10
Datsun 200SX	3255			IND	Gr.				Reg	Blk. & Wht. tr.	Chase Taxi Service		10
Datsun 200SX	3255			HK	Wht.				HO - Gold	Or., Red & Yl. stripes	200SX in Or.		6
Datsun 200SX	3255			MEX	Plum				HO - Gold	Blk. & Wht. racing tr.	Datsun 200SX		35
Datsun 200SX	3255			HK	Yl.				HO - Gold	Blk., Prp. & Blu. stripes	200SX Datsun		10
Datsun 200SX	3255			MAL	Wht.				HO - Gold	Or., Red & Yl. stripes	200SX in Dk. Red		7
Datsun 200SX	5083			HK	Maroon				HO - Gold	Blk. & Wht. racing tr.	Datsun 200SX		100
Datsun 200SX	5083			MAL	Gold MF.				HO - Gold	Or., Red & Wht. stripes	200SX in Dk. Red		5
Datsun 200SX	5083			MAL	Gold MF.				HO - Gold	Or., Red & Yl. stripes	260SX in Dk. Red		5
Datsun 200SX	5083			MAL	Maroon				HO - Gold	Blk. & Wht. racing tr.	Datsun 200SX		100
Deep Purple Nomad	1015			MAL	M. Prp.				RR - Grey	Red, Yl. & russet tr.	Nomad		20
Deep Purple Nomad	1015			MAL	M. Prp.				WW	Red, Yl. & russet tr.	Nomad		15
Delivery Truck	1578			MAL	Wht.				Reg	Red, Yl. & Blu. tr.	HW Mobile Tune Up		10
Delivery Truck	2808			MAL	Wht.				Reg		Wonder		5
Delivery Van		20th Ann.	Lines on side	MAL	Gold				Reg				15
Delivery Van		20th Ann.	Plain sides	MAL	Gold				Reg				15
Delivery Van	4790			MAL	Wht.				Reg	Blu. & Red tr.	Air Fra		10
Delivery Van	9643			MAL	Wht.				Reg		Frito Lay		75
Deora	10495 Vintage			CHN	Maroon				RL				4
Deora	10495 Vintage			CHN	Wht.				RL				4
Deora	10495 Vintage			CHN	M. Dk. Gr.				RL				4
Deora	10495 Vintage			CHN	M. Prp.				RL				4
Deora	10495 Vintage			CHN	M. Turquoise				RL				4
Deora	10495 Vintage			CHN	M. Olive Gr.				RL				4
Deora	10495 Vintage			CHN	M. Violet				RL				4
Deora	10495 Vintage			CHN	Gold				RL				4
Deora	10495 Vintage			CHN	M. Pale Pnk.				RL				4
Deora	10495 Vintage			CHN	M. Gold				RL				4
Deora	10495 Vintage			CHN	M. Royal Blu.				RL				4
Deora	10495 Vintage			CHN	Br. Red				RL				4
Deora	10495 Vintage			CHN	M. Red				RL				4
Deora	10495 Vintage			CHN	M. Pnk.				RL				4
Deora	10495 Vintage			CHN	M. Bro.				RL				4
Deora	10495 Vintage			CHN	M. Gr.				RL				4
Deora	10495 Vintage			CHN	M. Dk. Bro.				RL				4
Deora	10495 Vintage			CHN	M. Magenta				RL				4
Deora	10495 Vintage			CHN	M. Or.				RL				4
Deora	10495 Vintage			CHN	Gunmetal				RL				4

Name	#	Category	Casting	Ctry.	Color	Win.	Base	Interior	Wheels	Paint	Logo	Other	$
Decra	10495	Vintage		CHN	M. Br. Blu.				RL				4
Decra	10495	Vintage		CHN	M. Electric Gr.				RL				4
Decra	10495	Vintage		CHN	M. Blu.				RL				4
Deora	10495	Vintage		CHN	M. Lime				RL				4
Dinosaur Mudpit 4x4				MAL	Khk.		Blazer 4x4		4x4 SHb	Yl. tr.			12
Dinosaur Mudpit 4x4				MAL	Khk.		No Blazer 4x4		4x4 SHb	Yl. tr.			12
Dixie Challenger	3364			HK	Or.		US pat. pend.		Reg	No flag on rf.			6
Dixie Challenger	3364			HK	Or.				Reg	Confederate flag on rf.			6
Dixie Challenger	3364			MAL	Or.		US pat. pend.		Reg	No flag on rf.			6
Dixie Challenger	3364			MAL	Or.				Reg	No flag on rf.			6
Dixie Challenger	3364			MAL	Or.				Reg	Confederate flag on rf.			6
Dixie Challenger	3364			MAL	Or.		US pat. pend.		Reg	Confederate flag on rf.			6
Dixie Challenger	3364			HK	Or.				Reg	No flag on rf.			6
Dixie Challenger	3364			MEX	Or.				Reg	No flag on rf.			15
Dixie Challenger	3364			HK	Or.		US pat. pend.		Reg	Confederate flag on ff.			6
Dodge D-50	1133	Hiraker		HK	Red/Wht.		RWJU		Reg				6
Dodge D-50	1133	Hiraker		MAL	Red/Wht.		RWJU		Reg				6
Dodge D-50	4353	Hiraker		HK	Blu. MF./Wht.		RWJU		RR - Grey				15
Dodge D-50	4353	Hiraker		MAL	Blu. MF./Wht.		RWJU		Reg				6
Dodge D-50	4353	Hiraker		MAL	Blu. MF./Wht.		RWJU		RR - Wht.				6
Dodge D-50	9540			MEX	Wht.				Reg	Red & Yl. flames			20
Dodge D-50	9540			MAL	Wht.				RR - Wht.	Red & Yl. flames			15
Dodge Rampage	5903			HK	Red				RR - Grey				15
Dodge Rampage	5903			MAL	Red				RR - Wht.				15
Dodge Rampage	5903			MEX	Red				RR - Wht.				15
Dodge Viper RT/10	5265			MAL	Red				UH				5
Double Decker Bus	3291			IND	Wht.				Reg	Red & Blk. tr.	Chase, Falcon & San Jose		12
Double Decker Bus	3291			IND	Gr.				Reg	Blk. & Wht. tr.	Chase, Falcon & San Jose		12
Double Decker Bus	3291			IND	Light Blu.				Reg	Blk. & Wht. tr.	Chase, Falcon & San Jose		12
Double Decker Bus	3291			IND	Dk. Blu.				Reg	Wht. & tan tr.	Chase, Falcon & San Jose		12
Double Decker Bus	3291			IND	Yl.				Reg	Red & Blk. tr.			12
Double Decker Bus	3291			IND	Red				Reg	Blk. & Yl. tr.			12
Double Decker Bus	3291			MEX	Red				Reg				30
Double Decker Bus	3291			FRA	Wht.				Reg		Pepsi & Shell		40
Double Decker Bus	3291			FRA	Wht.				Reg		Pepsi		40
Double Demon	2057	Speed Demon		MAL	Gr.				UH			Leapin' Demons Chase	8
Double Demon	2057	Speed Demon		MAL	Yl.				UH				5
Double Demon	2057	Speed Demon		HK	Red				UH				5
Double Demon	2057	Speed Demon		MAL	Red				UH				5
Double Demon	2057	Speed Demon		HK	Gr.				UH			Leapin' Demons Chase	8
Double Header	5880			HK	Or.				RL				75
Double Header	5880			HK	Pale Blu.				RL				75
Double Header	5880			HK	Dk. Blu.				RL				75
Double Header	5880			HK	Pnk.				RL				75
Double Header	5880			HK	Red				RL				75

Name	#	Category	Casting	Ctry.	Color	Win.	Base	Interior	Wheels	Paint	Logo	Other	$
Double Header	5880			HK	Pale Yl.				RL				75
Double Header	5880			HK	Pale Gr.				RL				75
Double Header	5880			HK	Gr.				RL				75
Double Header	5880			HK	Plum				RL				75
Double Header	5880			HK	Flr. Lime				RL				75
Double Header	5880			HK	Dk. Yl.				RL				75
Double Vision	6975		No EXPS	FRA	Dk. Blu.				Reg				40
Double Vision	6975		No EXPS	HK	Gr.				RL				80
Double Vision	6975		No EXPS	HK	Pale Yl.				RL				80
Double Vision	6975		No EXPS	HK	Dk. Yl.				RL				80
Double Vision	6975		No EXPS	HK	Flr. Lime				RL				40
Double Vision	6975		No EXPS	FRA	Blu.				Reg				80
Double Vision	6975		No EXPS	HK	Pnk.				RL				80
Double Vision	6975		No EXPS	HK	Or.				RL				80
Double Vision	6975		No EXPS	HK	Pale Blu.				RL				80
Double Vision	6975		No EXPS	HK	Plum				RL				80
Double Vision	6975		No EXPS	HK	Red				RL				80
Double Vision	6975		No EXPS	HK	Pale Gr.				RL				80
Double Vision	6975		No EXPS	HK	Dk. Blu.				RL				80
Dragster				MAL	Wht./Blu.				P-C - Chr.	Red & Yl. tr.	HW		5
Dragster		McD's		CHN	Red				Uniq.				5
Dream Van XGW	5909			IND	Gr.				Reg				10
Dream Van XGW	5909			IND	Blu.				Reg				10
Dream Van XGW	5909			MAL	Blu. MF.				RR - Grey				15
Dream Van XGW	5909			HK	Blu. MF.				RR - Grey				15
Dream Van XGW	5909			MAL	Blu. MF.				RR - Wht.				15
Dream Van XGW	9350			MAL	Brg.				RR - Wht.				20
Dream Van XGW	9546			MAL	Gr.				RR - Grey				15
Dream Van XGW	9546			MEX	Gr.				RR - Grey				15
Driven To The Max	11847			MAL	N. Or.				Reg				3
Dumpin' A	2507			MEX	Or.				Reg	Prp. & Yl. tr.		Bro. chassis / Yl. dump	20
Dumpin' A	2507			HK	Or.				Reg	Yl. & Prp. tr.		Bro. chassis / Yl. dump	7
Dumpin' A	2507			MAL	Or.				Reg	Yl. & Prp. tr.		Bro. chassis / Yl. dump	7
Dumpin' A	2507			MAL	Yl.				Reg			Bro. chassis / Or. dump	7
Dumpin' A	2507			HK	Yl.				Reg			Bro. chassis / Or. dump	7
Dumpin' A	2507			MAL	Or.				Reg	Prp. & Yl. tr.		Bro. chassis / Yl. dump	7
Dumpin' A	2507			HK	Or.				Reg	Prp. & Yl. tr.		Bro. chassis / Yl. dump	7
Dune Daddy	6967			FRA	Pale Gr.	NW & rf.	Plst.	Blk.	Reg				20
Dune Daddy	6967			FRA	Blu.	NW & rf.	Plst.		Reg				20
Dune Daddy	6967			MEX	Pale Gr.	NW & rf.			Reg				20

Name	#	Category	Casting	Ctry.	Color	Win.	Base	Interior	Wheels	Paint	Logo	Other	S
Dune Daddy	6967			HK	Plum	wshld. & no rf.		Pale Bro.	RL				65
Dune Daddy	6967			HK	Plum	wshld. & no rf.		Wht.	RL				65
Dune Daddy	6967			HK	Pale Gr.	wshld. & no rf.		Blk.	RL				65
Dune Daddy	6967			HK	Dk. Blu.	wshld. & no rf.		Wht.	RL				65
Dune Daddy	6967			HK	Or.	wshld. & no rf.		Wht.	RL				65
Dune Daddy	6967			HK	Dk. Blu.	wshld. & no rf.		Pale Bro.	RL				65
Dune Daddy	6967			HK	Dk. Yl.	wshld. & no rf.		Wht.	RL				65
Dune Daddy	6967			HK	Flr. Lime	wshld. & no rf.		Blk.	RL				65
Dune Daddy	6967			HK	Red	wshld. & no rf.		Wht.	RL				65
Dune Daddy	6967			HK	Red	wshld. & no rf.		Pale Bro.	RL				65
Dune Daddy	6967			HK	Pale Blu.	wshld. & no rf.		Wht.	RL				65
Dune Daddy	6967			HK	Pale Yl.	wshld. & no rf.		Pale Bro.	RL				65
Dune Daddy	6967			HK	Plum	wshld. & no rf.		Blk.	RL				65
Dune Daddy	6967			HK	Dk. Yl.	wshld. & no rf.		Blk.	RL				65
Dune Daddy	6967			HK	Dk. Yl.	wshld. & no rf.		Pale Bro.	RL				65
Dune Daddy	6967			HK	Flr. Lime	wshld. & no rf.		Wht.	RL				65
Dune Daddy	6967			HK	Red	wshld. & no rf.		Blk.	RL				65
Dune Daddy	6967			HK	Pale Blu.	wshld. & no rf.		Pale Bro.	RL				65
Dune Daddy	6967			HK	Or.	wshld. & no rf.		Blk.	RL	Flowers on hood			65
Dune Daddy	6967			HK	Pnk.	wshld. & no rf.		Wht.	RL				65
Dune Daddy	6967			HK	Gr.	wshld. & no rf.		Pale Bro.	RL				65
Dune Daddy	6967			HK	Gr.	wshld. & no rf.		Wht.	RL				65
Dune Daddy	6967			HK	Gr.	wshld. & no rf.		Blk.	RL				65
Dune Daddy	6967			HK	Pale Yl.	wshld. & no rf.		Blk.	RL				65
Dune Daddy	6967			HK	Pale Blu.	wshld. & no rf.		Blk.	RL				65

Name	#	Category	Casting	Ctry.	Color	Win.	Base	Interior	Wheels	Paint	Logo	Other	$
Dune Daddy	6967			HK	Dk. Blu.	wshld. & no rf.		Blk.	RL				65
Dune Daddy	6967			HK	Pale Yl.	wshld. & no rf.		Wht.	RL				65
Dune Daddy	6967			HK	Pnk.	wshld. & no rf.		Pale Bro.	RL				65
Dune Daddy	6967			HK	Or.	wshld. & no rf.		Pale Bro.	RL				65
Dune Daddy	6967			HK	Pnk.	wshld. & no rf.		Blk.	RL				65
Dune Daddy	6967			HK	Flr. Lime	wshld. & no rf.		Pale Bro.	RL				65
Dune Daddy	6967			HK	Gr.	wshld. & no rf.		Blk.	RL	Flowers on hood			65
Dune Daddy	6967			HK	Pale Gr.	wshld. & no rf.		Wht.	RL				65
Dune Daddy	6967			HK	Or.	wshld. & no rf.		Blk.	RL				65
Dune Daddy	6967			HK	Pale Gr.	wshld. & no rf.		Pale Bro.	RL				65
Dune Daddy	6967 Wisconsin Toy Co			HK	Blu.	NW & rf.	Plst.	Wht.	RL	Flowers on hood			5
Ecolab Truck		Promotional	Taller deck cover	MAL	Wht.				4x4 SHb	Blu. & Red tr.	Ecolab		12
Ecolab Truck		Promotional	Taller deck cover	MAL	Wht.				Reg	Blu. & Red tr.	Ecolab		12
Eevil Weevil	2062	Speed Demon		MAL	Prp.				UH				5
Eevil Weevil	2062	Speed Demon		MAL	Blu.				UH				5
Eevil Weevil	2062	Speed Demon		MAL	Blu.				Reg				5
Eevil Weevil	2062	Speed Demon		HK	Blu.				UH				5
Eevil Weevil	2062	Speed Demon		HK	Blu.				Reg				5
Eevil Weevil	5143	Speed Demon		MAL	Yl.				Reg				5
Eevil Weevil	5143	Speed Demon		MAL	Yl.				UH				5
El Ray Special	8273			HK	Pale Gr.				RL				50
El Ray Special	8273			HK	Gr.				RL				50
El Ray Special	8273			HK	Blu.				RL				300
El Ray Special	8273			HK	Dk. Blu.				RL				250
Emergency Squad	7650			FRA	Red				Reg	Yl. & Wht. tr.	Oxygen, First Aid & Emergency Unit		10
Emergency Squad	7650			FRA	Red				Reg	Yl. & Wht. tr.	Oxygen, First Aid & Emergency Unit	Ananas on hood	10
Emergency Squad	9529			MAL	Yl.				Reg		Race Rescue & HW		10
Emergency Squad				IND	Red				Reg	Yl. & Wht. tr.	Oxygen, First Aid & Emergency Unit	Yl. roof light	10
Emergency Squad		Set		MAL	Yl.				Reg	Blk., Blu. & Red tr.	Airship Support Team on doors	Blimp & Support 5 Pack	8
Emergency Squad		Set		MAL	Yl.				Reg	Blk., Blu. & Wht. tr.	Airship Support Team on doors	Blimp & Support 5 Pack	5
Emergency Squad		Set		MAL	Yl.				Reg	Blk. & Blu. tr.	Airship Support Team on doors	Blimp & Support 5 Pack	8
Emergency Squad	7650			MAL	Red		Rsd. MAL		Reg	Yl. tr.			15
Emergency Squad	7650			HK	Red		BluT		RL				25

Name	#	Category	Casting	Ctry.	Color	Win.	Base	Interior	Wheels	Paint	Logo	Other	$
Emergency Squad	7650			HK	Red	GT			RL				25
Emergency Squad	7650			HK	Red	GT			Reg				15
Emergency Squad	7650			MAL	Red		MAL cast flat		Reg				15
Fangster	2059	Speed Demon		MAL	Gr.				Reg				8
Fangster	2059	Speed Demon		HK	Gr.		HW logo on Rsd. rectangle		UH				8
Fangster	2059	Speed Demon		HK	Gr.				UH				8
Fangster	2059	Speed Demon		MAL	Gr.		HW logo on Rsd. rectangle		Reg				8
Fast GT	9232	Park'n Plate		MAL	Yl.	Blk.			UH	Blu. & Red tr.	13		10
Fat Fendered 40	4315			MAL	Prp.				Reg				5
Fat Fendered 40		LE		MAL	Yl.				Dsh - Grey				18
Fat Fendered 40	9523			MAL	M. Red				RR				12
Fat Fendered 40	9523			HK	M. Red				RR				12
Fat Fendered 40	9523			MAL	M. Red				Reg				12
Fat Fendered 40	9523			HK	M. Red				Reg				12
Fat Fendered 40	9523			MEX	M. Red				Reg				15
Fat Fendered 40	9523			MEX	Brg.				Reg				15
Ferrari 308		Co. Rcr.		MAL	Dk. Red to Br. Red				Reg				5
Ferrari 308		Set		MAL	Russet Gr.				Reg			Sto & Go	8
Ferrari 308		Co. Rcr.		MAL	Red to Magnolia				Reg				5
Ferrari 312P		Pre-Pro		HK	Red				RL				100
Ferrari 312P	6973			HK	Pale Yl.				RL				100
Ferrari 312P	6973			HK	Flr. Lime				RL				100
Ferrari 312P	6973			HK	Dk. Blu.				RL				100
Ferrari 312P	6973			HK	Plum				RL				100
Ferrari 312P	6973			HK	Pale Gr.				RL				100
Ferrari 312P	6973			HK	Red		Plst.		RL	Blu. & Wht. tr.			25
Ferrari 312P	6973			HK	Red		Plst.		Reg	Blu. & Wht. tr.			25
Ferrari 312P	6973			HK	Or.				RL				100
Ferrari 312P	6973			HK	Red				RL	Blu. & Wht. tr.			45
Ferrari 312P	6973			HK	Red				RL				100
Ferrari 312P	6973			HK	Gr.				RL				100
Ferrari 312P	6973			HK	Pale Blu.				RL				100
Ferrari 312P	6973			HK	Pnk.				RL				100
Ferrari 312P	6973			HK	Dk. Yl.				RL				100
Ferrari 348		Aqua Fresh		MAL	N. Yl.				UH				5
Ferrari 348		Revealer		MAL	Bronze				UH - N. Gr.	Gr., Red & Blk. dollar notes tr.	$		5
Ferrari 348		Revealer		MAL	Ivory				UH - N. Pnk.	Gr., Red & Blk. dollar notes tr.	$		5
Ferrari 348		Revealer		MAL	N. Or.				UH - N. Or.	Gr., Red & Blk. dollar notes tr.	$		5
Ferrari 348		Set		MAL	N. Yl.				UH	Pnk., Blk. & Wht. tr.		Power Loop	10
Ferrari 348	459			MAL	Ivory				HO - Silver				4
Ferrari 348	459			MAL	Ivory				UH				4
Ferrari 348	4348			MAL	N. Blz.				UH				4
Ferrari 348	4348			MAL	N. Blz.				UH				4

Name	#	Category	Casting	Ctry.	Color	Win.	Base	Interior	Wheels	Paint	Logo	Other	S
Ferrari 348	5666			MAL	Yl.				UH - Gold				4
Ferrari 348	5666			MAL	Yl.				HO - Silver				4
Ferrari 348	5666			MAL	Yl.				UH				4
Ferrari F40		25th Ann.		MAL	Yl.				UH	Blu. tr.	Ferrari & 40		5
Ferrari F40		Revealer		MAL	Dk. Red				UH - N. Yl.	Blu. & Wht. check & Yl. tr.	F40		5
Ferrari F40		Revealer		MAL	Yl.				UH - N. Pnk.	Blu. & Wht. chequeRed tr.	F40		5
Ferrari F40		Revealer		MAL	Red				UH - N. Yl.	Blu. & Wht. check & Yl. tr.	F40		5
Ferrari F40	1468			MAL	Red				UH	Yl. tr.	Ferrari & 40		3
Ferrari F40	13582	Gold Medal Speed		MAL	Red				UH - Gold	Yl. tr.	Ferrari & 40		3
Ferrari Testarossa		20th Ann.		MAL	Chr.			Red	UH			Red tail lights	12
Ferrari Testarossa		25th Ann.		MAL	Ivory				UH				5
Ferrari Testarossa		Co. Rcr.		MAL	Red to Yl.			Blk. & Red	Reg				5
Ferrari Testarossa		Co. Rcr.		MAL	Prp. to Yl.			Red & Wht.	Reg	Blu., Red & Wht. arrow tr.			5
Ferrari Testarossa		Getty		MAL	M. Dk. Red			Red and Blk.	UH	Red, Wht. & Yl. tr.	Getty	Blk. tail lights	6
Ferrari Testarossa	2048	Park'n Plate		MAL	Silver		Lrg. logo	Wht. & tan	UH	Yl. & Blk. tr.	Ferrari	Wht. tail lights & tan rear valence	25
Ferrari Testarossa	2048	Park'n Plate		MAL	Silver		Lrg. logo	Red & silver	UH	Yl. & Blk. tr.	Ferrari	Red tail lights	7
Ferrari Testarossa	2048	Park'n Plate		MAL	Silver		Sm. logo	Wht. & tan	UH	Yl. & Blk. tr.	Ferrari	Wht. tail lights & tan rear valence	25
Ferrari Testarossa	2048	Park'n Plate		MAL	Silver		Sm. logo	Tan and silver	UH	Yl. & Blk. tr.	Ferrari	Tan tail lights	7
Ferrari Testarossa	2048	Park'n Plate		MAL	Silver		Sm. logo	Red & silver	UH	Yl. & Blk. tr.	Ferrari	Red tail lights	7
Ferrari Testarossa		Revealer		MAL	N. Pnk.			Blk. and Pnk.	UH - N. Or.	Blk. & Blu. guitar tr.		Blk. tail lights	5
Ferrari Testarossa		Revealer		MAL	N. Gr.			Blk. and Yl.	UH - N. Yl.	Blk. & Blu. guitar tr.		Blk. tail lights	5
Ferrari Testarossa		Revealer		MAL	N. Or.			Blk. and Gr.	UH - N. Pnk.	Blk. & Blu. guitar tr.		Blk. tail lights	5
Ferrari Testarossa		Revealer		MAL	Prp.				UH			Revealers 10 pack	10
Ferrari Testarossa		Set		MAL	Yl.			Blk. and Yl.	UH	Blu. stars & tr.	Ferrari & 75	Blk. tail lights - Speed Shift 500	8
Ferrari Testarossa		Set		MAL	Yl.			Blk. and Yl.	UH	Blu. stars & tr.	Ferrari, 75 & Longines	Blk. tail lights - Speed Shift 500	8
Ferrari Testarossa	1302	Cal Cus.		MAL	Prp. Chr.		Lrg. logo	N. Red and Blu.	RR - N. Yl.	Neon Prp. & Yl. tr.	Ferrari & 3	Neon Red tail lights	6
Ferrari Testarossa	1302	Cal Cus.		MAL	N. Blz.		Sm. logo	N. Yl. and Blu.	RR - N. Yl.			Red tail lights	6
Ferrari Testarossa	1302	Cal Cus.		MAL	Prp. Chr.		Sm. logo	N. Red and Blu.	RR - N. Yl.	Neon Prp. & Yl. tr.	Ferrari & 3	Neon Red tail lights	6
Ferrari Testarossa	1302	Cal Cus.		MAL	N. Blz.		Sm. logo	N. Yl. and Red	Rtr - Chr.	Blu. & Yl. tr.	Ferrari & 3	Neon Yl. tail lights	6
Ferrari Testarossa	1302	Cal Cus.		MAL	N. Blz.		Lrg. logo	N. Yl. and Red	RR - N. Yl.				6
Ferrari Testarossa	1302	Cal Cus.		MAL	N. Blz.		Lrg. logo	N. Yl. and Blu.	RR - N. Yl.				6
Ferrari Testarossa	1302	Cal Cus.		MAL	N. Blz.		Lrg. logo	N. Yl. and Red	Rtr - Chr.	Blu. & Yl. tr.	Ferrari & 3	Neon Yl. tail lights	6
Ferrari Testarossa	1302	Cal Cus.		MAL	N. Blz.		Sm. logo	N. Yl. and Red	RR - N. Yl.				6
Ferrari Testarossa	1684	Set		MAL	N. Yl.			Blk. and N. Yl.	UH	Blu. & Yl. tr.	Ferrari & prancing horse	G-Force	10
Ferrari Testarossa	1897			MAL	Wht.			Tan	UH			Tan tail lights	7
Ferrari Testarossa	1897			MAL	Blk.			Red and Blk.	UH			Red tail lights	7
Ferrari Testarossa	1897			MAL	Wht.			Red and Wht.	UH			Red tail lights	7
Ferrari Testarossa	1897	Set		MAL	Yl.			Blk. and Yl.	UH	Or. Prp. & Gr. geo. shps.		Blk. tail lights - Jump Buster	10
Ferrari Testarossa	3857	Set		MAL	Red			Red	UH	Luminous arrow		Red tail lights - Turbotrax Race	10
Ferrari Testarossa	5111			MAL	Red		Sm. logo	Red and Blk.	UH	Yl. tr.	Ferrari	Blk. tail lights	5
Ferrari Testarossa	5111			MAL	Red			Tan & Red	Reg	Yl. tr.	Ferrari	Tan tail lights	20
Ferrari Testarossa	5111			MAL	Wht.			Blk. and Wht.	UH	Red stars & tr.	Ferrari & 75	Blk. tail lights	5
Ferrari Testarossa	5111			MAL	Red		Lrg. logo	Red and Blk.	UH	Yl. tr.	Ferrari	Blk. tail lights	5

Name	# Category	Casting	Ctry.	Color	Win.	Base	Interior	Wheels	Paint	Logo	Other	S
Ferrari Testarossa	5111		MAL	Red		Lrg. logo	Tan & Red	UH	Yl. tr.	Ferrari	Tan tail lights	5
Ferrari Testarossa	5111		MAL	Red		Sm. logo	Tan	Reg	Yl. tr.	Ferrari	Tan tail lights and rear valence	5
Ferrari Testarossa	5111		MAL	Red			Tan	UH	Yl. tr.	Ferrari	Tan tail lights and rear valence	5
Ferrari Testarossa	5111		MAL	Red			Blk. & tan	UH	Yl. tr.	Ferrari	Blk. tail lights	5
Ferrari Testarossa	5111		MAL	Silver		Lrg. logo	Tan and silver	UH	Yl. & Blk. tr.	Ferrari	Tan tail lights	5
Ferrari Testarossa	5111		MAL	Red		Sm. logo	Tan & Red	UH	Yl. tr.	Ferrari	Tan tail lights	5
Fiat Ritmo	3287		IND	Red				Reg				10
Fiat Ritmo	3287		FRA	Grey		Blk.	Bro.	Reg	Blk. tr.			20
Fiat Ritmo	3287		FRA	Silver MF.		Blk.	Bro.	Reg	Blk. tr.			20
Fiat Ritmo	3287		FRA	Grey		Blk.	Wht.	Reg	No tr.			25
Fiat Ritmo	3287		FRA	Silver MF.		Silver	Bro.	Reg	No tr.			25
Fiat Ritmo	3287		MEX	Silver MF.		Blk.	Bro.	Reg				30
Fiera 2M4	476		MAL	Glt. Lime Gr.				UH				4
Fiero 2M4	9552		MAL	Blk.				HO - Silver	Blu., Red, Wht. & Yl. tr.	Large Fiero on hood		5
Fiero 2M4	9552		MAL	Blk.				UH	Blu., Red, Wht. & Yl. tr.	Large Fiero on hood		5
Fiero 2M4	9552		MAL	Blk.		Unpainted		Reg	Blu., Red, Wht. & Yl. tr.	Large Fiero on hood		5
Fiero 2M4	9552		MAL	Blk.		Painted		Reg	Blu., Red, Wht. & Yl. tr.	Large Fiero on hood		5
Fiero 2M4	9552		MAL	Glt. Lime Gr.				HO - Silver				5
Fiero 2M4	Co. Rcr.		MAL	Red to Yl.				Reg				5
Fiero 2M4	Set		MAL	Blk.				UH	Yl., Or. & Red tr.			10
Fiero 2M4	1458		MAL	Red		Fiero 2M4		Reg	US flag tr.	Small Fiero on sides		5
Fiero 2M4	1458		MAL	Red		N&N		HO - Gold	US flag tr.	Small Fiero on sides		5
Fiero 2M4	1458		MAL	Red		Fiero 2M4		UH	US flag tr.	Small Fiero on sides		5
Fiero 2M4	1458		MAL	Red		N&N		UH	US flag tr.	Small Fiero on sides		5
Fiero 2M4	1458		MAL	Red		N&N		Reg	US flag tr.	Small Fiero on sides		5
Fiero 2M4	1458		MAL	Red		No Fiero 2M4		HO - Gold	US flag tr.	Small Fiero on sides		5
Fiero 2M4	1458		MAL	Red		No Fiero 2M4		UH	US flag tr.	Small Fiero on sides		5
Fiero 2M4	1458		MAL	Red		No Fiero 2M4		Reg	US flag tr.	Small Fiero on sides		5
Fiero 2M4	1458		MAL	Red		Fiero 2M4		HO - Gold	US flag tr.	Small Fiero on sides		5
Fiero 2M4	7527		MAL	Wht.				HO - Gold	Blk., Yl. & Red tr.	Fiero		5
Fiero 2M4	7527		HK	Wht.				HO - Gold	Blk., Yl. & Red tr.	Fiero		5
Fire Chaser	2639		HK	Red		Flat HK & 1977	Blk.	Reg	Yl., Blk. & Wht. tr.	5 & Fire Chief		7
Fire Chaser	2639		MAL	Red		1977 cast in Rsd. rectangle	Blk.	Reg	Yl., Blk. & Wht. tr.	1 & Fire Chief		7

Name	#	Category	Casting	Ctry.	Color	Win.	Base	Interior	Wheels	Paint	Logo	Other	$
Fire Chaser	2639			HK	Red		Rsd. HK & 1977	Blk.	Reg	Yl., Blk. & Wht. tr.	5 & Fire Chief		7
Fire Chaser	2639			MAL	Red		HW, flat MAL & 1977	Blk.	Reg	Yl. & Blk. tr.	5 & Fire Chief		7
Fire Chaser	2639			MAL	Red		Rsd. MAL & 1977	Blk.	Reg	Yl., Blk. & Wht. tr.	5 & Fire Chief		7
Fire Chaser	2639			MAL	Red		1982	Blk.	Reg	Yl., Blk. & Wht. tr.	5 & Fire Chief		7
Fire Chaser	2639			MAL	Red		Logo, flat MAL & 1977	Blk.	Reg	Yl., Blk. & Wht. tr.	5 & Fire Chief		7
Fire Chaser	2639			HK	Red		Rsd. HK & 1977	Blk.	Reg	Yl. & Blk. tr.	5 & Fire Chief		7
Fire Chaser	2639			MAL	Red		Flat MAL & 1977	Blk.	Reg	Yl., Blk. & Wht. tr.	5 & Fire Chief		7
Fire Chaser	2639			HK	Red		Flat HK & 1977	Blk.	Reg	Yl. & Blk. tr.	5 & Fire Chief		7
Fire Chaser	2639			MAL	Red		Rsd. MAL & 1977	Blk.	Reg	Yl. & Blk. tr.	5 & Fire Chief		7
Fire Chaser	2639			MAL	Red		Rsd. MAL & 1982	Blk.	Reg	Yl. & Blk. tr.	5 & Fire Chief		7
Fire Chaser	2639			MAL	Red		1977 cast in Rsd. rectangle	Tan	Reg	Yl., Blk. & Wht. tr.	1 & Fire Chief		30
Fire Chaser	2639			MAL	Red		Logo, flat MAL & 1977	Blk.	Reg	Yl. & Blk. tr.	5 & Fire Chief		7
Fire Chief	4005			MAL	Red				Reg	Yl., Blk. & Wht. tr.	Fire Chief		5
Fire Chief	4005			HK	Red				Reg	Yl., Blk. & Wht. tr.	Fire Chief		5
Fire Eater	9640			FRA	Red				Reg	Blu. hose bed			15
Fire Eater	4001			MAL	Yl.				Reg	Red hose bed			8
Fire Eater	9640			MAL	Red		HW Logo		Reg	Blu. hose bed			7
Fire Eater	9640			MAL	Red		No holes		Reg	Blu. hose bed			7
Fire Eater	9640			MAL	Red		Fire Eater & holes		Reg	Blu. hose bed			7
Fire Eater	9640			HK	Red				RL	Blu. hose bed			20
Fire Eater	9640			HK	Red				Reg	Blu. hose bed			7
Fire Eater	9640			MAL	Red		Holes		Reg	Blu. hose bed			7
Firebird Funny Car	1483			MAL	Blu.				Reg	Red, Yl. & Wht. tr.	HW & 1 F/C		8
Firebird Funny Car		20th Ann.		MAL	Gold		ROA		Reg				8
Firebird Funny Car		20th Ann.		MAL	Silver		RAF & no SIS		Reg				8
Firebird Funny Car		20th Ann.		MAL	Silver		ROA		Reg				8
Firebird Funny Car		20th Ann.		MAL	Silver		RAF & SIS		Reg				8
Firebird Funny Car		20th Ann.		MAL	Gold		RAF & no SIS		Reg				8
Firebird Funny Car		20th Ann.		MAL	Gold		RAF & SIS		Reg				8
Firebird Funny Car		Pre-Pro		MAL	Gold				Reg	Or. & Mgta. firebird			
Firebird Funny Car		Set		MAL	Yl.		Pnk. w/ ROA		Reg	Red & Blk. tr.	Pennzoil	Funny Car Gift Pack	6
Firebird Funny Car		Set		MAL	Yl.		Pnk. w/ RAF & no SIS		Reg	Red & Blk. tr.	Pennzoil	Funny Car Gift Pack	6
Firebird Funny Car		Set		MAL	Yl.		Yl. w/ RAF & no SIS		Reg	Red & Blk. tr.	Pennzoil	Funny Car Gift Pack	6
Firebird Funny Car		Set		MAL	Yl.		Yl. w/ ROA		Reg	Red & Blk. tr.	Pennzoil	Funny Car Gift Pack	6
Firebird Funny Car		Set		MAL	Yl.		Yl. w/ RAF & SIS		Reg	Red & Blk. tr.	Pennzoil	Funny Car Gift Pack	6

Name	#	Category	Casting	Ctry.	Color	Win.	Base	Interior	Wheels	Paint	Logo	Other	$
Firebird Funny Car		Set		MAL	Yl.		Pnk. w/ RAF & SIS		Reg	Red & Blk. tr.	Pennzoil	Funny Car Gift Pack	6
Firebird Funny Car		Spawn Comic		MAL	Wht./Blk.		RAF & SIS		Reg	MulticoloRed tr. w/ no bats & headlights	Spawn		20
Firebird Funny Car		Spawn Comic		MAL	Wht./Blk.		RAF & SIS		Reg	MulticoloRed tr. w/ bats & headlights	Spawn		20
Firebird Funny Car		Spawn Comic		MAL	Wht./Blk.		ROA		Reg	MulticoloRed tr. w/ bats & headlights	Spawn		20
Firebird Funny Car		Spawn Comic		MAL	Wht./Blk.		RAF & no SIS		Reg	MulticoloRed tr. w/ bats & headlights	Spawn		20
Firebird Funny Car		Spawn Comic		MAL	Wht./Blk.		RAF & no SIS		Reg	MulticoloRed tr. w/ no bats & headlights	Spawn		20
Firebird Funny Car		Spawn Comic		MAL	Wht./Blk.		ROA		Reg	MulticoloRed tr. w/ no bats & headlights	Spawn		20
Firebird Funny Car	1483			MAL	Blu.		ROA		Reg	Red, Wht. & Blk. tr.	Speed Monster		7
Firebird Funny Car	1483			MAL	Blu.		RAF & no SIS		Reg	Red, Wht. & Blk. tr.	Speed Monster		7
Firebird Funny Car	1483			MAL	Blu.		RAF & SIS		Reg	Red, Wht. & Blk. tr.	Speed Monster		7
Firebird Funny Car	3003	Kelloggs		MAL	Blk.		RAF & no SIS		Reg	Or. & Prp. firebird on hood			8
Firebird Funny Car	3003	Kelloggs		MAL	Blk.		ROA		Reg	Or. & Prp. firebird on hood			8
Firebird Funny Car	3003	Kelloggs		MAL	Blk.		RAF & SIS		Reg	Or. & Prp. firebird on hood			8
Firebird Funny Car	3250			MAL	Magenta		RAF & SIS		Reg	Yl. & Blk. firebird on hood			6
Firebird Funny Car	3250			MAL	Wht.		RAF & SIS		Reg	Red, Yl. & Blk. flames	Fireball		7
Firebird Funny Car	3250			MAL	Magenta		RAF & no SIS		Reg	Yl. & Blk. firebird on hood			7
Firebird Funny Car	3250			HK	Magenta		RAF		Reg	Or. & Blk. firebird on hood			7
Firebird Funny Car	3250			HK	Magenta		RAF		Reg	Yl. & Blk. firebird on hood			7
Firebird Funny Car	3250			HK	Magenta		No rivet		Reg	Or. & Blk. firebird on hood			7
Firebird Funny Car	3250			HK	Wht.		RAF		Reg	Red, Yl. & Blk. flames	Fireball		7
Firebird Funny Car	3250			HK	Wht.		No rivet		Reg	Red, Yl. & Blk. flames	Fireball		7
Firebird Funny Car	3250			MAL	Magenta		ROA		Reg	Yl. & Blk. firebird on hood			7
Firebird Funny Car	3250			MAL	Wht.		RAF & no SIS		Reg	Red, Yl. & Blk. flames	Fireball		7
Firebird Funny Car	3250			HK	Magenta		No rivet		Reg	Yl. & Blk. firebird on hood			7
Firebird Funny Car	3955			MAL	Magenta MF.		RAF & no SIS		Reg	Yl. & Blk. firebird on hood			7
Firebird Funny Car	3955			MAL	Magenta MF.		ROA		Reg	Yl. & Blk. firebird on hood			7
Firebird Funny Car	3955			MAL	Magenta MF.		RAF & SIS		Reg	Yl. & Blk. firebird on hood			7
Firebird Funny Car	5121			MAL	Yl.		ROA		Reg	Or., Blu. & Blk. tr.	2		6
Firebird Funny Car	5121			MAL	Yl.		RAF & SIS		Reg	Or., Blu. & Prp. tr.	2		6
Firebird Funny Car	5121			MAL	Yl.		RAF & no SIS		Reg	Blu., Or. & Blk. tr.			6
Firebird Funny Car	5121			MAL	Yl.		RAF & SIS		Reg	Blu., Or. & Blk. tr.	2		6
Firebird Funny Car	5121			MAL	Yl.		RAF & no SIS		Reg	Or., Blu. & Prp. tr.	2		6
Firebird Funny Car	5121			MAL	Yl.		ROA		Reg	Blu., Or. & Blk. tr.	2		6
Firebird Funny Car	5121			MAL	Yl.		RAF & SIS		Reg	Or., Blu. & Blk. tr.	2		6
Firebird Funny Car	5121			MAL	Yl.		RAF & no SIS		Reg	Or., Blu. & Blk. tr.	2		6
Firebird Funny Car	5121			MAL	Yl.		ROA		Reg	Or., Blu. & Prp. tr.	2		6
Firebird Racer	2104			MAL	Chr.				Reg				8
Firebird Racer	2104	Cal Cus.		MAL	N. Yl./N. Blz.				Rtr - Chr.	Blu. & Wht. tr.		Large RWs	7
Firebird Racer	2104	Cal Cus.		MAL	N. Yl./N. Blz.				Rtr - Chr.	Blu. & Wht. tr.		Small RWs	7
Flame Rider		McD's	Plst.	CHN	Blk.				Uniq.	Red flames			5
Flame Funner		Co. Rcr.		MAL	Khk. to Yl.				Reg				5
Back Burner	2544	Ultra Hot		MAL	M. Red				UH				7
Back Burner	2544	Ultra Hot		HK	M. Red				UH				7

Name	# Category	Casting	Ctry.	Color	Win.	Base	Interior	Wheels	Paint	Logo	Other	S
Flame Runner	7293 Ultra Hot		HK	Gold				UH				7
Flame Runner	7293 Ultra Hot		MAL	Gold				UH				7
Flame Runner	9346 Ultra Hot		MAL	Silver				UH				10
Flame Runner	9346 Ultra Hot		HK	Silver				UH				10
Flame Stopper	5027		MAL	Red				4x4 SHb				5
Flame Stopper	5027		MAL	Red		Date comprised of different sized digits		4x4 SHb				5
Flame Stopper	5027		MAL	Red		Date comprised of different sized digits		4x4 SHb - Yl.				5
Flame Stopper	5027		MAL	Red		Date comprised of different sized digits		4x4 LHb				5
Flame Stopper	5027		MAL	Red				4x4 SHb - Yl.				5
Flame Stopper	5027		MAL	Red				4x4 LHb				5
Flashfire	25th Ann.		MAL	Pnk.				UH				5
Flashfire	Video Car		MAL	N. Pnk.				UH				8
Flashfire	3156		MAL	Blk.				HO - Silver				4
Flashfire	3156		MAL	Blk.				UH				4
Flat Out 442	2506		HK	Light Gr.				HO - Gold				75
Flat Out 442	2506		MAL	Light Gr.				HO - Gold				75
Flat Out 442	2506		MAL	Gold MF.				HO - Gold				5
Flat Out 442	2506		HK	Yl.		1978 to the right of HK		HO - Gold	Blu., Or. & Red tr.	442, no pentagon & Or. Goodyear		8
Flat Out 442	2506		HK	Yl.		1978 to the right of HK		Reg	Blu., Or. & Red tr.	442, pentagon & Blu. Goodyear		8
Flat Out 442	2506		HK	Or.		1978 to the right of HK		Reg	Blu., Wht. & Red tr.	442, pentagon & Blu. Goodyear		7
Flat Out 442	2506		HK	Yl.		1978 to the right of HK		Reg		442, no pentagon & Or. Goodyear		8
Flat Out 442	2506		HK	Gold MF.				HO - Gold				5
Flat Out 442	2506		HK	Or.				Reg	Blu., Wht. & Red tr.	442, no pentagon & Wht. Goodyear		7
Flat Out 442	2506		HK	Yl.				HO - Gold	Blu., Or. & Red tr.	442, no pentagon & Or. Goodyear		8
Flat Out 442	2506		HK	Yl.				Reg	Blu., Or. & Red tr.	442, pentagon & Blu. Goodyear		8
Flat Out 442	2506		HK	Yl.				Reg	Blu., Or. & Red tr.	442, no pentagon & Or. Goodyear		8
Food Service Truck	4548		FRA	Blu./Wht.				Reg				30
Ford Aerostar			MAL	Blk.				Reg	Red, Blu. & Yl. tr.	Rollerblade		4
Ford Aerostar	4695		MAL	M. Prp.				Reg	Yl. blob tr			5
Ford Aerostar	546		MAL	Wht.				Reg	Red, Blu. & Yl. tr.	Speedie Pizza & telephone number		5
Ford Aerostar	546		MAL	Wht.				Reg	Red, Blu. & Yl. tr.	Speedie Pizza & no telephone number		5

Name	#	Category	Casting	Ctry.	Color	Win.	Base	Interior	Wheels	Paint	Logo	Other	S
Ford Aerostar		Newsletter		MAL	Wht.				Reg	Red, Blu. & Yl. tr.	HW Newsletter		50
Ford Aerostar		Newsletter		MAL	Prp.				Reg	Red, Pnk. & Yl. tr.	HW Newsletter		50
Ford Aerostar		Newsletter		MAL	Blk.				Reg	Red, Pnk. & Yl. tr.	HW Newsletter		50
Ford Aerostar		Newsletter		MAL	Wht.				Reg	Red, Pnk. & Yl. tr.	HW Newsletter		50
Ford Aerostar		Promotional		MAL	Wht.				Reg	Red & Blu. tr.	Kinko's		15
Ford Aerostar	9767			MAL	Wht.				Reg	Blk. & Red tr.	Quantas		10
Ford Dump Truck	3253			MAL	Gr./Grey				Reg				8
Ford Dump Truck	3253			HK	Gr./Grey				Reg				8
Ford Escort	3288			HK	Red				Reg				30
Ford Escort	3288			MAL	Red				Reg				30
Ford Escort	3288			MEX	Red				Reg	Blu. & Wht. tr.			30
Ford Escort	3288			HK	Blk.				Reg	Bro. tr.			5
Ford Escort	3288			MAL	Blk.				Reg	Gold tr.			5
Ford Escort	3288			MEX	Yl.				Reg	Blu. & Red tr.			18
Ford Escort	3288			HK	Blk.				Reg	Gold tr.			5
Ford Escort	3288			MEX	Wht.				Reg	Blu. & Red tr.			30
Ford Escort	3288			FRA	Blk.				Reg	Gold tr.			20
Ford Escort	3288			MEX	Yl.				Reg	Blu. & Yl. tr.			30
Ford Escort	3288			FRA	Blk.				Reg				20
Ford Escort	5766			HK	Yl.				Reg				18
Ford Escort	5766			MAL	Yl.				Reg				18
Ford Stake Bed Truck	1561			HK	M. Blu./Yl.				Reg				5
Ford Stake Bed Truck	9551			MAL	Red/Yl.				Reg	Yl. & Wht. tr.	Rapid Delivery	Stake bed tips up	10
Ford Stake Bed Truck	1561			MAL	M. Blu./Yl.				Reg				4
Ford Stake Bed Truck	1561			MAL	M. Blu./Yl.		Inv. MAL		Reg	Red & Yl. tr.	Rapid Delivery	Stake bed tips up	4
Ford Stake Bed Truck	4018	Extras		MAL	Blu./Tan				Reg	Wht., Yl. & Blk. tr.	Sunset Trucking	Stake bed comes off	6
Ford Stake Bed Truck	4018	Extras		MAL	Blu./Tan				Reg	Wht., Yl. & Blk. tr.	Sunset Trucking	Stake bed comes off	6
Ford Stake Bed Truck	9551			MAL	M. Red/Yl.		Inv. MAL		Reg	Yl., Blu. & Wht. tr.	Rapid Delivery	Stake bed tips up	10
Ford Stake Bed Truck	9551			MAL	M. Red/Yl.				Reg	Yl., Blu. & Wht. tr.	Rapid Delivery	Stake bed tips up	10
Formula 5000	9119			FRA	Wht.				Reg				15
Formula 5000	9119			HK	Wht.		Rsd. rectangle		Reg				20
Formula 5000	9119			HK	Wht.		Plain		Reg				20
Formula 5000	9119			MEX	Wht.				Reg				15
Formula 5000	9119			HK	Wht.		Formula 5000		RL				25
Formula 5000	9511	Super Chr.		HK	Chr.				RL	Blu. & Red tr.	76		30
Formula 5000	9511	Super Chr.		HK	Chr.				RR - Grey	Blu. & Red tr.	76		15
Formula Fever	4366			MAL	Yl./Or.				Reg				15
Formula Fever	4366			MAL	Yl./Or.				RR - Wht.				5
Formula Fever	4366			MAL	Yl./Or.				Reg				15
Formula P.A.C.K.	9037			HK	Blk.				Reg	Yl. tr.	8		15
Formula P.A.C.K.	9037			MAL	Blk.				Reg	Red & Yl. w/ lightning	P.A.C.K.		30
Formula P.A.C.K.	9037			MAL	Blk.		Clr. sticker		Reg	Yl. tr.	8		15
Formula P.A.C.K.	9037			MAL	Blk.				Reg	Yl. tr.	8		15
Formula P.A.C.K.	9037			HK	Blk.				Reg	Red & Yl. w/ lightning	P.A.C.K.		15
Formula P.A.C.K.	9037			HK	Blk.				RL	Red & Yl. w/ lightning	P.A.C.K.		25
Formula P.A.C.K.	9037			HK	Blk.		Clr. sticker		Reg	Yl. tr.	8		15
Front Funnin' Fairmont		Color Changer		HK	Grey via Blu. to Magnolia				Reg				5
Front Funnin' Fairmont		Color Changer		MAL	Grey via Blu. to Magnolia				Reg				5

Name	#	Category	Casting	Ctry.	Color	Win.	Base	Interior	Wheels	Paint	Logo	Other	S
Front Runnin' Fairmont	3257			HK	Red				HO - Gold	Wht., Blk. & Yl. tr.	Fireball Jr & 27		10
Front Runnin' Fairmont	3257			MAL	M. Red				Reg				10
Front Runnin' Fairmont	3257			HK	M. Red				Reg				10
Front Runnin' Fairmont	3257			MAL	Red				HO - Gold	Wht., Blk. & Yl. tr.	Fireball Jr & 27		10
Fuji Blimp	12341			MAL	Wht./Gr.					Red tr.	Fuji Film		3
Funny Car		McD's		CHN	Red				Uniq.				5
Funny Car		McD's		CHN	Wht.				Uniq.				5
Funny Money	7621			HK	Grey				Reg		Brinks		25
Funny Money	7621			HK	Magenta				RL	Yl.,Or. & Gr. flowers			45
Funny Money	7621			HK	Grey				RL		Brinks		30
Funny Money	7621 Pre-Pro			HK	Magenta				RL				45
Gas Hog		McD's	Plst.	CHN	Red				Uniq.				5
Geoffrey's 4x4 Bronco	5094 Toys R Us			HK	Wht.				Reg	Yl., Or. & Blk. tr.	Geoffrey		30
Geoffrey's Pickup	1537 Toys R Us			HK	Wht.			No TB	Reg	Or., Blk. & Prp. tr.	Geoffrey		40
Geoffrey's Van	1337 Toys R Us			HK	Wht.				RL		Toys R Us		50
Gleamer Patrol	1691 Gleamer	Plst. w/ etched pattern		MAL	Smokey Silver			Tan	Reg				4
Gleamer Patrol	1691 Gleamer	Plst. w/ etched pattern		MAL	Silver			Blk.	Reg				4
GM Lean Machine	11084 Demo Man			MAL	Gunmetal				UH				10
GM Lean Machine	12361			MAL	Blk./Yl.				UH		SAPD		3
GM Ultralite	11083 Demo Man			MAL	Wht./Blk				UH		No SAPD		10
GM Ultralite	11083 Demo Man			MAL	Wht./Blk.				UH				10
GMC Motor Home	9645			IND	Dk. Gr.		Plst.		Reg				10
GMC Motor Home	9645			MEX	Dk. Gr.		Plst.		Reg				20
GMC Motor Home	9645			IND	Red				Reg				10
GMC Motor Home	9645			IND	Gr.		Plst.		Reg				10
GMC Motor Home	9645			IND	Red				Reg				10
GMC Motor Home	9645			IND	Blu.		Plst.		Reg				10
GMC Motor Home		Gold Manager		HK	Gold plate		Gold plate		Reg				400
GMC Motor Home	9645			MEX	Gr.				Reg				20
GMC Motor Home	9645			HK	Or.		Plst.		Reg				15
GMC Motor Home	9645			HK	Gr.		Plst.		Reg				15
GMC Motor Home	9645			HK	Or.				RL				300
GMC Motor Home	9645			HK	Or.				Reg				15
Good Humor Truck	5904		lg. r.wndw	MAL	Wht.				Reg	Red striped awning	Strawberry on sign		5
Good Humor Truck	5904		lg. r.wndw	MAL	Wht.				Reg	Blu. striped awning	Strawberry on sign		5
Good Humor Truck	5904		lg. r.wndw	MAL	Wht.				Reg	Blu. striped awning	Sign Blk.ed out		35
Good Humor Truck	5904		lg. r.wndw	HK	Wht.				Reg	Blu. striped awning	Popsicle on sign		12
Good Humor Truck	5904		sm. r.wndw	MAL	Wht.				Reg	Red striped awning	Strawberry on sign		5
Good Ol' Pick-Um-Up	9541			MAL	Brg.				RR - Wht.				25
Good Ol' Pick-Um-Up	9541			MEX	M. Brg.				RR - Wht.				50
Goodyear Blimp	5518			MAL	Grey					Blk., Gr., Yl. & Blu. tr.	The best tires in the world...		6
Goodyear Blimp	1384			MAL	Grey					Red, Gr., Yl. & Blu. tr.	Rev it up! Rip it up!		5

Name	#	Category	Casting	Ctry.	Color	Win.	Base	Interior	Wheels	Paint	Logo	Other	S
Goodyear Blimp	1384			MAL	Grey					Blk. tr.	Goodyear #1 in tires		5
Goodyear Blimp	5518			MAL	Grey					Blk. tr.	The best tires in the world...		6
Goodyear Blimp	1384			MAL	Grey					Blk., Gr., Yl. & Blu. tr.	Goodyear #1 in tires		6
Goodyear Blimp	1384			MAL	Grey					Blk., Red & Yl. tr.	Rev it up! Rip it up!		6
Goodyear Blimp		Gulf		MAL	Grey					Blk., Or. & Wht. tr.	Gulf		5
Goodyear Blimp		LE		MAL	Chr.								100
Goodyear Blimp		Pre-Pro		MAL	Grey					Blu. tr.	Goodyear		
Grass Hopper	7622			HK	Gr.			Blk.	RL	Blu. & Or. tr.		No rear engine or canvas top	40
Grass Hopper	7622		Engine does not protrude	HK	Gr.			Blk.	RL	Blu. & Or. tr.		No rear engine or canvas top	100
Grass Hopper	7622	Pre-Pro		HK	Gr.			Blk.	RL	Blk.	Hopper		
Grass Hopper	7622	Pre-Pro		HK	Gr.			Blk.	RL				
Greased Gremlin	2502			MEX	Red				RR - Wht.				100
Greased Gremlin	2502			HK	Red				Reg				15
Greased Gremlin	2502			MAL	Red				Reg				15
Gremlin Grinder	7652			HK	Gr.				RL				35
Gremlin Grinder	9116	Herfy's		HK	Gr.				RL		Herfy's		100
Gremlin Grinder	9201	Super Chr.		HK	Chr.				RL				30
Gremlin Grinder	9201	Super Chr.		HK	Chr.				Reg				25
Greyhound MC-8	1127			MEX	Silver/Wht.				Reg				30
Greyhound MC-8	1127			HK	Silver/Wht.				Reg				12
Greyhound MC-8	1127			MAL	Silver/Wht.				Reg				15
GT Racer	9224	Park'n Plate		MAL	Red				UH				8
GT Racer		Revealer		MAL	Blu.				Reg			Revealers 10 pack	10
GT Racer		Video Car		MAL	Silver				Reg	Wht., Yl. & Prp. tr.	5		10
GT Racer	450			MAL	Blk.	Solid silver			Reg	Red, Prp., Yl. & Pnk. tr.	5		4
GT Racer	1789			MAL	Prp.				Reg	Or., Wht. & Blu. tr.	5 & V		4
GT Racer	1789			MAL	Prp.				Reg	Or., Wht. & Blu. tr.	5 & no V		4
GT Racer	1789			MAL	Prp.				UH	Or., Wht. & Blu. tr.	5 & no V		4
GT Racer	1789			MAL	M. Blu.				UH	Or., Wht. & Blk. tr.	5		35
GT Racer	1789			MAL	Prp.				UH	Or., Wht. & Blu. tr.	5 & V		4
GT Racer	2680	Set		MAL	Ivory				Reg	Or., Mgta. & Blu. tr.	5	Dash'n'Crash	10
GT Racer	2680	Set		MAL	Ivory				Reg	Or., Pnk. & Prp. tr.	5	Dash'n'Crash	10
Gulch Stepper				IND	Red				4x4 SHb	Bro., Wht. & Blk. tr.			10
Gulch Stepper	4320			MAL	N. Yl.		Rsd. MAL		4x4 SHb				4
Gulch Stepper		Kool Aid		MAL	Gr. to Yl.		Rsd. MAL		4x4 SHb	Blu., Wht. & Gr. tr.	Kool Aid 4x4 Wacky		10
Gulch Stepper		Mall		MAL	Wht.		Rsd. MAL		4x4 SHb	Pnk., Blu. & Gr. tr.			10
Gulch Stepper	1516			MAL	Red		Flat MAL		4x4 LHb				4
Gulch Stepper	1516			MAL	Red		Rsd. MAL		4x4 SHb	Blu., Yl. & Wht. tr.	15		4
Gulch Stepper	1516			MAL	Red		Rsd. MAL		4x4 LHb				4
Gulch Stepper	1516			MAL	Red		Flat MAL		4x4 SHb	Blu., Yl. & Wht. tr.			4
Gulch Stepper	7532			HK	Yl.				4x4 SHb	Or., Red & Prp. tr.			5
Gulch Stepper	7532			HK	Yl.				4x4 LHb	Or., Red & Prp. tr.			5
Gun Bucket	9090			HK	Khk.				RL				25

Name	#	Category	Casting	Ctry.	Color	Win.	Base	Interior	Wheels	Paint	Logo	Other	$
Gun Bucket	9090			MAL	Khk. Cmflg.				Reg - Blk.				5
Gun Bucket	9090			HK	Khk. Cmflg.				Reg - Blk.				20
Gunslinger	7664		Engine does not protrude	HK	Khk.	Gun bracket on wshld.		Blk.	RL				35
Gunslinger	7664		Engine does not protrude	HK	Khk.	Gun bracket		Blk.	Reg				25
Gunslinger	7664		Engine does not protrude	HK	Khk.			Blk.	RL				35
Hammer Down				MAL	Red				Reg			Great American Truck Race	60
Hammer Down				HK	Red				Reg			Great American Truck Race	60
Hare Splitter	2504			IND	Red				Reg				10
Hare Splitter	2504			MAL	Yl.				Reg			Spare wheel on roof	10
Hare Splitter	2504			MAL	Wht.				Reg			Spare wheel on roof	10
Hare Splitter	2504			HK	Wht.				Reg			Spare wheel on roof	10
Hare Splitter	2504			HK	Yl.				Reg			Spare wheel on roof	10
Hare Splitter	2504			MEX	Wht.				Reg				20
Heavy Chevy	6189 Super Chr.			HK	Chr.				Reg	Light & Dk. Gr. tr.	7		50
Heavy Chevy	6189 Super Chr.			US	Chr.				Reg	Light & Dk. Gr. tr.	7		50
Heavy Chevy	7619			HK	Yl.				RL	Red & Or. tr.	7		60
Heavy Chevy	7619			HK	Gr.				RL	Red & Or. tr.	7		200
Heavy Chevy	9212 Super Chr.			HK	Chr.				Reg	Red & Or. tr.	7		50
Heavy Chevy	9212 Super Chr.			HK	Chr.				RL	Red & Or. tr.	7		50
Heavy Chevy	9212 Super Chr.			HK	Chr.				RL	Light & Dk. Gr. tr.	7		50
Highway Hauler	700 Millionth	DRA		MAL	Wht.				Reg		HW		200
Highway Hauler	1174 Workhorse	DRA		MAL	Gr.				Reg		Mountain Dew		20
Highway Hauler	1174 Workhorse	DRA		HK	Wht.				Reg		North American		20
Highway Hauler	1174 Workhorse	DRA		MAL	Gr.		Inv. MAL		Reg		Mountain Dew		20
Highway Hauler	1174 Workhorse	DRA		HK	Yl.				Reg		Pennzoil		20
Highway Hauler	1174 Workhorse	DRA		MAL	Wht.				Reg		North American		20
Highway Hauler	1174 Workhorse	DRA		MAL	Yl.				Reg		Pennzoil		20
Highway Hauler	1174 Workhorse	DRA		HK	Yl.				Reg		Mayflower		12
Highway Hauler	1174 Workhorse	DRA		HK	Gr.				Reg		Mountain Dew		20
Highway Hauler	1174 Workhorse	DRA		MAL	Yl.				Reg		Mayflower		12
Highway Heat	2524			MAL	Or.				HO - Gold				8
Sheriff Patrol	1549			MAL	Blk./Wht.				Reg	Yl. star on hood & doors	123 on roof & Police		4
Sheriff Patrol	9228 Park'n Plate			MAL	Blk./Wht.				Reg	Yl. tr.	Police & 104 on roof		10
Highway Patrol	2019			HK	Wht./Blk.		Rsd. HK & 1977				12 on roof & Highway Patrol		8
Highway Patrol	2019			HK	Wht./Blk.		Rsd. HK & 1977		Reg				12
Highway Patrol	2019			HK	Wht./Blk.		Flat HK & 1977		Reg		Highway Patrol		8
Highway Patrol	2019			HK	Wht./Blk.		Flat HK & 1977		Reg		12 on roof & Highway Patrol		12
Hiway Hauler	3782			MAL	Red/Wht.				Reg	Blu, Red & Yl. tr.	Kool-Aid	Thick Red wavy line	5

Name	#	Category	Casting	Ctry.	Color	Win.	Base	Interior	Wheels	Paint	Logo	Other	S
Hiway Hauler	3782			MAL	Red/Wht.				Reg	Blu., Red & Yl. tr.	Kool-Aid	Thin Red wavy line	5
Hiway Hauler		Dinty Moore		MAL	Red/Wht.				Reg	Blk., Red & Bro. tr.	Dinty Moore		12
Hiway Hauler		1174 Workhorse	DRA	MAL	Aq./Wht.				Reg		Ocean Pacific		5
Hiway Hauler	1565		DRA	MAL	Blu./Wht.				Reg		Goodyear		8
Hiway Hauler	1565		DRA	HK	Blu./Wht.				Reg		Goodyear		8
Hiway Hauler	1565		DRA	MAL	Dk. Blu./Wht.				Reg		Goodyear Racing Tires		8
Hiway Hauler	1565		DRA	HK	Dk. Blu./Wht.				Reg		Goodyear Racing Tires		8
Hiway Hauler	2548		DRA	MAL	Wht.				Reg	Red, Blu. & Blk. tr.	Masters Of The Universe		8
Hiway Hauler	2548		DRA	HK	Wht.				Reg	Red, Blu. & Blk. tr.	Masters Of The Universe		8
Hiway Hauler	2806		DRA	MAL	Red/Wht.				Reg	Red & Blu. tr. covering whole side	Pepsi		8
Hiway Hauler	2806		DRA	MAL	Red/Wht.				Reg	Red & Blu. tr. not covering whole side	Pepsi		6
Hiway Hauler	2806		DRA	HK	Red/Wht.				Reg	Red & Blu. tr. not covering whole side	Pepsi		6
Hiway Hauler	2806		DRA	HK	Red/Wht.				Reg	Red & Blu. tr. covering whole side	Pepsi		8
Hiway Hauler	4642			MAL	Prp./Wht.				Reg	Red, Yl., Blu. & Gr. tr.	HW logo & Delivery		8
Hiway Hauler	5144		DRA	MAL	Wht.				Reg		NASA		8
Hiway Hauler	5144		DRA	HK	Wht.				Reg		NASA		8
Hiway Hauler	9549		DRA	MAL	Wht.				Reg	Red, Blu. & Yl. tr.	HW Racing Team		8
Hiway Hauler	9549		DRA	HK	Wht.				Reg	Red, Blu. & Yl. tr.	HW Racing Team		8
Hiway Robber	6979			HK	Plum			Dk. Bro.	RL				75
Hiway Robber	6979			HK	Red			Blk.	RL				75
Hiway Robber	6979			HK	Light Gr.			Dk. Bro.	RL				75
Hiway Robber	6979			HK	Dk. Blu.			Blk.	RL				75
Hiway Robber	6979			HK	Pnk.			Dk. Bro.	RL				75
Hiway Robber	6979			HK	Gr.			Grey	RL				75
Hiway Robber	6979			HK	Red			Blk.	RL				75
Hiway Robber	6979			HK	Dk. Blu.			Dk. Bro.	RL				75
Hiway Robber	6979			HK	Pnk.			Grey	RL				75
Hiway Robber	6979			HK	Pale Blu.			Grey	RL				75
Hiway Robber	6979			HK	Gr.			Dk. Bro.	RL				75
Hiway Robber	6979			HK	Pale Blu.			Dk. Bro.	RL				75
Hiway Robber	6979			HK	Dk. Blu.			Grey	RL				75
Hiway Robber	6979			HK	Pnk.			Blk.	RL				75
Hiway Robber	6979			HK	Pale Blu.			Dk. Bro.	RL				75
Hiway Robber	6979			HK	Red			Dk. Bro.	RL				75
Hiway Robber	6979			HK	Pale Yl.			Blk.	RL				75
Hiway Robber	6979			HK	Pale Yl.			Dk. Bro.	RL				75
Hiway Robber	6979			HK	Flr. Lime			Blk.	RL				75
Hiway Robber	6979			HK	Dk. Yl.			Blk.	RL				75
Hiway Robber	6979			HK	Light Gr.			Grey	RL				75
Hiway Robber	6979			HK	Light Gr.			Dk. Bro.	RL				75
Hiway Robber	6979			HK	Or.			Grey	RL				75
Hiway Robber	6979			HK	Plum			Grey	RL				75

Name	#	Category	Casting	Ctry.	Color	Win.	Base	Interior	Wheels	Paint	Logo	Other	$
Hiway Robber	6979			HK	Pale Yl.			Grey	RL				75
Hiway Robber	6979			HK	Flr. Lime			Blk.	RL				75
Hiway Robber	6979			HK	Plum			Blk.	RL				75
Hiway Robber	6979			HK	Dk. Yl.			Grey	RL				75
Hiway Robber	6979			HK	Or.			Grey	RL				75
Hiway Robber	6979			HK	Gr.			Blk.	RL				75
Hiway Robber	6979			HK	Dk. Yl.			Dk. Bro.	RL				75
Hiway Robber	6979			HK	Or.			Blk.	RL				75
Hiway Robber	6979			HK	Flr. Lime			Grey	RL				75
Holden Commodore	9713			MAL	Wht.				Reg				10
Hot Bird		Set		MAL	M. Blu.	BluT		37 Grey	UH	Grey & Or. tr.		Double Barrel Stunt	10
Hot Bird		Set		MAL	M. Blu.	BluT		37 Grey	HO - Gold	Grey & Or. tr.		Double Barrel Stunt	10
Hot Bird	462			MAL	Git. Blk.				UH				4
Hot Bird		Color Changer		MAL	Prp. to Mauve				Reg				5
Hot Bird		Pre-Pro		MAL	M. Pale Blu.				HO - Gold	Yl. firebird			5
Hot Bird		Ralston		MAL	Silver			Tan	HO - Gold	Red, Blu. & Yl. flames & bird			8
Hot Bird	1451			MAL	Wht.			Tan	UH	Red & Blu. stars & stripes	All American Firebird		12
Hot Bird	1451			MAL	M. Blu.	CL		37 Tan	UH	Red & Yl. flames & Wht. bird	Firebird		5
Hot Bird	1451			MAL	Wht.			Red	HO - Gold	Red & Blu. stars & stripes	All American Firebird		5
Hot Bird	1451			MAL	M. Blu.	CL		44 Grey	UH	Red & Yl. flames & Wht. bird	Firebird		15
Hot Bird	1451			MAL	M. Blu.	CL		37 Tan	UH	Red & Yl. flames & Wht. bird	Firebird		5
Hot Bird	1451			MAL	M. Blu.	CL		44 Tan	UH	Red & Yl. flames & Wht. bird	Firebird		5
Hot Bird	1451			MAL	M. Blu.	CL		44 Grey	UH	Red & Yl. flames & Wht. bird	Firebird		15
Hot Bird	1451			MAL	M. Blu.	CL		44 Tan	HO - Gold	Red & Yl. flames & Wht. bird	Firebird		5
Hot Bird	1451			MAL	Wht.			37 Red	UH	Red & Blu. stars & stripes	All American Firebird		5
Hot Bird	1451			MAL	M. Blu.	CL		44 Tan	UH	Red & Yl. flames & Wht. bird	Firebird		5
Hot Bird	1451			MAL	M. Blu.	CL		37 Grey	HO - Gold	Red & Yl. flames & Wht. bird	Firebird		5
Hot Bird	1451			MAL	M. Blu.	CL		37 Tan	HO - Gold	Red & Yl. flames & Wht. bird	Firebird		5
Hot Bird	2014			MAL	Gold				Reg				5
Hot Bird	2014			HK	Blk.		HW logo		Reg	Red & Yl. stripes & Yl. firebird			5
Hot Bird	2014			HK	Blk.			44	HO - Gold	Red & Yl. stripes & Yl. firebird			5
Hot Bird	2014			HK	Blk.			44	Reg	Red & Yl. stripes & Yl. firebird			5
Hot Bird	2014			MAL	Blk.			44	Reg	Red & Yl. stripes & Yl. firebird			5

Name	#	Category	Casting	Ctry.	Color	Win.	Base	Interior	Wheels	Paint	Logo	Other	$
Hot Bird	2014			HK	Blk.		HW logo		HO - Gold	Red & Yl. stripes & Yl. firebird			5
Hot Bird	2014			MAL	Blk.		HW logo		Reg	Red & Yl. stripes & Yl. firebird			5
Hot Bird	2014			HK	Bro.				Reg				5
Hot Bird	2014			HK	Blk.		HW	Tan	Reg	Red & Yl. stripes & Yl. firebird			5
Hot Bird	2014			MAL	Blk.		HW logo		HO - Gold	Red & Yl. stripes & Yl. firebird			5
Hot Bird	2014			HK	Blk.		HW	Red	HO - Gold	Red & Yl. stripes & Yl. firebird			5
Hot Bird	2014			MAL	Bro.				Reg				75
Hot Bird	2014			MAL	Blk.		HW	Red	HO - Gold	Red & Yl. stripes & Yl. firebird			5
Hot Bird	2014			HK	Blu.				Reg				50
Hot Bird	2014			MAL	Blk.			44	HO - Gold	Red & Yl. stripes & Yl. firebird			5
Hot Bird	2014			MAL	Blk.		HW	Tan	Reg	Red & Yl. stripes & Yl. firebird			5
Hot Bird	2014			HK	Gold				Reg				18
Hot Bird	2014			HK	Blk.		HW	Tan	HO - Gold	Red & Yl. stripes & Yl. firebird			5
Hot Bird	2014			MAL	Blk.		HW	Tan	HO - Gold	Red & Yl. stripes & Yl. firebird			5
Hot Bird	2014			MAL	Blu.				Reg				50
Hot Bird	9518			MAL	Wht.			Red	UH - Gold	Red & Blu. stars & stripes	All American Firebird		8
Hot Bird	9518			MAL	Wht.			Red	HO - Silver	Red & Blu. stars & stripes	All American Firebird		8
T-Bucket - (Hot Rod)	9223	Park'n Plate		MAL	Prp.	BluT			Reg				20
T-Bucket - (Hot Rod)	9223	Park'n Plate		MAL	Prp.	CL			Reg				20
Hot Wheels Race Team	3305	Scene Machine		HK	Yl.				Reg				40
Human Torch	2881	Heroes		HK	Blk.		RAF		Reg				15
Human Torch	2881	Heroes		HK	Blk.		No rivet		Reg				15
Hummer	773			MAL	Des. Cmflg.				4x4 SHb				6
Hummer	773			MAL	Des. Cmflg.				4x4 SHb	Pnk. tinge to camouflage			5
Ice Cream Truck	3855		lg. r.wndw	MAL	Red				Reg		Pepsi		12
Ice Cream Truck	3206			MAL	N. Yl.				Reg - N. Gr.				10
Ice Cream Truck	3855		sm. r.wndw	MAL	Red				Reg		No Pepsi		12
Ice T	6980			MEX	Dk. Gr.				Reg			Yl. top	20
Ice T	6980			FRA	Yl.				Reg			Wht. top	20
Ice T	6980			FRA	Light Blu.				Reg			Yl. top	30
Ice T	6980			FRA	Bro.				Reg			Wht. top	30
Ice T	6980			FRA	Yl.				Reg			Yl. top	20
Ice T	6980			FRA	Light Blu.				Reg	Or. & Dk. Gr. tr.		Wht. top	20
Ice T	6980			HK	Pale Blu.				RL				90
Ice T	6980			HK	Dk. Yl.				RL				90
Ice T	6980			HK	Pale Gr.				RL	Or. & Dk. Gr. tr.		Wht. top	50
Ice T	6980			HK	Dk. Blu.				RL				90
Ice T	6980			HK	Plum				RL				90

Name	#	Category	Casting	Ctry.	Color	Win.	Base	Interior	Wheels	Paint	Logo	Other	$
Ice T	6980			HK	Pale Gr.				RL				90
Ice T	6980			HK	Flr. Lime				RL				90
Ice T	6980			HK	Red				RL				90
Ice T	6980			HK	Gr.				RL				90
Ice T	6980			HK	Pale Gr.				Reg			Wht. top	20
Ice T	6980			HK	Yl.				RL	Or. & Dk. Gr. tr.		Wht. top	50
Ice T	6980			HK	Pale Yl.				RL			Wht. top	90
Ice T	6980			HK	Or.				RL				90
Ice T	6980			HK	Pnk.				RL				90
Inferno	9186			HK	Yl.				RL				40
Inside Story				IND	Gr.				Reg	Yl. & Blk. tennis tr.			10
Inside Story				IND	Blu.				Reg				10
Inside Story				IND	Gr.				Reg	Wht. & Blk. tennis tr.			10
Inside Story				IND	Yl.				Reg	Red & Gr. tennis tr.			10
Inside Story	2510			MAL	Yl.	YT			Reg				7
Inside Story	2510			HK	Grey	BluT			Reg				7
Inside Story	2510			MAL	Grey	BluT			Reg				7
Inside Story	2510			HK	Yl.	YT			Reg				7
Inside Story	2510			HK	Yl.	BluT			Reg				7
Inside Story	2510			MAL	Yl.	YT			Reg				7
Inside Story	4234			MEX	Blk.	YT			Reg				35
Inside Story	4234			MEX	Tan	YT			Reg				25
Iron Man		3301 Heroes		MAL	Wht.			Tan	Reg				15
Iron Man		3301 Heroes		HK	Wht.			Tan	Reg				15
Iron Man		3301 Heroes		MAL	Wht.			Red	Reg				25
Jaguar XJ220		25th Ann.	CSRS	MAL	Chr.				UH				5
Jaguar XJ220		25th Ann.	CSFS	MAL	Chr.				UH				5
Jaguar XJ220		Revealer	CSFS	MAL	M. Prp.				UH - N. Yl.				5
Jaguar XJ220		Revealer	CSFS	MAL	M. Blu.				UH - N. Gr.				5
Jaguar XJ220		Revealer	CSRS	MAL	M. Blu.				UH - N. Gr.				5
Jaguar XJ220		Revealer	CSRS	MAL	Crimson				UH - N. Yl.				5
Jaguar XJ220		Revealer	CSRS	MAL	M. Prp.				UH - N. Yl.				5
Jaguar XJ220		Revealer	CSFS	MAL	Crimson				UH - N. Yl.				5
Jaguar XJ220	3026		CSFS	MAL	Silver				UH				3
Jaguar XJ220	3026		CSRS	MAL	Silver				UH				3
Jaguar XJ220	3026		OSFS	MAL	Silver				UH				3
Jaguar XJ220	3026		OSRS	MAL	Silver				UH				3
Jaguar XJS	2012			FRA	Dk. Bro. MF.				Reg	Jaguar cat on door	XJS		20
Jaguar XJS	2012			FRA	Dk. Bro. MF.				Reg				20
Jaguar XJS	2012			FRA	Wht.				Reg				20
Jaguar XJS	2012			FRA	Grey				Reg				20
Jaguar XJS	2012			HK	Grey				Reg	Jaguar cat on door	XJS		8
Jaguar XJS	2012			MEX	Dk. Bro. MF.				Reg	Jaguar cat on door	XJS		40
Jaguar XJS	2012			MEX	Wht.				Reg	Yl., Red & Blk. tr.	10		40
Jaguar XJS	2012			HK	Blu.				Reg	Jaguar cat on door	XJS		8
Jaguar XJS	2012			MAL	Dk. Bro. MF.				Reg	Jaguar cat on door	XJS		40
Jaguar XJS	2012			MEX	Dk. Bro. MF.				UH	Yl., Gr. & Blk. tr.	10		40
Jaguar XJS	2012			MEX	Dk. Bro. MF.				Reg	Yl., Gr. & Blk. tr.	10		40
Jaguar XJS	2012			HK	Gold				Reg	Jaguar cat on door	XJS		20
Jaguar XJS	2012			MAL	Blu.				Reg	Jaguar cat on door	XJS		8

Name	#	Category	Casting	Ctry.	Color	Win.	Base	Interior	Wheels	Paint	Logo	Other	S
Jaguar XJS	2012			MEX	Dk. Bro. MF.				Reg	Jaguar cat on door & triangle	XJS		40
Jaguar XJS	2012			MEX	Wht.				Reg	Yl., Blu. & Blk. tr.	10		40
Jaguar XJS	2012			MEX	Dk. Bro. MF.				HO - Gold	Yl., Gr. & Blk. tr.	10		40
Jaguar XJS	2012			MEX	Wht.				HO - Gold	Yl., Blu. & Blk. tr.	10		40
Jaguar XJS	2012			MEX	Dk. Bro. MF.				UH	Jaguar cat on door & triangle	XJS		40
Jeep CJ7		Co. Rcr.		MAL	Gr. to Yl.			Blk.	Reg				5
Jeep CJ7		Pre-Pro		MAL	Gr.				Reg	Red & Or. eagle			
Jeep CJ7	2539			HK	Wht.		Jeep CJ 7	Red	4x4 SHb	Red, Or. & Prp. tr.	Jeep		6
Jeep CJ7	2539			HK	Wht.		No Jeep CJ 7	Red	Reg	Red, Or. & Prp. tr.	Jeep		6
Jeep CJ7	2539			MAL	Wht.		MAL cast flat & HW logo	Red	Reg	Red, Or. & Prp. tr.	Jeep		6
Jeep CJ7	2539			MAL	Wht.		MAL cast flat & no Jeep CJ	Red	4x4 SHb	Red, Or. & Prp. tr.	Jeep		6
Jeep CJ7	2539			HK	Wht.		Jeep CJ 7	Red	RR - Wht.	Red, Or. & Prp. tr.	Jeep		15
Jeep CJ7	2539			HK	Wht.		Jeep CJ 7	Red	Reg	Red, Or. & Prp. tr.	Jeep		6
Jeep CJ7	2539			MAL	Wht.		Jeep CJ 7	Red	Reg	Red, Or. & Prp. tr.	Jeep		6
Jeep CJ7	2539			MAL	Wht.		MAL cast flat & HW logo	Red	RR - Wht.	Red, Or. & Prp. tr.	Jeep		15
Jeep CJ7	2539			MAL	Wht.		Jeep CJ 7	Red	RR - Wht.	Red, Or. & Prp. tr.	Jeep		15
Jeep CJ7	2539			MAL	Wht.		No Jeep CJ 7	Red	RR - Wht.	Red, Or. & Prp. tr.	Jeep		6
Jeep CJ7	2539			MAL	Wht.		MAL cast flat & HW logo	Red	4x4 SHb	Red, Or. & Prp. tr.	Jeep		6
Jeep CJ7	2539			MAL	Wht.		No Jeep CJ 7	Red	RR - Wht.	Red, Or. & Prp. tr.	Jeep		15
Jeep CJ7	2539			MAL	Wht.		MAL cast flat & HW logo	Red	RR - Wht.	Red, Or. & Prp. tr.	Jeep		15
Jeep CJ7	2539			HK	Wht.		No Jeep CJ 7	Red	RR - Wht.	Red, Or. & Prp. tr.	Jeep		15
Jeep CJ7	2539			HK	Wht.		No Jeep CJ 7	Red	4x4 SHb	Red, Or. & Prp. tr.	Jeep		6
Jeep CJ7	2539			MAL	Wht.		MAL cast flat & no Jeep CJ	Red	Reg	Red, Or. & Prp. tr.	Jeep		6
Jeep CJ7	2539			MAL	Wht.		Jeep CJ 7	Red	4x4 SHb	Red, Or. & Prp. tr.	Jeep		6
Jeep CJ7	2539			MAL	Wht.		No Jeep CJ 7	Red	4x4 SHb	Red, Or. & Prp. tr.	Jeep		6
Jeep CJ7	3005 Kelloggs			HK	Yl.			Blk.	Reg	Red, Or. & Prp. tr.	Jeep		10
Jeep CJ7	3005 Kelloggs			MAL	Yl.			Blk.	Reg	Red, Or. & Prp. tr.	Jeep		10
Jeep CJ7	3259			HK	Wht.	CF		Blk.	Reg	Red & Or. eagle			6
Jeep CJ7	3259			MAL	Wht.	WF		Blk.	Reg	Red & Or. eagle			6
Jeep CJ7	3259			MAL	Wht.	CF		Blk.	Reg	Red & Or. eagle			6
Jeep CJ7	3259			HK	Wht.	WF		Blk.	Reg	Red & Or. eagle			6
Jeep CJ7	3953			MAL	Wht.		Rsd. MAL	Blk.	Reg	Red & Or. eagle			6
Jeep CJ7	3954			HK	Yl.			Blk.	Reg	Red, Or. & Prp. eagle			6
Jeep CJ7	3954			MAL	Yl.			Blk.	Reg	Red, Or. & Prp. eagle			6
Jeep CJ7	4362			HK	Dk. Bro. MF.			Tan	RR - Grey				15
Jeep CJ7	4362			MAL	Dk. Bro. MF.			Blk.	Reg				6
Jeep CJ7	4362			MAL	Dk. Bro. MF.			Tan	RR - Wht.				15
Jeep CJ7	4362			MAL	Dk. Bro. MF.			Tan	RR - Grey				15
Jeep CJ7	4362			MAL	Dk. Bro. MF.			Tan	Reg				6
Jeep CJ7	4362			HK	Dk. Bro. MF.			Tan	RR - Wht.				15
Jeep CJ7	4362			HK	Dk. Bro. MF.			Blk.	Reg				6
Jeep CJ7	9543			HK	Yl.			Blk.	RR - Wht.	Gr. dragon			15

Name	#	Category	Casting	Ctry.	Color	Win.	Base	Interior	Wheels	Paint	Logo	Other	S
Jeep CJ7	9543			MAL	Yl.			Blk.	RR - Wht.	Gr. dragon			15
Jeep CJ7	9543	Pre-Pro		MAL	Yl.			Tan	RR - Wht.	Gr. dragon			7
Jeep Scrambler	2541			MAL	M. Blu.				Reg				15
Jeep Scrambler	2541			MAL	M. Blu.				RR - Wht.				15
Jeep Scrambler	4370			HK	Grey				RR - Grey				15
Jeep Scrambler	4370			HK	Grey				RR - Wht.				15
Jeep Scrambler	4370			HK	Grey MF.				RR - Grey				15
Jeep Scrambler	4370			MAL	Grey MF.				RR - Wht.				25
Jeep Scrambler	4370			MAL	Blk.				RR - Wht.				15
Jeep Scrambler	5146			MAL	M. Red				4x4 SHb				7
Jeep Scrambler	5146			MAL	M. Red				Reg				7
Jeep Scrambler	9547			MAL	Brg.				RR - Wht.				15
Jet Sweep X5	2546	Ultra Hot		MAL	Silver				UH				6
Jet Sweep X5	7528	Ultra Hot		MAL	Gold				UH				6
Jet Sweep X5	7528	Ultra Hot		HK	Gold				UH				6
Khaki Kooler	9183			HK	Khk.				Reg				20
Khaki Kooler	9183			HK	Khk.		Plst.		RL				25
Khaki Kooler	9183			HK	Khk.				RL				25
King Radio Van	9133	Herfy's		HK	Blk.	BluT			RL	Or. tr.	King		100
King Radio Van	9133	Herfy's		HK	Blu.	BluT			RL	Or. tr.	King		100
King Radio Van	9133	Herfy's		HK	Blk.	BluT			RL	Yl. tr.	King		100
Thunderstreak	2199	Park'n Plate	Short rear wing	MAL	Blu./Yl.				Reg		Kraco 18		6
Lamborghini Countach		25th Ann.	Wing integral to body	MAL	Gunmetal	CL		Red	UH				5
Lamborghini Countach		Co. Rcr.	Wing separate from body	MAL	Prp. to Wht.	BluT		Wht.	Reg				5
Lamborghini Countach		Co. Rcr.	Wing separate from body	MAL	Pnk. to Wht.	BluT		Red	Reg				5
Lamborghini Countach	9222	Park'n Plate	Wing integral to body	MAL	Red	CL		Wht.	UH				8
Lamborghini Countach		Revealer		MAL	Gold				UH - Gold			Revealers first prize car	125
Lamborghini Countach		Revealer		MAL	Wht.				UH - N. Gr.	Blk., Yl. & Red coins tr.			5
Lamborghini Countach		Revealer		MAL	N. Blz.				UH - N. Pnk.	Blk., Yl. & Red coins tr.			5
Lamborghini Countach		Revealer		MAL	Silver				UH - N. Yl.	Blk., Yl. & Red coins tr.			5
Lamborghini Countach	4384			MAL	Wht.	DT		Red	UH	Blu. & Red tr. on sides	Countach		5
Lamborghini Countach	4384		Wing integral to body	MAL	Wht.	DT		Red	UH - Gold	Blu. & Red tr. on sides	Countach		12
Lamborghini Countach	4384		Wing integral to body	MAL	Wht.	DT		Red	UH	No tr.	Countach		5
Lamborghini Countach	4384		Wing separate from body	MAL	Wht.	DT		Red	UH	Blu. & Red tr. on sides	Countach		5
Lamborghini Countach	4384		Wing integral to body	MAL	Wht.	DT		Red	UH	Blu. & Red tr. on sides & hood	Countach		5
Lamborghini Countach	4384		Wing integral to body	MAL	Wht.	LT		Red	UH	No tr.	Countach		5
Lamborghini Countach	4384		Wing integral to body	MAL	Wht.	DT		Red	UH	Dk. Blu. & Red tr. on sides	Countach		5
Lamborghini Countach	4553		Wing integral to body	MAL	Red	DT		Blk.	UH	Blk. & Wht. tr. on sides	Countach		5

Name	#	Category	Casting	Ctry.	Color	Win.	Base	Interior	Wheels	Paint	Logo	Other	s
Lamborghini Countach	13577		Wing integral to body	MAL	Red	DT		Blk.	UH - Gold	Blk. & Wht. tr. on sides	Countach		5
Lamborghini Diablo		25th Ann.		MAL	Blk.				UH				5
Lamborghini Diablo		Revealer		MAL	Red				UH	Prp. & Yl. tr.		Revealers 10 pack	10
Lamborghini Diablo		Revealer		MAL	M. Blu.				UH - N. Gr.	Or., & Pnk. tr.			5
Lamborghini Diablo		Revealer		MAL	Crimson				UH - N. Yl.	Or., & Pnk. tr.			5
Lamborghini Diablo		Revealer		MAL	Blk.				UH - N. Pnk.	Or., & Pnk. tr.			5
Lamborghini Diablo	460			MAL	Glt. Blu.				UH			Dk. Blu. wing	3
Lamborghini Diablo	460			MAL	Glt. Blu.				UH			Pale Blu. wing	3
Lamborghini Diablo	4406			MAL	Yl.				UH				4
Lamborghini Diablo	5672			MAL	Red				UH				4
Landlord	3260			HK	Or.				Reg				7
Landlord	3260			HK	Or.		Rsd. HK		Reg				7
Landlord	3260			MAL	Or.		MAL cast on one of two Rsd. bars		Reg				7
Landlord	3260			MAL	Or.				Reg				7
Large Charge	8272			HK	Or.				Reg	Red, Yl. & Blk. electrical tr.			10
Large Charge	8272			MEX	Or.				Reg	Yl. & Prp. electrical tr.			20
Large Charge	8272			HK	Or.				Reg	Prp., Wht. & Mgta. tr.			10
Large Charge	8272			MEX	Or.				Reg	Prp. & Yl. electrical tr.			20
Large Charge	8272			HK	Gr.				RL	Red, Yl. & Blk. electrical tr.			40
Large Charge	9211	Super Chr.		HK	Chr.				RL				30
Large Charge	9211	Super Chr.		HK	Chr.				Reg				20
Letter Getter	9643			HK	Wht.				Reg		US Mail		10
Letter Getter	9643			HK	Wht.		Plst.		RL		US Mail		300
Letter Getter	9643			HK	Wht.		Plst.		Reg		US Mail		10
Letter Getter	9643			HK	Wht.				RL		US Mail		300
Letter Getter	9643			MAL	Wht.		Plst.		Reg		US Mail		10
Lexus SC 400	5263			MAL	M. Dk. Red				UH				3
Lexus SC 400	5263			MAL	M. Blk.				UH				3
Lickety Six	2017			FRA	Blu.				Reg				20
Lickety Six	2017			MEX	Wht.				Reg				40
Lickety Six	2017			MEX	Blu.		No MEX		Reg				30
Lickety Six	2017			MEX	Blu.				Reg				30
Lickety Six	2017			MAL	Blu.				Reg				15
Lickety Six	2017			HK	Blu.				Reg				15
Lightning Gold	3004	Kelloggs		MAL	Blu.				Reg				18
Lightning Gold	4372			MAL	Yl.				RR - Wht.				15
Lightning Gold	4372			MAL	Yl.				RR - Grey				18
Lightning Gold	4372			MAL	Yl.				Reg				12
Limozeen	5638			MAL	Glt. Blu.				WW				4
Limozeen	5638			MAL	Wht.				WW				5
Limozeen	4347			MAL	Glt. Blk.				WW				4
Long Shot	3921			MEX	Wht.				Reg	Dk.er Red flames		All wheels are small	15
Long Shot	3921			HK	Wht.				Reg	Paler Red flames		RWs are larger than front	6
Long Shot	3921			MAL	Wht.				Reg	Paler Red flames		RWs are larger than front	6

Name	#	Category	Casting	Ctry.	Color	Win.	Base	Interior	Wheels	Paint	Logo	Other	$
Long Shot	5768			HK	Yl.				Reg			RWs are larger than front	8
Long Shot	5768			MAL	Yl.				Reg			RWs are larger than front	8
Lowdown	9185			FRA	Wht.				Reg	Blu., Yl. & Red tr.			40
Lowdown	9185			MEX	Blu.				Reg	Gr. & Wht. tr.			40
Lowdown	9185			MEX	Blu.				HO - Gold	Gr. & Wht. tr.			40
Lowdown	9185			FRA	Blu.				Reg	Red, Yl. & Wht. tr.			40
Lowdown	9185			MEX	Blu.		Blk. Plst.		HO - Gold	Gr. & Wht. tr.			40
Lowdown	9185			HK	Gold				RL	Red, Wht. & Blu. tr.			25
Lowdown	9185			HK	Gold				Reg	Red, Wht. & Blu. tr.			20
Lowdown	9185			MAL	Gold				Reg	Red, Wht. & Blu. tr.			20
Lowdown	9185			HK	Blu.				RL	Prp. & Yl. tr.	Flying Low		40
Malibu Grand Prix	9037			MAL	Blk.				RR - Grey				15
Malibu Grand Prix	9037			HK	Blk.				Reg				12
Malibu Grand Prix	9037			MAL	Blk.				Reg				12
Malibu Grand Prix	9037			HK	Blk.				RR - Grey				15
Maxi Taxi	9184		Cast roof sign	HK	Yl.				RL				35
Maxi Taxi	9184		Cast roof sign	HK	Yl.				Reg				20
Mazda Miata	2920			MAL	Yl.				Five Spoke - Lime Gr.		Miata on sides		4
Mazda Miata	2920			MAL	Yl.				Reg	Blu., Pnk. & Blk. tr.	Miata on sides		4
Mazda Miata		Getty		MAL	Red				Reg	Yl., Blu. & Wht.	Getty		5
Mazda Miata		Pre-Pro		MAL	Yl.				Five Spoke - Yl.	Blu., Pnk. & Blk. tr.	Miata on sides		
Mazda Miata	2920	Set		MAL	N. Or.				Serrated			G-Force	10
Mazda Miata	2920			MAL	Red				Reg	Pnk., Yl. & Gr. tr. on hood	Miata on hood		4
Mazda Miata	2920			MAL	Red				Reg				4
Mazda Miata	2920			MAL	Red				Reg	Pnk., Yl. & Gr. tr. on hood & door	Miata on hood		4
Mean Gr. Passion	12356			MAL	Gr.				WW	Blu. & olive flames	Blu. logo		3
Mean Gr. Passion	12356	Pre-Pro		MAL	Gr.				WW	Blu. & olive flames	Wht. logo		
Megadestroyer 1	5269	Mega Force		MAL	Tan				Reg - Blk.				20
Megadestroyer 2	5268	Mega Force		MAL	Blk.				Reg - Blk.				20
Megadestroyer 2	5268	Mega Force		MAL	Blk.				Reg - Grey				20
Megafighter	5271	Mega Force		MAL	Tan								20
Mercedes 380 SEL	9220	Park'n Plate		MAL	Blk.			Tan	HO - Gold				8
Mercedes 380 SEL		Pre-Pro		MAL	Blk.				UH - N. Or.	Prp., Blu. & Pnk. graffiti tr.			
Mercedes 380 SEL		Revealer		MAL	Silver				UH - N. Or.	Prp., Blu. & Pnk. graffiti tr.			5
Mercedes 380 SEL		Revealer		MAL	N. Yl.				UH - N. Or.	Prp., Blu. & Pnk. graffiti tr.			5
Mercedes 380 SEL		Revealer		MAL	Wht.				UH - N. Pnk.	Prp., Blu. & Pnk. graffiti tr.			5
Mercedes 380 SEL	491			MAL	Glt. Blu.				HO - Silver				3
Mercedes 380 SEL	491			MAL	Glt. Blu.				UH				3
Mercedes 380 SEL	3261			FRA	Blk./Silver				Reg				20
Mercedes 380 SEL	3261			HK	Grey	Blk.		Tan	HO - Gold				8
Mercedes 380 SEL	3261			FRA	Blk./Silver			Wht.	HO - Gold				20
Mercedes 380 SEL	3261	Set		MAL	Blu MF				UH			Sto & Go	10

Name	#	Category	Casting	Ctry.	Color	Win.	Base	Interior	Wheels	Paint	Logo	Other	$
Mercedes 380 SEL	3368	Cal Cus.		MAL	Chr./N. Pnk.	CL			Rtr - Chr.				8
Mercedes 380 SEL	3368	Cal Cus.		MAL	Chr./N. Pnk.	DT			Rtr - Chr.				8
Mercedes 380 SEL	3850			MAL	Blk.			Tan	Reg				4
Mercedes 380 SEL	3850			MAL	Blk.			Tan	UH				4
Mercedes 380 SEL	4206			MAL	Wht.			Tan	UH				4
Mercedes 380 SEL	4363			HK	Grey MF.		Blk.	Tan	Reg				4
Mercedes 380 SEL	4363			HK	Grey MF.		Blk.	Tan	RR - Grey				4
Mercedes 380 SEL	4363			MEX	Grey		Blk.	Wht.	Reg				20
Mercedes 380 SEL	4363			MEX	Grey		Unpainted		Reg				20
Mercedes 380 SEL	4363			HK	Grey MF.		Blk.	Tan	HO - Gold				4
Mercedes 380 SEL	4408			MAL	Glt. Pnk.				UH				4
Mercedes 380 SEL	9986			MAL	Blk.			Tan	HO - Silver				4
Mercedes 380 SEL	9986			MAL	Blk.			Tan	UH - Gold				4
Mercedes 380 SEL	9986			MAL	Blk./Silver			Tan	Reg				4
Mercedes 380 SEL	9986			MAL	Blk./Silver			Tan	RR - Grey				4
Mercedes 380 SEL	12346			MAL	M. Dk. Red				UH				3
Mercedes 500 SL	9770			MAL	Chr.				HO - Silver				8
Mercedes 500 SL	9770			MAL	Chr.				UH				8
Mercedes 500 SL	9770	Pre-Pro		MAL	Grey				UH			Small wheels	
Mercedes 540K	422			MAL	Glt. Blu.				Reg				4
Mercedes 540K	3911			FRA	Red				Reg				15
Mercedes 540K	3911			MAL	Wht.				Reg				
Mercedes 540K	3911	20th Ann.		MAL	Silver		Letters of MAL close together		WW				10
Mercedes 540K		20th Ann.		MAL	Gold		Letters of MAL close together		WW				10
Mercedes 540K		20th Ann.		MAL	Silver		Letters of MAL further apart		WW				10
Mercedes 540K		20th Ann.		MAL	Gold		Letters of MAL further apart		WW				10
Mercedes 540K		20th Ann.		MAL	Gold		HW logo		WW				10
Mercedes 540K		Gold Ser.		MAL	M. Dk. Red				SS - Gold			FAOSc	25
Mercedes 540K	3911			HK	Red				WW				6
Mercedes 540K	3911			MAL	Red		MAL cast flat		WW				6
Merceces 540K	3911			MAL	Red				Reg				6
Mercedes 540K	3911			MAL	Red		MAL cast flat		Reg				6
Mercedes 540K	3911			MAL	Red		HW logo		Reg				6
Mercedes 540K	3911			HK	Red		HW		Reg				6
Mercedes 540K	5142			MAL	Blk.		HW		Reg				5
Mercedes 540K	5142			HK	Blk.		HW logo		Reg				5
Mercedes 540K	5142			HK	Blk.		HW logo		WW				5
Mercedes 540K	5142			HK	Blk.		HW		WW				5
Mercedes 540K	5142			MAL	Blk.		HW logo		Reg				5
Mercedes 540K	5142			HK	Blk.		HW		Reg				5
Mercedes 540K	5142			MAL	Blk.		HW logo		WW				5
Mercedes 540K	5142			MAL	Blk.		HW		WW				5
Mercedes C111	6978			HK	Red		Plst.		Reg			Blu., Wht. & Yl. tr.	25

Name	#	Category	Casting	Ctry.	Color	Win.	Base	Interior	Wheels	Paint	Logo	Other	$
Mercedes C111	6978			HK	Red		Plst.		RL	Blu., Wht. & Yl. tr.			30
Mercedes C111	6978			HK	Red				RL	Blu., Wht. & Yl. tr.	C111 on engine deck		40
Mercedes C111	6978			HK	Red				RL	Blu., Wht. & Yl. tr.			40
Mighty Maverick	7653			HK	Blu.				RL	Or. & Wht. tr.		No wing	50
Mighty Maverick	7653			HK	Pale Gr.				RL	Blu. & Gr. tr.		No wing	75
Mighty Maverick	9209	Super Chr.		HK	Chr.				RL			No wing	35
Mighty Maverick	9209	Super Chr.		HK	Chr.				Reg			No wing	30
Mini Truck	2099			MAL	N. Or.				UH	Blu., Blk. & Wht. tr.		Large FWs	4
Mini Truck	2099			MAL	N. Or.				UH	Blu., Blk. & Wht. tr.		Small FWs	4
Mini Truck	2099			MAL	Aq.				HO - Silver	Prp., Blu. & Yl. tr.			20
Mini Truck	2099			MAL	Aq.				UH	Prp., Blu. & Yl. tr.			4
Mini Truck	2099	Set		MAL	Yl.				UH	Gr., Blu. & Pnk. tr.		Sto & Go	10
Mini Truck	2099	Set		MAL	Yl.				UH - Gold	Gr., Blu. & Pnk. tr.		Sto & Go	15
Minitrek	1697			FRA	Silver				Reg	Red & Blu. tr.			35
Minitrek	1697			FRA	Silver				Reg	Red tr.			20
Minitrek	1697			MEX	Blk.				Reg				40
Minitrek	1697			HK	Tan				Reg				7
Minitrek	1697			HK	Wht.		Blk.		Reg				7
Minitrek	1697			MAL	Wht.		Blk.		Reg				7
Minitrek	1697			MAL	Wht.		Bro.		Reg				30
Minitrek	1697			MAL	Tan				Reg				7
Minitrek	1697			HK	Wht.		Bro.		Reg				30
Mirada Stocker	1700			MAL	Red			Wht.	HO - Gold				10
Mirada Stocker	1700			HK	Red			Blk.	HO - Gold				10
Mirada Stocker	1700			HK	Red			Wht.	HO - Gold				10
Mirada Stocker	1700			MEX	Red			Tan	HO - Gold				20
Mirada Stocker	1700			FRA	Red			Blk.	HO - Gold				20
Mirada Stocker	1700			MAL	Red			Blk.	HO - Gold				10
Mirada Stocker	1700			MAL	Red			Tan	Reg	Blk., Yl. & Wht. tr.	10		10
Mirada Stocker	1700			HK	Red			Tan	HO - Gold	Blk., Yl. & Wht. tr.	10		10
Mirada Stocker	1700			HK	Yl.				HO - Gold	Blk., Red & Wht. tr.	10		10
Mirada Stocker	1700			MAL	Red			Tan	HO - Gold	Blk., Yl. & Wht. tr.	10		10
Mirada Stocker	1700			HK	Gold MF.				HO - Gold	Blk., Red & Wht. tr.	10		10
Mirada Stocker	1700			MAL	Gold MF.			Tan	HO - Gold	Blk., Red & Wht. tr.	10		10
Mirada Stocker	1700			HK	Red				Reg	Blk., Yl. & Wht. tr.	10		10
Mirada Stocker	1700			MAL	Yl.				HO - Gold	Blk., Red & Wht. tr.	10		10
Mongoose	6970			HK	Blu.	NW			RL	Red flames			500
Mongoose	6970			HK	Red	NW			RL	Red flames			500
Mongoose	10783	Vintage		CHN	M. Or.				RL				5
Mongoose	10783	Vintage		CHN	M. Aq.				RL				5
Mongoose	10783	Vintage		CHN	Dk. Blu.				RL	Red, Wht. & Yl. tr.			5
Mongoose	10783	Vintage		CHN	M. Pale Blu.				RL				5
Mongoose	10783	Vintage		CHN	M. Dk. Red				RL				5
Mongoose	10783	Vintage		CHN	M. Red				RL				5
Mongoose	10783	Vintage		CHN	M. Pnk.				RL				5
Mongoose	10783	Vintage		CHN	Dk. Blu.				RL	Red, Prp. & Wht. tr.			5
Monster Vette		20th Ann.		MAL	Gold				4x4 SHb				8
Monster Vette		20th Ann.		MAL	Silver				4x4 LHb				8
Monster Vette		20th Ann.		MAL	Silver				4x4 SHb				8
Monster Vette	2177			MAL	Prp.				4x4 SHb	Red & Blu. flames			5

Name	#	Category	Casting	Ctry.	Color	Win.	Base	Interior	Wheels	Paint	Logo	Other	$
Monster Vette	2177			MAL	Prp.				4x4 LHb	Red & Blu. flames			5
Monster Vette	3716			MAL	Yl.	DTW			4x4 LHb	Or. & Prp. flames			5
Monster Vette	3716			MAL	Yl.	BluCW			4x4 LHb	Or. & Prp. flames			5
Monster Vette	3716			MAL	Yl.	DTW			4x4 SHb	Or. & Prp. flames			5
Monte Carlo Stocker	7660			MEX	Blu.		Blk. Plst.		Reg	Gr., Wht. & Yl. tr.			30
Monte Carlo Stocker	7660			HK	Yl.				Reg	Red, Wht. & Blu. tr.	38		25
Monte Carlo Stocker	7660			MEX	Blu.				Reg	Gr., Wht. & Yl. tr.			30
Monte Carlo Stocker	7660			MAL	Yl.				Reg	Red, Wht. & Blu. tr.	38		30
Monte Carlo Stocker	7660			MAL	Blu.				Reg	Gr., Wht. & Yl. tr.	38		25
Monte Carlo Stocker	7660			HK	Blu.				Reg	Gr., Wht. & Yl. tr.	38		25
Monte Carlo Stocker	7660			MEX	Blu.				HO - Gold	Gr., Wht. & Yl. tr.			25
Monte Carlo Stocker	7660			HK	Yl.				RL	Red, Wht. & Blu. tr.	38		40
Chevy Monza 2+2	9202 Christmas Ball			HK	Chr.				RL	Red & Gr. tr.	MMA 1975 Winter Ball		400
Motocross 1	7668		No headlight	HK	Red				Reg				60
Motocross Team	2853 Scene Machine			MAL	Red				Reg				40
Movin On				HK	Wht.				Reg			Great American Truck Race	60
Movin On				MAL	Wht.				Reg			Great American Truck Race	60
Mustang Stocker	7644		PBH	FRA	Yl.				Reg	Or. & Mgta. tr.	450 HP		75
Mustang Stocker	7644		No PBH	FRA	Wht.			Tan	Reg	Blu. stripes	GT 350		50
Mustang Stocker	7644		No PBH	MEX	Wht.			Wht.	Reg	Yl. & Red tr.	450 HP		75
Mustang Stocker	7644		PBH	FRA	Yl.				Reg				50
Mustang Stocker	7644		No PBH	MAL	Wht.			Wht.	Reg	Blu. stripes	GT 350		30
Mustang Stocker	7644		No PBH	HK	Wht.			Blk.	RL	Red & Blu. tr.	450 Ford		30
Mustang Stocker	7644		No PBH	HK	Wht.			Wht.	Reg	Yl. & Mgta. tr.	450 HP		30
Mustang Stocker	7644		PBH	HK	Yl.				Reg	Or. & Mgta. tr.	450 HP		100
Mustang Stocker	7644		No PBH	MAL	Wht.			Wht.	Reg	Yl. & Mgta. tr.	450 HP		50
Mustang Stocker	7644		PBH	HK	Yl.				RL	Or. & Mgta. tr.	450 HP		75
Mustang Stocker	7644		PBH	MAL	Yl.				Reg	Or. & Mgta. tr.	450 HP		50
Mustang Stocker	7644		PBH	HK	Yl.				RL	Red & Blu. tr.	450 Ford		300
Mustang Stocker	9203 Super Chr.		PBH	HK	Chr.				Reg	Red, Wht. & Blu. US flag tr.			40
Mustang Stocker	9203 Super Chr.		PBH	HK	Chr.				RL	Red, Wht. & Blu. US flag tr.			50
Mustang Stocker	9203 Super Chr.		PBH	HK	Chr.				RL	Or. & Mgta.	450 Ford		50
Mustang SVO	9531			MAL	Blk.				HO - Gold	Red, Wht. & Yl. tr.	Mustang SVO		10
NASCAR Stocker	3927 Racing Stocker			MAL	Wht.		Mountain Dew Stocker		HO - Gold	Pale Gr. tr.	Mountain Dew		75
NASCAR Stocker	3927 Racing Stocker			HK	Wht.		Mountain Dew Stocker		HO - Gold	Pale Gr. tr.	Mountain Dew		75
NASCAR Stocker	3927 Racing Stocker			HK	Wht.		NASCAR Stocker		Reg	Gr. & Red tr.	Mountain Dew		75
NASCAR Stocker	3927 Racing Stocker			HK	Wht.		Racing Stocker		HO - Gold	Dk. Gr. tr.	Mountain Dew		25
NASCAR Stocker	3927 Racing Stocker			MAL	Wht.		Racing Stocker		HO - Gold	Dk. Gr. tr.	Mountain Dew		25
NASCAR Stocker	3927 Racing Stocker			MAL	Wht.		NASCAR Stocker		Reg	Gr. & Red tr.	Mountain Dew		75
Neet Streeter	9244			MAL	Blu.				Reg				15

Name	#	Category	Casting	Ctry.	Color	Win.	Base	Interior	Wheels	Paint	Logo	Other	S
Neet Streeter	9244			HK	Dk. Red				Reg				10
Neet Streeter	9244			MAL	Dk. Red				Reg				10
Neet Streeter	9244			HK	Magenta				Reg				10
Neet Streeter	9244			HK	Blu.				RL				25
Neet Streeter	9244			HK	Red MF.		HK cast in a different place		Reg				10
Neet Streeter	9244			HK	Red MF.				Reg				10
Neet Streeter	9244			HK	Blu.				Reg				15
Neet Streeter	9244			MEX	Maroon MF.		Rsd. MEX		Reg				25
Neet Streeter	9244			MEX	Blu.				Reg	Prp. Ford logo			25
Neet Streeter	9244			MAL	Red MF.				Reg				10
Neet Streeter	9244			MAL	Magenta				Reg				10
Neet Streeter	9244			MEX	Maroon MF.				Reg				25
Neet Streeter	9510 Super Chr.			HK	Chr.				Reg				25
Neet Streeter	9510 Super Chr.			HK	Chr.				RL				35
Nightstreaker	1497 Ultra Hot			MAL	Silver				UH				8
Nightstreaker	9537 Ultra Hot			MAL	M. Prp.	Blk.	Predator		UH				8
Nightstreaker	9537 Ultra Hot			MAL	M. Prp.	Blk.	No Predator		UH				8
Nightstreaker	9537 Ultra Hot			MAL	M. Prp.	Sil.	Predator		UH				8
Nissan 300ZX	1454			MAL	Yl.		No Nissan 300ZX		HO - Gold	Wht., Red & Blu. tr.	300ZX sideways on hood		6
Nissan 300ZX	1454			MAL	Yl.		Nissan 300ZX		HO - Gold	Wht., Red & Blu. tr.	300ZX sideways on hood		6
Nissan 300ZX		Getty		MAL	Wht.		Painted Wht.		UH	Red, Wht. & Yl. tr.	Getty		6
Nissan 300ZX		Getty		MAL	Wht.		Unpainted		UH	Red, Wht. & Yl. tr.	Getty		7
Nissan 300ZX	2140 Park'n Plate			MAL	Wht.		Unpainted		HO - Gold	Yl., Red & Blu. tr.	300ZX sideways on hood		18
Nissan 300ZX	2140 Park'n Plate			MAL	Wht.		Painted Wht.		HO - Gold	Yl., Red & Blu. tr.	300ZX sideways on hood		8
Nissan 300ZX	1099 Set			MAL	M. Blu.				HO - Gold	Yl., Wht. & Prp. lightning tr.	Turbo	Turbotrax Race & Speed Trigger	10
Nissan 300ZX	1454			MAL	Yl.		No Nissan 300ZX		UH	Wht., Red & Blu. tr.	300ZX sideways on hood		5
Nissan 300ZX	1454			MAL	Wht.				HO - Gold	Blu., Red & Yl. tr.	300ZX on hood & doors		5
Nissan 300ZX	1454			MAL	Wht.				UH	Blu., Red & Yl. tr.	300ZX on hood & doors		5
Nissan 300ZX	1454			MAL	Yl.		Nissan 300ZX		UH	Wht., Red & Blu. tr.	300ZX sideways on hood		5
Nissan 300ZX	7529			MAL	Red				HO - Gold				6
Nissan 300ZX	7529			HK	Red				HO - Gold				6
Nissan Hardbody		Kool Aid		MAL	Wht.				4x4 SHb	Pnk., Gr. & Blu. tr.	Kool Aid		10
Nissan Hardbody		Kraft		MAL	Wht.		Blk. Plst.	N. Or.	4x4 SHb	Yl., Blu. & Red tr.	Cheesasaurus Rex	Neon Or. RB & Grl.	10
Nissan Hardbody	4392			MAL	Wht.		Blk. Plst.	Blk.	4x4 SHb			Blk. RB & Grl.	6
Nissan Hardbody	4392			MAL	Wht.			Blk.	4x4 LHb			Blk. RB & Grl.	6
Nissan Hardbody	4392			MAL	Wht.			N. Pnk.	4x4 SHb			Neon Pnk. RB & Grl.	8
Nissan Hardbody	4392			MAL	Wht.		Blk. Plst.	Blk.	4x4 SHb			Blk. RB & Grl.	5
Nissan Hardbody	4392			MAL	Wht./Red			Blk.	4x4 SHb			Blk. RB & Grl.	5
Nissan Hardbody	9588			MAL	Blk.		Blk. Plst.	N. Yl.	4x4 SHb	Gr., Blu. & Yl.	10	Neon Yl. RB & Grl.	6
Nissan Hardbody	9588			MAL	Blk.			N. Pnk.	4x4 SHb	Gr., Blu. & Pnk.	10	Neon Pnk. RB & Grl.	6
Nissan Hardbody	9588			MAL	Blk.		Blk. Plst	N Pnk	4x4 SHb	Gr., Blu. & Pnk.	10	Neon Pnk. RB & Grl.	6

Name	#	Category	Casting	Ctry.	Color	Win.	Base	Interior	Wheels	Paint	Logo.	Other	S
No Fear Race Car	11846			MAL	Blk.				Reg	Red & Wht. tr.	1 & No Fear		3
Odd Job	6981			HK	Pale Blu.			Blk.	RL				90
Odd Job	6981			HK	Red			Blk.	RL				90
Odd Job	6981			HK	Flr. Lime			Blk.	RL				90
Odd Job	6981			HK	Dk. Blu.			Blk.	RL				90
Odd Job	6981			HK	Pale Yl.			Blk.	RL				90
Odd Job	6981			HK	Or.			Blk.	RL				90
Odd Job	6981			HK	Gr.			Blk.	RL				90
Odd Job	6981			HK	Plum			Blk.	RL				90
Odd Job	6981			HK	Pale Gr.			Blk.	RL				90
Odd Job	6981			HK	Dk. Yl.			Blk.	RL				90
Odd Job	6981			HK	Pnk.			Blk.	RL				90
Odd Rod	9642			IND	Red				Reg				10
Odd Rod	9642			FRA	Yl.				Reg				20
Odd Rod	9642			MAL	Plum				Reg				200
Odd Rod	9642			HK	Plum				Reg				200
Odd Rod	9642			MEX	Yl.				Reg				25
Odd Rod	9642			HK	Yl.				Reg				20
Odd Rod	9642			MAL	Yl.				Reg				20
Old Number 5	1695		Louvres on both sides of engine	MAL	Red		All of name visible		Reg				8
Old Number 5	1695		Louvres on both sides of engine	MAL	Red		Name on outer edge		WW				8
Old Number 5	1695		Louvres on both sides of engine	HK	Red		Name on outer edge		Reg				8
Old Number 5	1695		Louvres on both sides of engine	MAL	Red		Name visible		WW				8
Old Number 5	1695			HK	Red		Name visible		Reg				12
Old Number 5	1695			HK	Red		Part of name covered by plate		Reg				12
Old Number 5	1695		Louvres on both sides of engine	MAL	Red		Name on outer edge		Reg				8
Old Number 5	1695		Louvres on both sides of engine	HK	Red		Name visible		Reg				8
Old Number 5	9403 LE		Louvres on both sides of engine	MAL	Yl.				SS - Yl.				15
Oldsmobile 442 W-30	11082	Demo Man		MAL	Red				Reg				12
Oldsmobile 442 W-30		LE		MAL	Blk.				Dsh - Grey				15
Oldsmobile 442 W-30	12360			MAL	Yl.				Reg	Blk. tr.			3
Oldsmobile Aurora	11086	Demo Man		MAL	Silver				Reg				15
Oldsmobile Aurora	12358			MAL	M. Electric Gr.	DT			Reg				3
Oldsmobile Aurora	12358			MAL	M. Electric Gr.	CL			Reg				5
Oldsmobile Funny Car	2743	Pro-Circuit		CHN	Wht.	PT			P-C - Chr.	Gr., Red & Blk. tr.	Castrol GTX	Strut inside & 3 headlights	5
Oldsmobile Funny Car	2743	Pro-Circuit		CHN	Wht.	PT			P-C - Chr.	Gr., Red & Blk. tr.	Castrol GTX	Strut inside & 4 headlights	5
Oldsmobile Funny Car		Set		MAL	Wht.	DT	Pnk. w/ RAF & no SIS		Reg	Gr., Red & Blk. tr.	Castrol GTX & Jolly Rancher	SI-FCGP	6
Oldsmobile Funny Car		Set		MAL	Wht.	DT	Pnk. w/ ROA		Reg			SI-FCGP	6

Name	#	Category	Casting	Ctry.	Color	Win.	Base	Interior	Wheels	Paint	Logo	Other	$
Oldsmobile Funny Car		Set		MAL	Wht.	DT	Pnk. w/ ROA		Reg	Gr., Red & Blk. tr.	Castrol GTX & Jolly Rancher	Sl-FCGP	6
Oldsmobile Funny Car		Set		MAL	Wht.	DT	Pnk. w/ ROA & no SIS					Sl-FCGP	6
Oldsmobile Funny Car		Set		MAL	Wht.	DT	Blu. w/ ROA		Reg	Gr., Red & Blk. tr.	Castrol GTX & Jolly Rancher	Sl-FCGP	6
Oldsmobile Funny Car		Set		MAL	Wht.	DT	Pnk. w/ RAF & SIS		Reg	Gr., Red & Blk. tr.	Castrol GTX	Sl-FCGP	6
Oldsmobile Funny Car		Set		MAL	Wht.	DT	Blu. w/ RAF & SIS		Reg	Gr., Red & Blk. tr.	Castrol GTX & Jolly Rancher	Sl-FCGP	6
Oldsmobile Funny Car		Set		MAL	Wht.	DT	Pnk. w/ RAF & SIS		Reg	Gr., Red & Blk. tr.	Castrol GTX & Jolly Rancher	Sl-FCGP	6
Oldsmobile Funny Car		Set		MAL	Wht.	DT	Blu. w/ RAF & no SIS		Reg	Gr., Red & Blk. tr.	Castrol GTX & Jolly Rancher	Sl-FCGP	6
Omni 024	1692			FRA	Gold				Reg	Prp., Red & Yl. tampo			20
Omni 024	1692			HK	Grey				Reg				6
Omni 024	1692			HK	Gold				Reg	Prp., Red & Yl. tampo			20
Omni 024	1692			MAL	Gold				Reg	Prp., Red & Yl. tampo			20
Omni 024	1692			HK	Blu.				Reg				10
Omni 024	1692			MEX	Gold		Unpainted		Reg				40
Omni 024	1692			MAL	Grey				Reg				6
Omni 024	1692			MEX	Gold		Unpainted		Reg	Prp., Red & Yl. tampo			40
Omni 024	1692			MAL	Blu.				Reg				10
Omni 024	1692			MEX	Gold		Blk. Plst.		Reg				40
Oscar Mayer Weinermobile	3029			MAL	Red/Yl.				Reg				6
Oscar Mayer Weinermobile	3029			MAL	Red/Yl.				Reg - Blk.				4
Oshkosh Cement Mixer	2074			MAL	Wht./Red/Blu.				Reg				5
Oshkosh Cement Mixer	12362			MAL	Yl./Blk.				Reg				5
Oshkosh Snow Plow	5905		Metal top	MAL	Or.		Oshkosh Snow Plow & HW logo		4x4 SHb - Or.				5
Oshkosh Snow Plow	5905		Plst. top	HK	Or.		Oshkosh Snow Plow & HW logo		4x4 SHb				5
Oshkosh Snow Plow	5905		Plst. top	MAL	Or.		Oshkosh Snow Plow		4x4 SHb - Or.				5
Oshkosh Snow Plow	5905		Metal top	MAL	Gr.		Oshkosh Snow Plow & HW logo		4x4 LHb				6
Oshkosh Snow Plow	5905		Plst. top	HK	Or.		Oshkosh Snow Plow		4x4 SHb - Or.				5
Oshkosh Snow Plow	5905		Plst. top	MAL	Or.		Oshkosh Snow Plow & HW logo		4x4 SHb				5
Oshkosh Snow Plow	5905		Metal top	MAL	Or.		Oshkosh Snow Plow		4x4 SHb - Or.				5
Oshkosh Snow Plow	5905		Metal top	HK	Or.		Oshkosh Snow Plow & HW logo		4x4 SHb - Or.				15

Name	#	Category	Casting	Ctry.	Color	Win.	Base	Interior	Wheels	Paint	Logo	Other	S
Oshkosh Snow Plow	5905		Plst. top	MAL	Gr.				4x4 SHb				6
Oshkosh Snow Plow	5905		Metal top	MAL	Gr.				4x4 SHb				6
Oshkosh Snow Plow	5905		Metal top	HK	Or.		Oshkosh Snow Plow & HW logo		4x4 SHb				15
Oshkosh Snow Plow	5905		Metal top	HK	Or.		No Oshkosh Snow Plow		4x4 SHb - Or.				15
Oshkosh Snow Plow	5905		Plst. top	MAL	Gr.				4x4 LHb				6
Oshkosh Snow Plow	5905		Metal top	MAL	Or.		No Oshkosh Snow Plow		4x4 SHb				5
Oshkosh Snow Plow	5905		Plst. top	HK	Or.		No Oshkosh Snow Plow		4x4 SHb				5
Oshkosh Snow Plow	5905		Plst. top	MAL	Or.		No Oshkosh Snow Plow		4x4 SHb				5
Oshkosh Snow Plow	5905		Metal top	MAL	Or.		No Oshkosh Snow Plow		4x4 SHb - Or.				5
Oshkosh Snow Plow	5905		Metal top	HK	Or.		No Oshkosh Snow Plow		4x4 SHb				15
Oshkosh Snow Plow	5905		Metal top	MAL	Or.		Oshkosh Snow Plow & HW logo		4x4 SHb				5
Oshkosh Snow Plow	5905		Metal top	HK	Or.		Oshkosh Snow Plow		4x4 SHb - Or.				5
Oshkosh Snow Plow	5905		Plst. top	MAL	Or.		No Oshkosh Snow Plow		4x4 SHb - Or.				5
Oshkosh Snow Plow	5905		Plst. top	HK	Or.		Oshkosh Snow Plow & HW logo		4x4 SHb - Or.				5
Oshkosh Snow Plow	5905		Plst. top	HK	Or.		No Oshkosh Snow Plow		4x4 SHb - Or.				5
Oshkosh Snow Plow	5905 Extras		Metal top	HK	Or.		Oshkosh Snow Plow		4x4 SHb				15
Oshkosh Snow Plow	5905 Extras		Metal top	MAL	Or.		Oshkosh Snow Plow		4x4 SHb				10
P-911	9206			FRA	Blk.				HO - Gold	Red, Yl. & Wht. tr.	95		20
P-911	9206			HK	Blk.				Reg - Gold	Red, Yl. & Wht. tr.	95		6
P-911	9206			HK	Blk.				HO - Gold	Red, Yl. & Wht. tr.	95		6
P-911	9206			MAL	Blk.				HO - Gold	Red, Yl. & Wht. tr.	95		6
P-911	9206			MAL	Blk.				Reg - Gold	Red, Yl. & Wht. tr.	95		6
P-911	2108	Cal Cus.		MAL	N. Biz.		Flat MAL		Rtr - N. Yl.				8
P-911	2108	Cal Cus.		MAL	Prp. Chr.		Flat MAL		Rtr - N. Yl.				8
P-911	2108	Cal Cus.		MAL	N. Biz.		Rsd. MAL		Rtr - N. Yl.				8
P-911	2108	Cal Cus.		MAL	Prp. Chr.		Rsd. MAL		Rtr - N. Yl.				8
P-911		Video Car		MAL	Blk.				Reg	Red, Yl. & Wht. tr.	95		10
P-911	3969	Ziploc		MAL	Wht.				Reg	Red, Blk. & Yl. tr.	95		8
P-911	3968			HK	Blk.				Reg				6
P-911	3968			HK	Blk.				Reg - Gold				6
P-911	3968			MAL	Blk.				Reg - Gold				6

Name	#	Category	Casting	Ctry.	Color	Win.	Base	Interior	Wheels	Paint	Logo	Other	$
P-911	3968			MAL	Blk.				Reg	Red tr.			6
P-911	3968 HW Conv.			HK	Blk.				Reg - Gold		HW Convention 90		150
P-911	3969			MAL	Wht.				Reg - Gold	Red, Yl. & Blk. tr.	95		6
P-911	3969			HK	Wht.				Reg - Gold	Red, Yl. & Blk. tr.	95		6
P-911	9206		Porsche cast on rear	HK	Wht.				RL	Red & Blu. stripes			6
P-911	9206			MAL	Blk.		MAL on Rsd. bar		Reg	Red, Yl. & Wht. tr.	95		6
P-911	9206			MAL	Blk.				Reg	Red, Yl. & Wht. tr.	95		6
P-911	7648			HK	Yl.		P-911		RL	Red & Blu. stripes			45
P-911	9206			HK	Wht.				Reg	Red, Blk. & Blu. tr. & stripes	Turbo 6		6
P-911	7648			HK	Yl.		P-911 w/ Rsd. bar		RL	Red & Blu. stripes	95		45
P-911	9206			HK	Blk.				Reg	Red, Yl. & Wht. tr.	95		6
P-911	7648		Porsche cast on rear	HK	Yl.		Porsche Carrera		RL	Red & Blu. stripes			45
P-911	9206			HK	Wht.				HO - Gold	Red, Blk. & Blu. tr. & stripes	Turbo 6		6
P-911	7648			HK	Blk.		HK on Rsd. bar		Reg		6 95		6
P-911	7648 Gold Manager			MAL	Gold				RL				300
P-911	7648 Set			HK	Blk.				Reg	Red, Or. & Yl. swirls			7
P-911	9115 Herfy's			HK	Yl.				RL	Red & Blu. stripes	Herfy's		100
P-911	9206 Super Chr.			HK	Chr.				Reg	Red, Or. & Yl. swirls			25
P-911	9206 Super Chr.			HK	Chr.				RL	Red, Or. & Yl. swirls			30
P-911	9206 Super Chr.			HK	Chr.		P-911		RL	Red & Gr. stripes			30
P-911	9206 Super Chr.			HK	Chr.		Porsche Carrera		RL	Red & Gr. stripes			30
P-911	9345			HK	Yl.		New base w/ long bar		RL	Red & Blu. stripes			45
P-911	9345			HK	Yl.		P-911 cast over		RL	Red & Blu. stripes			45
P-911	9345			HK	Yl.		Rsd. HK		RL	Red & Blu. stripes			45
P-911	9345 Set			HK	Red				HO - Gold	Yl. & Wht. racing tr.	95	Stamper 3 Pack	12
P-911	9345 Set			MAL	Red				HO - Gold	Yl. & Wht. racing tr.	95	Stamper 3 Pack	12
P-917	6972			HK	Dk. Yl.			Blk.	RL				125
P-917	6972			HK	Pale Gr.			Blk.	RL				125
P-917	6972			HK	Flr. Lime			Blk.	RL				125
P-917	6972			HK	Or.		Plst.		Reg	Yl. & Prp. tr.	P-917		15
P-917	6972			HK	Plum			Blk.	RL				125
P-917	6972			HK	Or.				RL	Yl. & Prp. tr.	Porsche		35
P-917	6972			HK	Red			Blk.	RL				125
P-917	6972			HK	Red				RL	Yl., Or. & Prp. tr.	Porsche		250
P-917	6972			HK	Gr.			Blk.	RL				125
P-917	6972			HK	Pnk.			Blk.	RL				140
P-917	6972			HK	Dk. Blu.			Blk.	RL				125
P-917	6972			HK	Red				RL	Yl. & Prp. tr.	Porsche		250
P-917	6972			HK	Or.				RL	Yl. & Prp. tr.	P-917		25
P-917	6972			HK	Pale Yl.			Blk.	RL				125
P-917	6972			HK	Or.			Blk.	RL				125

Name	#	Category	Casting	Color	Ctry.	Win.	Base	Interior	Wheels	Paint	Logo	Other	S
P-917	6872			Pale Blu.	HK			Blk.	RL				125
P-917	9204	Super Chr.		Chr.	HK				RL	Red, Prp. & Or. tr.	P-917		40
P-917	9204	Super Chr.		Chr.	HK				RL	Red, Prp. & Or. tr.	Porsche		40
P-928	4371			Wht.	HK				HO - Gold				12
P-928	5180			Red	HK				RR - Grey				15
P-928	5180			Red	HK				Reg				10
P-928	5180			Red	HK				HO - Gold				10
Packin' Pacer	2015			Or.	HK				HO - Gold	Red, Blu. & Mgta. tr.	Packin' Pacer		8
Packin' Pacer	2015			Wht.	HK				HO - Gold	Prp., Red & Yl. arrow tr.			10
Packin' Pacer	2015			Yl.	MEX				Reg	Prp., Red & Or. tr.			20
Packin' Pacer	2015			Yl.	HK				Reg	Prp., Red & Or. arrow tr.			8
Packin' Pacer	2015			Yl.	HK				Reg	Or., Blu. & Mgta. tr.	Packin' Pacer		8
Paddy Wagon	6966			Navy Blu.	FRA				Reg			Blu. top	25
Paddy Wagon	6966			Pale Bro.	FRA				Reg			Bro. top	25
Paddy Wagon	6966			Blu.	MEX				Reg			Pale Blu. top	25
Paddy Wagon	6966			Dk. Bro.	FRA				Reg			Bro. top	25
Paddy Wagon		Pre-Pro		M. Blu.	US				RL		Blu.	Blu. top	
Paddy Wagon		Pre-Pro		M. Or.	US				RL		Blk.	Or.	
Paddy Wagon		Set	Lower top	Dk. Blu.	US				RL			Low Blk. top - Great Getaway	20
Paddy Wagon	5707	25th Ann.		M. Turquoise	CHN				RL			Blu. top	4
Paddy Wagon	5707	25th Ann.		M. Violet	CHN				RL			Blu. top	4
Paddy Wagon	5707	25th Ann.		M. Blu.	CHN				RL			Blu. top	4
Paddy Wagon	5707	25th Ann.		M. Lime	CHN				RL			Blu. top	4
Paddy Wagon	5707	25th Ann.		M. Olive Gr.	CHN				RL			Blu. top	4
Paddy Wagon	5707	25th Ann.		M. Bro.	CHN				RL			Blu. top	4
Paddy Wagon	5707	25th Ann.		M. Red	CHN				RL			Blu. top	4
Paddy Wagon	5707	25th Ann.		M. Magenta	CHN				RL			Blu. top	4
Paddy Wagon	5707	25th Ann.		M. Gr.	CHN				RL			Blu. top	4
Paddy Wagon	5707	25th Ann.		M. Or.	CHN				RL			Blu. top	4
Paddy Wagon	5707	25th Ann.		M. Pnk.	CHN				RL			Blu. top	4
Paddy Wagon	5707	25th Ann.		Navy Blu.	CHN				RL			Blu. top	4
Paddy Wagon	5707	25th Ann.		Gold	CHN				RL			Blu. top	4
Paddy Wagon	5707	25th Ann.		Navy Blu.	CHN				RL			Blk. top	4
Paddy Wagon	5707	Gold Ser.		M. Emerald Gr.	CHN				RL - Gold			Blk. top & GEng - FAO	25
Paddy Wagon	5707	RL Conv.		Navy Blu.	CHN				RL		Redline Conv 03	Blu. top	50
Paddy Wagon	5707	Vintage		M. Prp.	CHN				RL			Blk. top	4
Paddy Wagon	5707	Vintage		M. Dk. Gr.	CHN				RL			Blu. top	4
Paddy Wagon	5707	Vintage		Gunmetal	CHN				RL			Blu. top	4
Paddy Wagon	5707	Vintage		Maroon	CHN				RL			Blk. top	4
Paddy Wagon	5707	Vintage		M. Br. Blu.	CHN				RL			Blu. top	4
Paddy Wagon	5707	Vintage		M. Gold	CHN				RL			Blu. top	4
Paddy Wagon	5707	Vintage		M. Electric Gr.	CHN				RL			Blu. top	4
Paddy Wagon	5707	Vintage		Wht.	CHN				RL			Blu. top	4
Paddy Wagon	5707	Vintage		M. Dk. Bro.	CHN				RL			Blu. top	4
Paddy Wagon	5707	Vintage		M. Royal Blu.	CHN				RL			Blk. top	4
Paddy Wagon	5707	Vintage		M. Pale Pnk.	CHN				RL			Blk. top	4
Paddy Wagon	5707	Vintage		M. Sea Blu.	CHN				RL			Blk. top	4
Paddy Wagon	5707	Vintage		Br. Red	CHN				RL			Blk. top	4
Paddy Wagon	6966			Navy Blu.	HK		Plst.		Reg				15

Name	#	Category	Casting	Ctry.	Color	Win.	Base	Interior	Wheels	Paint	Logo	Other	$
Paddy Wagon	6966			HK	Navy Blu.				Reg			Blu. top	15
Paramedic	7661			HK	Yl.	GT	Metal base		Reg				25
Paramedic	7661			HK	Wht.	BluT			RL				35
Paramedic	7661			HK	Wht.	GT			RL				35
Paramedic	7661			HK	Yl.	GT	Metal base		Reg				25
Paramedic	7661			HK	Yl.	GT			Reg				25
Passion	9401 LE			MAL	Red				WW	Wht., Or. & Prp. tr.			15
Path Beater		Co. Rcr.		HK	Gr. to Yl.				Reg				5
Path Beater	2534			MAL	Blk.				Reg				8
Path Beater	2534			HK	Blk.				RR - Grey				15
Path Beater	2534			MAL	Blk.				RR - Grey				15
Path Beater	2534			HK	Blk.				RR - Wht.				20
Path Beater	2534			HK	Blk.				Reg				8
Path Beater	2534			HK	Blk.				Reg			Larger wheels	8
Path Beater	2534			MAL	Blk.				Reg			Larger wheels	8
Path Beater	2534			MAL	Blk.				RR - Wht.				20
Pavement Pounder	9542			HK	Gr.			TB	Reg	Blk., Yl. & Blu. tr.	Henry's Hauling		7
Pavement Pounder	9542			MAL	Gr.		MAL cast flat	No TB	RR	Blk., Yl. & Blu. tr.	Henry's Hauling		15
Pavement Pounder	9542			MAL	Gr.		Rsd. MAL	TB	Reg	Blk., Yl. & Blu. tr.	Henry's Hauling		7
Pavement Pounder	9542			MAL	Gr.		MAL cast flat	TB	Reg	Blk., Yl. & Blu. tr.	Henry's Hauling		15
Pavement Pounder	9542			MAL	Gr.		Rsd. MAL	TB	RR - Wht.	Blk., Yl. & Blu. tr.	Henry's Hauling		7
Pavement Pounder	9542			MAL	Gr.		MAL cast flat	No TB	Reg	Blk., Yl. & Blu. tr.	Henry's Hauling		7
Pavement Pounder	9542			MAL	Gr.		1982 & flat MAL	TB	Reg	Blk., Yl. & Blu. tr.	Henry's Hauling		7
Pavement Pounder	9542			MAL	Gr.		Rsd. MAL	No TB	RR - Wht.	Blk., Yl. & Blu. tr.	Henry's Hauling		15
Pavement Pounder	9542			MAL	Gr.		MAL cast flat	TB	RR - Wht.	Blk., Yl. & Blu. tr.	Henry's Hauling		15
Pavement Pounder	9542			HK	Gr.			TB	RR - Wht.	Blk., Yl. & Blu. tr.	Henry's Hauling		15
Pavement Pounder	9542			MAL	Gr.		1982 & flat MAL	No TB	Reg	Blk., Yl. & Blu. tr.	Henry's Hauling		7
Pavement Pounder	9542			MAL	Gr.		Rsd. MAL	No TB	Reg	Blk., Yl. & Blu. tr.	Henry's Hauling		7
Pavement Pounder	9542			MAL	Gr.		1982 & flat MAL	TB	RR - Wht.	Blk., Yl. & Blu. tr.	Henry's Hauling		15
Pavement Pounder	9542			HK	Gr.			No TB	RR	Blk., Yl. & Blu. tr.	Henry's Hauling		7
Pavement Pounder	9542			HK	Gr.			No TB	Reg	Blk., Yl. & Blu. tr.	Henry's Hauling		7
Pavement Pounder	9542			MAL	Gr.		1982 & flat MAL	No TB	RR - Wht.	Blk., Yl. & Blu. tr.	Henry's Hauling		15
Pepsi Challenger	2023			MAL	Yl.		ROA		Reg		No Don Prudhomme		25
Pepsi Challenger	2023			MAL	Yl.		RAF & no SIS		Reg		No Don Prudhomme		25
Pepsi Challenger	2023			MAL	Yl.		ROA		Reg		Don Prudhomme		12
Pepsi Challenger	2023			HK	Yl.		RAF		Reg		Don Prudhomme		12
Pepsi Challenger	2023			HK	Yl.		No rivet		Reg		Don Prudhomme		12
Pepsi Challenger	2023			MAL	Yl.		RAF & SIS		Reg		No Don Prudhomme		25
Pepsi Challenger	2023			MAL	Yl.		RAF & SIS		Reg		Don Prudhomme		12
Pepsi Challenger	2023			MAL	Yl.		RAF & no SIS		Reg		Don Prudhomme		12
Personnel Carrier	5270	Mega Force		MAL	Wht./Red			Chr. motorcycles	Reg				20
Personnel Carrier	5270	Mega Force		MAL	Wht./Red			Tan motorcycles	Reg				20
Peterbilt Cement			Non RES	IND	Yl./Wht.				Reg				12
Peterbilt Cement	1169	Workhorse	Non RES	MAL	Red/Grey				Reg				7

Name	#	Category	Casting	Ctry.	Color	Win.	Base	Interior	Wheels	Paint	Logo	Other	S
Peterbilt Cement	1169	Workhorse	RES	HK	Red/Grey				Reg				7
Peterbilt Cement	1169	Workhorse	RES	MAL	Red/Grey				Reg				7
Peterbilt Cement	1169	Workhorse	Non RES	HK	Red/Grey				Reg				7
Peterbilt Dump Truck	1560		Non RES	MAL	Red				Reg				6
Peterbilt Dump Truck	1560		Non RES	HK	Red				Reg				6
Peterbilt Dump Truck	4017	Extras	RES	HK	Yl./Grey				Reg			Dumper comes off	6
Peterbilt Dump Truck	4017	Extras	RES	MAL	Yl./Grey				Reg			Dumper comes off	6
Peterbilt Dump Truck	9550		RES	HK	M. Blu./Wht.				Reg				6
Peterbilt Dump Truck	9550		RES	HK	M. Blu./Wht.				Reg				6
Peterbilt Dump Truck	9550		RES	MAL	Blu./Wht.				Reg				6
Peterbilt Dump Truck	9550		RES	HK	Blu./Wht.				Reg				6
Peterbilt Dump Truck	9550		RES	MAL	M. Blu./Wht.				Reg				6
Peterbilt Dump Truck	9550		RES	MAL	M. Blu./Wht.				Reg				6
Peterbilt Tank Truck		Set	Non RES	MAL	Gr./Grey				Reg		Helium gas carefull	Blimp & Support Pack	5
Peterbilt Tank Truck	1689	Pre-Pro	Non RES	MAL	Red/Silver				Reg		Shell		6
Peterbilt Tank Truck	1689	Workhorse	RES	MAL	Or./Silver				Reg		California Construction Company		6
Peterbilt Tank Truck	1689	Workhorse	RES	HK	Or./Silver				Reg		California Construction Company		6
Peterbilt Tank Truck	2547		Non RES	HK	Red/Silver				Reg		Railroad		6
Peterbilt Tank Truck	2547		RES	HK	Red/Silver				Reg		Railroad		6
Peterbilt Tank Truck	2547		Non RES	MAL	Yl./Silver				Reg		Railroad		30
Peterbilt Tank Truck	2547		RES	MAL	Red/Silver				Reg		Railroad		6
Peterbilt Tank Truck	2547		Non RES	HK	Blu./Silver				Reg		Railroad		6
Peterbilt Tank Truck	2547		Non RES	MAL	Red/Silver				Reg		Railroad		6
Peterbilt Tank Truck	2547		Non RES	HK	Yl./Silver				Reg		Railroad		6
Peterbilt Tank Truck	2547	Set	Non RES	MAL	Blu./Silver				Reg		Railroad		6
Peterbilt Tank Truck	2800		Non RES	HK	Or./Grey				Reg		Shell		6
Peterbilt Tank Truck	2800		Non RES	MAL	Or./Grey				Reg		Shell		6
Peterbilt Tank Truck	2800		Non RES	HK	Yl./Grey				Reg		Shell		5
Peterbilt Tank Truck	2800		Non RES	MAL	Yl./Grey				Reg		Shell		5
Peugeot 205 Rallye	1469			MAL	Wht.				Reg	Red, Yl. & Blu. stripes & Blk. tr.	2		4
Peugeot 205 Rallye	2307			MAL	Wht.				Reg	Red, Blk. & Blu. tr.	3		4
Peugeot 405	3204			MAL	Blu.				Reg				8
Peugeot 405	5670			MAL	Blk.				Reg				8
Peugeot 505	3281			FRA	Bro.				Reg				20
Peugeot 505	3281			FRA	Bro. MF.				Reg				20
Peugeot 505	3281			FRA	Blk.				Reg				20
Peugeot 505	3281			MEX	Blk.				Reg				30
Peugeot 505	3281			MEX	Blk.				Reg			Bro. fdrs	40
Peugeot 505	3281			HK	Gold MF.				Reg				6
Peugeot 505	3281			MEX	Blu.				Reg				30
Peugeot 505	3281			HK	Blu.				Reg				6
Phantomachine	3851	Speed Demon		MAL	M.				UH				8
Phone Truck	5906			MAL	Wht.				Reg		Marks Phone Truck		8
Phone Truck	5906			MAL	Wht.				Reg		Phone Truck		8

Name	#	Category	Casting	Ctry.	Color	Win.	Base	Interior	Wheels	Paint	Logo	Other	$
Phone Truck	5906			MEX	Wht.				Reg		Phone Truck		20
Phone Truck	5906			HK	Wht.				Reg		Phone Truck		8
Bywayman		9230 Park'n Plate		MAL	Wht.				4x4 SHb	Gr. & Or. tr.			8
Pnk. Passion	12537 LE			MAL	N. Pnk.				WW	Wht., Or. & Prp. tr.			15
Pipe Jammer	3036			MAL	Yl.				UH				3
Poison Pinto	9508			FRA	Gr.				Reg	Blk., Wht. & Gr. tr.			20
Poison Pinto	9508			FRA	Gr.				Reg	Blk., Wht. & Yl. tr.			20
Poison Pinto	9508			FRA	Dk. Gr.				Reg				30
Poison Pinto	9240			MAL	Gr.				Reg				15
Poison Pinto	9240			HK	Gr.				Reg				15
Poison Pinto	9240			HK	Gr.				RL				25
Poison Pinto	9508 Super Chr.			HK	Chr.				Reg				35
Poison Pinto	9508 Super Chr.			HK	Chr.				RL				15
Police Cruiser	6963		Hood does not open	HK	Wht.				Reg		Blk. police label	Blu. roof light	35
Police Cruiser	6963		Hood does not open	HK	Wht.				RL		Blk. police label	Blu. roof light	40
Police Cruiser	6963			HK	Wht.				RL		Blk. police label	Red roof light	50
Police Cruiser	6963			HK	Wht.				RL		Wht. police label	Red roof light	125
Pontiac J 2000	3917		smr. sunroof	MEX	Red		Rsd. HK		HO - Gold	Blk. & Yl. tr.			75
Pontiac J 2000	3917		lgr. sunroof	HK	Yl.				Reg				7
Pontiac J 2000	3917		smr. sunroof	MEX	Gr.		Rsd. MEX		Reg	Red & Yl. dragon tr.			75
Pontiac J 2000	3917		smr. sunroof	MEX	Yl.				HO - Gold				40
Pontiac J 2000	3917		smr. sunroof	MEX	Wht.		Rsd. MEX		HO - Gold	Blu. & Yl. tr.			75
Pontiac J 2000	3917		lgr. sunroof	HK	Yl.				Reg				7
Pontiac J 2000	3917		smr. sunroof	MEX	Gr.				Reg	Red & Yl. dragon tr.			75
Pontiac J 2000	3917		smr. sunroof	MAL	Yl.				Reg				7
Pontiac J 2000	3917		smr. sunroof	MEX	Wht.				HO - Gold	Blu. & Yl. tr.			75
Pontiac J 2000	3917		smr. sunroof	MEX	Gr.		Rsd. MEX		HO - Gold	Red & Yl. dragon tr.			75
Pontiac J 2000	3917		smr. sunroof	MAL	Gr.				HO - Gold	Red & Yl. dragon tr.			100
Pontiac J 2000	3917		smr. sunroof	MEX	Yl.				Reg				75
Pontiac J 2000	3917		smr. sunroof	MEX	Gr.				HO - Gold	Red & Yl. dragon tr.			75
Pontiac Salsa	11087 Demo Man			MAL	Or.				Reg - Or.				10
Pontiac Stocker		Auto Palace		CHN	Blu./Wht.				P-C - Blu.	Red & Blk. tr.	AC Delco 9		15
Pontiac Stocker	2623 Pro-Circuit			CHN	Blk.				P-C - Grey	Yl., Red & Wht. tr.	Pontiac Excitement 2		5
Pontiac Stocker	2623 Pro-Circuit			CHN	Blk./N. Gr.				P-C - Grey	Red, Yl. & Gr. tr.	Mello Yello 42		5
Pontiac Stocker	Prototype			MAL	Yl.				P-C - Yl.	Red & Blk. tr.	Pennzoil		
Pontiac Stocker	2623 Pro-Circuit			CHN	Blu./N. Red			Grey	P-C - Grey	Red, Wht. & Blu. tr.	STP 43	No Blu. border - oil treatment	6
Pontiac Stocker	2623 Pro-Circuit			CHN	Blu./N. Red			Grey	P-C - Grey	Red, Wht. & Blu. tr.	STP 43	Blu. border - oil treatment	6
Pontiac Stocker	2623 Pro-Circuit			CHN	Blu./N. Red			Blu.	P-C - Grey	Red, Wht. & Blu. tr.	STP 43	Blu. border - oil treatment	6
Pontiac Stocker	2623 Pro-Circuit			CHN	Matt N. Blu./N. Red			Blu.	P-C - Grey	Red, Wht. & Blu. tr.	STP 43	No Blu. border - oil treatment	6
Pontiac Stocker	2623 Pro-Circuit			CHN	Blu./N. Red			Blu.	P-C - Grey	Red, Wht. & Blu. tr.	STP 43	No Blu. border - oil treatment	6
Pontiac Stocker	2623 Pro-Circuit			CHN	N. Blu./N. Red			Blu.	P-C - Grey	Red, Wht. & Blu. tr.	STP 43	Blu. border - oil treatment	6

Name	#	Category	Casting	Ctry.	Color	Win.	Base	Interior	Wheels	Paint	Logo	Other	$
Pontiac Stocker	2623	Pro-Circuit		CHN	N. Blu./N. Red			Blu.	P-C - Grey	Red, Wht. & Blu. tr.	STP 43	No Blu. border - oil treatment	6
Pontiac Stocker	12873								P-C - Red	Red tr.	Mattel #1		15
Poppa Vette	2528			MAL	Wht.		ROA		Reg	Red, Blk. & Yl. tr.			25
Poppa Vette	2528			MAL	Wht.		RAF & no SIS		Reg	Red, Blk. & Yl. tr.			25
Poppa Vette	2528			MAL	Wht.		RAF & SIS		Reg	Red, Blk. & Yl. tr.			25
Porsche 930	7607			MAL	M. Dk. Red				Reg				6
Porsche 930		Revealer		MAL	Maroon				UH - N. Pnk.	Wht., Red & Yl. exploding gems tr.			5
Porsche 930		Revealer		MAL	N. Or.				Reg			Revealers 10 pack	10
Porsche 930		Revealer		MAL	M. Gr.				UH - N. Yl.	Wht., Red & Yl. exploding gems tr.			5
Porsche 930		Revealer		MAL	M. Blu.				UH - N. Yl.	Wht., Red & Yl. exploding gems tr.			5
Porsche 930		Set		MAL	Prp.				Reg			Double Barrel Set	10
Porsche 930		Set		MAL	Glt. Gr.				Serrated	Blu., Pnk. & Yl. tr.		Double Barrel Set	10
Porsche 930		Set		MAL	Gr.y Yl.				Reg			Double Barrel Set	10
Porsche 930	7607			MAL	Red				Reg				6
Porsche 959		Co. Rcr.		MAL	Blu. to Wht.				Reg				5
Porsche 959		Co. Rcr.		MAL	Red to Yl.				Reg				5
Porsche 959	2038	Park'n Plate		MAL	Wht.	BluT		Blu.	UH	Blu. & Red tr.	Porsche 959		7
Porsche 959	2038	Park'n Plate		MAL	Wht.	CL		Blk.	Reg	Blu. & Red tr.	Porsche 959		7
Porsche 959	2038	Park'n Plate		MAL	Wht.	CL		Blk.	UH	Blu. & Red tr.	Porsche 959		7
Porsche 959	2038	Park'n Plate		MAL	Wht.	CL		Tan	UH	Blu. & Red tr.	Porsche 959		25
Porsche 959	2038	Park'n Plate		MAL	Wht.	BluT		Blk.	UH	Blu. & Red tr.	Porsche 959		7
Porsche 959	2038	Park'n Plate		MAL	Wht.	BluT		Blk.	Reg	Blu. & Red tr.	Porsche 959		25
Porsche 959	2038	Park'n Plate		MAL	Wht.	BluT		Blu.	Reg	Blu. & Red tr.	Porsche 959		25
Porsche 959		Set		CHN	Yl.				Reg	Red flames		Triple level garage	10
Porsche 959		Set		MAL	Dirty Yl. to clean Yl.				Reg	Blu. stripes		Car Wash	10
Porsche 959		Set		CHN	Red				Reg			Stop & Go	10
Porsche 959	463			MAL	M. Prp.				HO - Silver	Yl., grey & Pnk. computer circuit tr.	5		4
Porsche 959	463			MAL	M. Prp.				UH	Yl., grey & Pnk. computer circuit tr.	5		4
Porsche 959	1403			MAL	Red				UH	Yl., Blu. & grey tr.	Porsche & 59		4
Porsche 959	1403			MAL	Red				UH	Wht. & Blk. tr.	Porsche & 7		4
Porsche 959	1403			MAL	Red				UH	Yl., Dk. Blu. & grey tr.	Porsche & 59		4
Porsche 959	1403			MAL	Blu.				UH	Wht. & Blk. tr.	Porsche & 7		7
Porsche 959		Getty		MAL	Yl.				Reg	Red, Wht. & Blu. tr.	Getty		4
Porsche 959	1794	Gleamer	Plst. w/ etched pattern	MAL	Silver				UH			Power Loop	5
Porsche 959	1794	Gleamer	Plst. w/ etched pattern	MAL	M. Pnk.				UH				4
Porsche 959	1794	Gleamer	Plst. w/ etched pattern	MAL	M. Pnk.				UH				4
Porsche 959	1794	Pre-Pro	Plst. w/ etched pattern	MAL	Gold				UH				5
Porsche 959	4631			MAL	M. Dk. Red		Lg. logo		UH	Or. & Yl. stripes	Porsche		5
Porsche 959	4631			MAL	M. Dk. Red		Sm. logo		UH	Or. & Yl. stripes	Porsche	No side tampo	5
Porsche 959	4631			MAL	M. Dk. Red		Sm. logo		UH	Or. & Yl. stripes	Porsche		5

Name	#	Category	Casting	Ctry.	Color	Win.	Base	Interior	Wheels	Paint	Logo	Other	$
Porsche 959	4631	Set		MAL	M. Blu.				UH	Wht. & Blk. tr.	Porsche & 7	Speed Shift 500 Set	10
Porsche 959	9519			MAL	Red				HO - Silver	Yl., Blu. & grey tr.	Porsche & 59		5
Porsche 959	9519			MAL	Red				UH - Gold	Yl., Blu. & grey tr.	Porsche & 59		5
Power Plower	9580			MAL	Prp. MF.				4x4 SHb	Yl., Or. & Blu. tr.			4
Power Plower	9580			MAL	Prp.				4x4 SHb	Yl., Or. & Blu. tr.			4
Power Plower	9580			MAL	N. Yl.				4x4 SHb	Blu., Wht. & Bro. tr.	Ecology Center & recycle		4
Power Plower	2538			HK	Red				RR - Wht.				15
Power Plower	2538			MAL	Red		MAL cast flat	TB	Reg	Blu., Yl. & Prp. tr.	Brian's Removal		10
Power Plower	2538			MAL	Red				RR - Wht.				15
Power Plower	2538			HK	Red			No TB	RR - Wht.	Blu., Yl. & Prp. tr.	Brian's Removal		15
Power Plower	2538			MAL	Red		MAL cast flat	TB	Reg	Blu., Yl. & Prp. tr.	Brian's Removal		10
Power Plower	2538			MAL	Red		MAL cast Rsd.	No TB	RR - Wht.	Blu., Yl. & Prp. tr.	Brian's Removal		15
Power Plower	2538			MAL	Red		Rsd. MAL	No TB	Reg	Blu., Yl. & Prp. tr.	Brian's Removal		10
Power Plower	2538			MAL	Red		MAL cast flat	TB	RR - Wht.	Blu., Yl. & Prp. tr.	Brian's Removal		15
Power Plower	2538			MAL	Red		MAL cast Rsd.	No TB	RR - Wht.	Blu., Yl. & Prp. tr.	Brian's Removal		15
Power Plower	2538			HK	Red			No TB	Reg	Blu., Yl. & Prp. tr.	Brian's Removal		10
Power Plower	2538			HK	Red			TB	Reg	Blu., Yl. & Prp. tr.	Brian's Removal		10
Power Plower	2538			HK	Red			TB	RR - Wht.	Blu., Yl. & Prp. tr.	Brian's Removal		15
Power Plower	2538			MAL	Red		MAL cast Rsd.	No TB	Reg	Blu., Yl. & Prp. tr.	Brian's Removal		10
Power Plower	2538			MAL	Red		MAL cast flat	TB	RR - Wht.	Blu., Yl. & Prp. tr.	Brian's Removal		15
Power Plower	5113			HK	Blk.				4x4 SHb	Or. & Prp. tr.	Midnight Removal		5
Power Plower	5113			MAL	Blk.				Reg	Or. & Prp. tr.	Midnight Removal		5
Power Plower	5113			MAL	Blk.		MAL cast Rsd.		Reg	Or. & Prp. tr.	Midnight Removal		5
Power Plower	5113			HK	Blk.				Reg	Red & Or. tr.	Midnight Removal		5
Power Plower	5113			MAL	Blk.				4x4 SHb	Or. & Prp. tr.	Midnight Removal		5
Power Plower	5113			HK	Blk.				Reg	Or. & Prp. tr.	Midnight Removal		5
Power Plower	5113			MAL	Blk.		MAL cast Rsd.		4x4 SHb	Or. & Prp. tr.	Midnight Removal		5
Power Plower	5113			MAL	Blk.				Reg	Red & Or. tr.	Midnight Removal		5
Predator	7292	Ultra Hot		HK	M. Gr.				UH				8
Predator	7292	Ultra Hot		MAL	M. Gr.				UH				8
Probe Funny Car		Pre-Pro		CHN	Red/Wht.				P-C - Chr.	Yl. & Blk.	McDonalds		6
Probe Funny Car		Set		MAL	Red	DT	RAF & no SIS		Reg	Wht. & Blu. tr.	Motorcraft & Ford	Strut inside-Funny Car Gift Pack	6
Probe Funny Car		Set		MAL	Red	DT	ROA		Reg	Wht. & Blu. tr.	Motorcraft & Ford	Strut inside-Funny Car Gift Pack	6
Probe Funny Car		Set		MAL	Red	DT	RAF & SIS		Reg	Wht. & Blu. tr.	Motorcraft & Ford	Strut inside-Funny Car Gift Pack	6
Probe Funny Car	7608			MAL	Red	DT	ROA		Reg	Wht. & Blu. tr.	Motorcraft & Ford	No strut inside	6
Probe Funny Car	7608			MAL	Red	DT	RAF & SIS		Reg	Wht. & Blu. tr.	Motorcraft & Ford	No strut inside	6
Probe Funny Car	7608			MAL	Red	DT	RAF & no SIS		Reg	Wht. & Blu. tr.	Motorcraft & Ford	No strut inside	6
Propper Chopper	492			MAL	Wht.				Reg	Blk., Yl. & Or. tr.	Police Unit 45		5
Propper Chopper	9112			MAL	Wht.					Red, Blu. & Yl. tr. w/ triangle on rear	Newschopper 2		8
Propper Chopper	9112			MAL	Wht.					Red, Blu. & Yl. tr. w/ bandit	Newschopper 2		4
Prowler	9207			FRA	Chr.				Reg	Blk., Blu. & Yl. tr.			30

Name	#	Category	Casting	Ctry.	Color	Win.	Base	Interior	Wheels	Paint	Logo	Other	S
Prowler	9207			FRA	Wht.				Reg	Red & Blk. tr. w/ bandit			50
Prowler	9207			FRA	Or.				Reg	Blk. & Blu. tr. w/ bandit			50
Prowler	9207			FRA	Or.				Reg	Red & Yl. flames w/ devil			30
Prowler				IND	Blk.				Reg			Enclosed engine	15
Prowler	6965			HK	Pale Yl.			Blk.	RL				200
Prowler	6965			HK	Dk. Blu.			Blk.	RL				200
Prowler	6965			HK	Or.				RL	Red & Yl. flames & devil			45
Prowler	6965			HK	Pale Blu.			Blk.	RL				200
Prowler	6965			HK	Pnk.			Blk.	RL				200
Prowler	6965			HK	Pale Gr.			Blk.	RL				200
Prowler	6965			HK	Wht.				Reg	Red & Blk. tr. w/ bandit			50
Prowler	6965			HK	Plum			Blk.	RL				200
Prowler	6965			HK	Dk. Yl.			Blk.	RL				200
Prowler	6965			HK	Pale Gr.				RL	Red & Yl. flames & devil			300
Prowler	6965			HK	Flr. Lime			Blk.	RL				200
Prowler	6965			HK	Or.			Blk.	RL				200
Prowler	6965			HK	Gr.			Blk.	RL				200
Prowler	6965			HK	Red			Blk.	RL				200
Prowler	9207			MEX	Chr.				Reg	Red, Blk. & Wht. tr. w/ bandit			50
Prowler	9207	Super Chr.		HK	Chr.				Reg	Red & Yl. flames w/ devil			25
Prowler	9207	Super Chr.		HK	Chr.				RL	Red & Yl. flames w/ devil			35
Prowler	9207	Super Chr.		HK	Chr.				Reg	Red, Blk. & Wht. tr. w/ bandit			25
Purple Passion		Gold Ser.		MAL	Gold				WW - Gold			FAOSc	25
Purple Passion		Pre-Pro		MAL	Blu.	CL			WW			Revealers 10 pack	10
Purple Passion		Revealer		MAL	M. Blu.	TNT			WW			Revealers 10 pack	10
Purple Passion		Revealer		MAL	M. Blu.	CL			WW			Revealers 10 pack	10
Purple Passion		Set		MAL	Blk.				WW	Or. & Red tr. on hood & sides			12
Purple Passion		Set		MAL	Wht.				WW	Or. & Prp. tr. on hood & sides			12
Purple Passion		Shell		MAL	Yl.				WW				5
Purple Passion		Toy Fair		MAL	Gold				WW	Red & Blk. flames	New York Toy Fair 1992		30
Purple Passion	2173			MAL	M. Prp.				WW	Yl. & Blu. flames			4
Purple Passion	2173			MAL	M. Prp.				WW	Gr. & Blu. tr. on hood & sides			4
Purple Passion	2173			MAL	M. Prp.				WW	Gr. & Blu. tr. on hood			4
Quik T-rik	7295	Ultra Hot		MAL	M. Prp.				UH				6
Quik T-rik	7295	Ultra Hot		HK	M. Prp.				UH				6
Race Ace	2620			MAL	Wht.				HO - Gold				20
Race Ace	2620			HK	Wht.				HO - Gold				20
Race Bait 308		HW Conv.		MAL	Red				Reg		HW Convention 1989		150
Race Bait 308		HW Conv.		HK	Red				Reg		HW Convention 1989		150
Race Bait 308	2021			HK	Grey MF.				HO - Gold		308 Turbo		8
Race Bait 308	2021			HK	Grey MF.				RR - Grey		308 Turbo		15
Race Bait 308	2021			HK	Grey MF.				Reg - Gold		308		8
Race Bait 308	2021			HK	Grey				HO - Gold	Red, Yl. & Blk. tr.	GTB Turbo		12

Name	#	Category	Casting	Ctry.	Color	Win.	Base	Interior	Wheels	Paint	Logo	Other	$
Race Bait 308	2021			MAL	Red		Plst.		Reg		308 & GTB		8
Race Bait 308	2021			MAL	Grey				HO - Gold	Red, Yl. & Blk. tr.	GTB Turbo		12
Race Bait 308	2021			HK	Red		Plst.		Reg		308 & GTB		8
Race Bait 308	2021			HK	Gold				Reg		308 & GTB		20
Race Bait 308	2021			MAL	Gold				Reg		308 & GTB		20
Race Bait 308	2021			HK	Grey MF.				Reg		308 Turbo		7
Race Bait 308	2021			MAL	Grey MF.				Reg		308 Turbo		7
Race Bait 308	2021			MAL	Red				Reg		308 & GTB		8
Race Bait 308	2021			MAL	Grey MF.				RR - Grey		308 Turbo		15
Race Bait 308	2021			HK	Grey				Reg		GTB		7
Race Bait 308	2021			MAL	Grey MF.				Reg - Gold		308		7
Race Bait 308	2021			MAL	Grey MF.				HO - Gold		308 Turbo		7
Race Bait 308	2021			HK	Red				Reg		308 & GTB		7
Race Bait 308	2021			MAL	Grey				Reg		GTB		7
NASCAR Stocker	3927			HK	Wht.				HO - Gold	Gr. & Red tr.	Mountain Dew		25
NASCAR Stocker	3927			MAL	Wht.				HO - Gold	Gr. & Red tr.	Mountain Dew		25
Radar Ranger	5022			MAL	Silver				4x4 LHb				7
Radar Ranger	5022			MAL	Silver				4x4 SHb				7
Radar Ranger	5022			MAL	Silver				4x4 SHb - Blk.				7
Ramblin' Wrecker	7659			HK	Wht.	GT			Reg		No telephone number		20
Ramblin' Wrecker	7659			HK	Yl.				Reg				10
Ramblin' Wrecker	7659			HK	Wht.	BluT			RL		Telephone number		25
Ramblin' Wrecker	7659			HK	Wht.	GT			RL		Telephone number		25
Ramp Truck	700			MAL	Yl./Wht.				Reg				5
Ramp Truck	5343			MAL	Wht.	CL			Reg				8
Ramp Truck	5343			MAL	Wht.	Blk.			Reg				5
Range Rover		Cadbury	WWA	MAL	Plum				4x4 SHb	Wht. tr.	Cadbury		175
Range Rover		Cadbury	WWA	MAL	Yl.				4x4 SHb	Plum tr.	Cadbury Flake		175
Range Rover		Getty	WWA	MAL	Wht.				4x4 SHb		Getty		4
Range Rover	4322		WWA	MAL	Blk.				4x4 SHb	Blk. & Bro. tr.	Range Rover		4
Range Rover	9738		NWA	MAL	Wht.				4x4 SHb	Dk. Blu. & Red tr.	Range Rover		4
Range Rover	9738		NWA	MAL	Wht.				4x4 SHb	Pale Blu. & Red tr.	Range Rover		4
Range Rover	9738		WWA	MAL	Wht.				4x4 SHb	Pale Blu. & Red tr.	Range Rover		4
Ranger Rig	7666			HK	Gr.	GT			RL				35
Ranger Rig	7666			HK	Gr.	BluT			RL				35
Rapid Transit	3256		1 roof vent	MAL	Br. Yl.				Reg				5
Rapid Transit	3256		1 roof vent	HK	Br. Yl.				Reg				5
Rapid Transit	3256		1 roof vent	HK	Wht.				Reg	Blu. & Red US flag tr.	American Football Team		15
Rapid Transit	3256		2 roof vents	MAL	Wht.				Reg		Blk. sign on rear		25
Rapid Transit	3256		2 roof vents	HK	Wht.				Reg		Blk. sign on rear		25
Rapid Transit	3256		2 roof vents	MAL	Wht.				Reg		Blu. sign on rear		8
Rapid Transit	3256		1 roof vent	MAL	Wht.				Reg	Blu. & Red US flag tr.	American Football Team		15
Rapid Transit	3256		1 roof vent	MAL	Yl.	DT			Reg				5
Rapid Transit	3256		1 roof vent	HK	Br. Yl.				Reg		Blu. sign on rear		5
Rapid Transit	3256		2 roof vents	HK	Wht.				Reg		Blu. sign on rear		5
Rapid Transit	3256		1 roof vent	HK	Wht.				Reg				5
Rapid Transit	3256		1 roof vent	MAL	Br. Yl.	DT			Reg				5
Rapid Transit	3256		2 roof vents	MAL	Yl.				Reg				5

Name	#	Category	Casting	Ctry.	Color	Win.	Base	Interior	Wheels	Paint	Logo	Other	S
Rapid Transit	3256		1 roof vent	MAL	Wht.				Reg		Blu. sign on rear		5
Rapid Transit	3256		2 roof vents	HK	Yl.				Reg				5
Rapid Transit	3256		1 roof vent	HK	Yl.				Reg				5
Rash 1	7616			HK	Gr.			Wht.	RL	Yl. & Red tr.			50
Rash 1	7616			HK	Gr.			Blk.	RL	Yl. & Red tr.			50
Rash 1	7616			HK	Blu.			Blk.	RL	Yl. & Red tr.			300
Rash 1	7616			HK	Pale Gr.			Blk.	RL	Yl. & Red tr.			60
Ratmobile	5028	Speed Demon	Plst.	MAL	Wht.				HO - Silver	Wht. head			5
Ratmobile	5028	Speed Demon	Plst.	MAL	Wht.				UH	Wht. head			5
Ratmobile	5028	Speed Demon	Plst.	MAL	Wht.				UH	Cream head			5
Recycling Truck	2073		No hole	MAL	Or.				Reg				4
Recycling Truck	2073		Hole	MAL	Or.				Reg				4
Red Baron	5700	25th Ann.		CHN	M. Or.				RL				4
Red Baron	5700	25th Ann.		CHN	M. Violet				RL				4
Red Baron	5700	25th Ann.		CHN	Br. Red MF.				RL				4
Red Baron	5700	25th Ann.		CHN	Navy Blu.				RL				4
Red Baron	5700	25th Ann.		CHN	M. Br. Red				RL				4
Red Baron	5700	25th Ann.		CHN	M. Lime				RL				4
Red Baron	5700	25th Ann.		CHN	Gold				RL				4
Red Baron	5700	25th Ann.		CHN	M. Olive Gr.				RL				4
Red Baron	5700	25th Ann.		CHN	M. Turquoise				RL				4
Red Baron	5700	25th Ann.		CHN	M. Pnk.				RL				4
Red Baron	5700	25th Ann.		CHN	M. Bro.				RL				4
Red Baron	5700	25th Ann.		CHN	M. Gr.				RL				4
Red Baron	5700	25th Ann.		CHN	M. Blu.				RL				4
Red Baron	5700	25th Ann.		CHN	M. Magenta				RL				4
Red Baron	5700	Gold Ser.		CHN	M. Sea Blu.				RL - Gold			GEng - FAOSc	25
Red Baron	5700	Vintage		CHN	M. Electric Gr.				RL				4
Red Baron	5700	Vintage		CHN	M. Dk. Gr.				RL				4
Red Baron	5700	Vintage		CHN	M. Dk. Bro.				RL				4
Red Baron	5700	Vintage		CHN	M. Pale Pnk.				RL				4
Red Baron	5700	Vintage		CHN	Maroon				RL				4
Red Baron	5700	Vintage		CHN	M. Prp.				RL				4
Red Baron	5700	Vintage		CHN	Wht.				RL				4
Red Baron	5700	Vintage		CHN	M. Gold				RL				4
Red Baron	5700	Vintage		CHN	Br. Red				RL				4
Red Baron	5700	Vintage		CHN	M. Sky Blu.				RL				4
Red Baron	5700	Vintage		CHN	M. Royal Blu.				RL				4
Red Baron	5700	Vintage		CHN	Gunmetal				RL				4
Red Baron	5700	Vintage		CHN	M. Br. Blu.				RL				4
Red Baron	6964			HK	Red			Blk.	RL				40
Red Baron	6964		No spike on helmet	HK	M. Red			Blk.	RL				20
Red Baron	6964			HK	Red			Blk.	Reg				12
Redliner	9534	Ultra Hot		HK	Gold				UH				7
Redliner	9534	Ultra Hot		MAL	Gold				UH				7
Renault LeCar	3292			FRA	Blk.				Reg				25
Renault LeCar	3292			FRA	Pale Gr.				Reg				25
Renault LeCar	3292			MEX	Red				Reg				35
Renault LeCar	3292			FRA	Red				Reg				25
Renault LeCar	3292			FRA	M. Pale Blu.				Reg				25

Name	#	Category	Casting	Ctry.	Color	Win.	Base	Interior	Wheels	Paint	Logo	Other	$
Renault 5 Turbo	3205			MAL	Wht.				Reg				8
Renault 5 Turbo	9749			MAL	Blu.				Reg				6
Rescue Ranger	2537			MAL	Gr.		No holes		Reg				6
Rescue Ranger	2537			MAL	Gr.		Holes		Reg				6
Rescue Ranger	2537			MAL	Gr.		Holes		RR - Wht.				15
Rescue Ranger	2537			MAL	Gr.		No holes		RR - Wht.				15
Rescue Ranger	5145			MAL	Red		No holes		Reg	Red, Wht. & Blk. tr.	HW logo & Rescue Unit		5
Rescue Ranger	5145			MAL	Red		Holes		Reg	Red, Wht. & Blk. tr.	HW logo & Rescue Unit		5
Rescue Squad	3304	Scene Machine Set		HK	Red				Reg				50
Rig Wrecker	5145			MAL	Wht.				Reg	Blu. & Red tr.	Airship Tug	Blimp & Support 5 Pack	5
Rig Wrecker	3916			MAL	Wht.		Inserted MAL cstg.		Reg				5
Rig Wrecker	3916			MAL	Wht.				Reg				5
Rig Wrecker	3916			MAL	Wht.				Reg				5
Rig Wrecker	3916			MAL	Wht.		HW logo		Reg	Dk.er Red stripes			5
Rig Wrecker	3916			HK	Wht.		HW logo		Reg	Dk.er Red stripes			5
Rig Wrecker	3916			MAL	Wht.		Plst.		Reg				5
Rig Wrecker	3916			HK	Wht.		Plst.		Reg				5
Rig Wrecker	3916			HK	Wht.		HW logo		Reg				5
Rigor-Motor	11849			MAL	Magenta				Reg				3
Road King	7615	Set		HK	Yl.				RL			Mountain Mining	600
Road Pirate		Set		CHN	Red				Reg			Criss Cross Crash	10
Road Torch	1500	Ultra Hot		MAL	Red				UH				7
Rock Buster	9088			MEX	Yl.				Reg				40
Rock Buster	9088			HK	Yl.				RL				15
Rock Buster	9088			HK	Gr.				Reg				12
Rock Buster	9088			HK	Yl.				Reg				20
Rock Buster	9213	Super Chr.		HK	Chr.				RL				40
Rock Buster	9213	Super Chr.		HK	Chr.				Reg				35
Rockettank	9380			MAL	Tan								5
Rockettank	9380			MAL	Khk.								5
Rodger Dodger	8259			HK	Magenta				RL	Red, Prp. & Wht. tr.		Highway Drive-Ins Set	50
Rodger Dodger	8259			HK	Magenta		Plst.		RL	Or. & Red flames			50
Rodger Dodger	8259			HK	Magenta				Reg	Or. & Red flames			45
Rodger Dodger	8259			HK	Blu.				RL	Or. & Red flames			400
Rodger Dodger	8259			HK	Gold		Wht.		Reg	Red, Prp. & Wht. tr.			30
Rodger Dodger	8259			HK	Gold				Reg	Mgta. & Or. flames			30
Rodzilla	4389	Speed Demon		MAL	Gr.				UH	Yl. eyes		GEng	4
Rodzilla	4389	Speed Demon		MAL	Prp.		Red		UH	Red eyes			30
Rodzilla	4389	Speed Demon		MAL	Prp.				HO - Silver	Yl. eyes			4
Rodzilla	4389	Speed Demon		MAL	Prp.		Pale purple		UH	Yl. eyes			4
Rodzilla	4389	Speed Demon		MAL	Prp.		Wht.		UH	Yl. eyes			4
Rodzilla	4389	Speed Demon		MAL	Prp.				UH	Yl. eyes			4
Rodzilla	4389	Speed Demon		MAL	Prp.		Red		UH	Yl. eyes			4
Roll Patrol	9375			MAL	Des. Cmflg.				Reg - Blk.	Desert camouflage on			4
Roll Patrol	9375			MAL	Khk. Cmflg.				4x4 SHb - Blk.	Desert camouflage on			4

Name	# Category	Ctry.	Color	Win.	Base	Interior	Wheels	Paint	Logo	Other	S
Roll Patrol	9375	MAL	Des. Cmflg.				4x4 SHb	Desert camouflage on			4
Roll Patrol	419	MAL	Des. Scrub		HW logo	Pnk.ish tan	4x4 SHb - Blk.				4
Roll Patrol	9375	MAL	Des. Cmflg.				4x4 SHb - Blk.	Desert camouflage on hood & sides			4
Roll Patrol	419	MAL	Des. Scrub		HW	Blk.	Reg - Blk.				4
Roll Patrol	419	MAL	Des. Scrub		HW logo	Tan	4x4 SHb - Blk.				4
Roll Patrol	9375	MAL	Khk. Cmflg.		CJ7	Khaki	Reg - Blk.				4
Roll Patrol	9375	MAL	Khk. Cmflg.		N&N	Khaki	4x4 SHb - Blk.				4
Roll Patrol	9375	HK	Khk. Cmflg.		CJ7	Khaki	Reg - Blk.				4
Roll Patrol	9375	MAL	Khk. Cmflg.		HW logo, MAL cast flat	Khaki	Reg - Blk.				4
Roll Patrol	9375	HK	Des. Cmflg.		HW logo	Tan	Reg			Military 4 Pack	4
Roll Patrol	9375	MAL	Khk. Cmflg.		No CJ7	Khaki	Reg - Blk.				4
Roll Patrol	9375	MAL	Des. Cmflg.		HW logo	Blk.	Reg				4
Roll Patrol	9375	MAL	Des. Cmflg.		HW logo	Tan	Reg			Military 4 Pack	4
Roll Patrol	9375	MAL	Khk. Cmflg.		No CJ7 & MAL cast flat	Khaki	Reg - Blk.				4
Roll Patrol	9375	HK	Khk. Cmflg.		N&N	Khaki	Reg - Blk.				4
Roll Patrol	9375	HK	Khk. Cmflg.		No CJ7	Khaki	Reg - Blk.				4
Roll Patrol	9375	MAL	Khk. Cmflg.		No CJ7 & MAL cast flat	Khaki	4x4 SHb - Blk.				4
Roll Patrol	9375	HK	Des. Cmflg.		HW logo, MAL cast flat	Blk.	Reg				4
Roll Patrol	9375	MAL	Khk. Cmflg.			Khaki	4x4 SHb - Blk.				4
Roll Patrol	9375	HK	Des. Cmflg.		HW logo	Blk.	Reg				4
Roll Patrol	9375	HK	Khk. Cmflg.		N&N	Khaki	4x4 SHb - Blk.				4
Roll Patrol	9375	MAL	Des. Cmflg.			Blk.	Reg				4
Roll Patrol	9375	MAL	Khk. Cmflg.		CJ7	Khaki	4x4 SHb - Blk.				4
Roll Patrol	9375	MAL	Khk. Cmflg.		No CJ7	Khaki	4x4 SHb - Blk.				4
Roll Patrol	9375	HK	Khk. Cmflg.		No CJ7	Khaki	4x4 SHb - Blk.				4
Roll Patrol	9375	HK	Khk. Cmflg.		CJ7	Khaki	4x4 SHb - Blk.				4
Roll Patrol	9375	MAL	Khk. Cmflg.		N&N	Khaki	Reg - Blk.				4
Rolls Royce Phantom II	1931	FRA	Silver				Reg				30
Rolls Royce Phantom II	1931	FRA	Silver				WW				30
Rolls Royce Phantom II	3290	HK	M. Blu.		No NOB		WW				5
Rolls Royce Phantom II	3290	MAL	M. Blu.		NOB		WW				5
Rolls Royce Phantom II	3290	HK	M. Blu.		NOB		WW				5
Rolls Royce Phantom II	3290	MAL	M. Blu.		No NOB		WW				5
Rolls Royce Phantom II	3290	MAL	Silver		NOB		Reg				5
Rolls Royce Phantom II	3290	MAL	M. Blu.		No NOB		Reg				5
Rolls Royce Phantom II	3290	MAL	M. Blu.		NOB		Reg				5

Name	#	Category	Casting	Ctry.	Color	Win.	Base	Interior	Wheels	Paint	Logo	Other	$
Rolls Royce Phantom II	3290			HK	Silver		NOB		Reg				5
Rolls Royce Phantom II	3290			HK	M. Blu.		NOB		Reg				5
Rolls Royce Phantom II	3290			HK	M. Blu.		No NOB		Reg				5
Royal Flash	2501			FRA	Or.	DT			Reg	Red, Wht. & Blu. Union Flag tr.	Lotus		25
Royal Flash	2501			FRA	Wht.				Reg			Tan bmps	25
Royal Flash	2501			MAL	Wht.	BluT			Reg				7
Royal Flash	2501			HK	Wht.	BluT			Reg				7
Royal Flash	2501			MAL	Or.				Reg				7
Royal Flash	2501			MEX	Or.	BluT			Reg	Red, Wht. & Blu. Union Flag tr.	Lotus		25
Royal Flash	2501			HK	Wht.	GT			Reg				7
Royal Flash	2501			MAL	Or. MF.				Reg				7
Ruby Red Passion				MAL	M. Ruby				WW	Yl. & Blu. flames			15
Ruby Red Passion		HW Conv.		MAL	M. Ruby				WW	Yl. & Blu. flames	HW 7th Annual Convention		100
Sand Drifter	7651			FRA	Or.				WW				30
Sand Drifter	7651			FRA	Yl.				Reg				30
Sand Drifter	7651			HK	Yl.				Reg				35
Sand Drifter	7651			MAL	Yl.				Reg				35
Sand Drifter	7651			FRA	Or.				Reg				30
Sand Drifter	7651			FRA	Yl.				Reg	Red & Prp. flames			30
Sand Drifter	7651			HK	Yl.				Reg	Red & Prp. flames			30
Sand Drifter	7651			MAL	Yl.				Reg	Red & Prp. flames			30
Sand Drifter	7651			HK	Gr.				RL				200
Sand Drifter	7651			HK	Yl.				RL	Red & Prp. flames			30
Sand Witch	6974			HK	Pale Blu.			Blk.	RL				75
Sand Witch	6974			FRA	Plum				Reg				40
Sand Witch	6974			HK	Dk. Yl.			Blk.	RL				75
Sand Witch	6974			HK	Pnk.			Blk.	RL				75
Sand Witch	6974			MEX	Red				RL				40
Sand Witch	6974			HK	Plum			Blk.	RL				75
Sand Witch	6974			HK	Gr.			Blk.	RL				75
Sand Witch	6974			HK	Red			Blk.	RL				75
Sand Witch	6974			HK	Or.			Blk.	RL				75
Sand Witch	6974			HK	Dk. Blu.			Blk.	RL				75
Sand Witch	6974			HK	Pale Yl.			Blk.	RL				75
Sand Witch	6974			HK	Pale Gr.			Blk.	RL				75
Sand Witch	6974			HK	Flr. Lime			Blk.	RL				75
School Bus	1795			MAL	Pale Yl.				Reg	Thin Blk. stripe	School Bus		7
School Bus	1795			MAL	Yl.				Reg	Thick Blk. stripe	School Bus		5
Science Friction	2018			MAL	Wht.				Reg				5
Science Friction	2018			HK	Wht.				Reg				8
Science Friction	2018			MAL	Wht.				HO - Gold				8
Science Friction	2018			HK	Wht.				HO - Gold				8
Science Friction	2018			MAL	Magenta				HO - Gold				8
Science Friction	2018			HK	M. Red				Reg				7
Science Friction	2018			MAL	M. Red				Reg				7

Name	#	Category	Casting	Ctry.	Color	Win.	Base	Interior	Wheels	Paint	Logo	Other	$
Science Friction	2018			MAL	Magenta				Reg				8
Science Friction	2018			HK	Magenta				HO - Gold				8
Science Friction	2018			HK	Magenta				Reg				8
S'Coo Bus	11533 Vintage			CHN	M. Br. Yl.				RL				10
S'Coo Bus	11533 Vintage			CHN	M. Gold				RL				10
S'Cooi Bus	11533 Vintage			CHN	Yl.				RL				10
Screamin'	2532			MAL	Pale Gr.		RAF & no SIS		Reg				20
Screamin'	2532			MAL	Pale Gr.		RAF & SIS		Reg				20
Screamin'	2532			MAL	Pale Gr.		ROA		Reg				20
Screamin'	9521			MAL	Red		RAF & no SIS		Reg				12
Screamin'	9521			MAL	Red		RAF & SIS		Reg				12
Screamin'	9521			MAL	Red		ROA		Reg				12
Second Wind	9644			IND	Gr.				Reg				10
Second Wind	9644			FRA	Wht.				Reg	Red number 5			20
Second Wind	9644			IND	Blu.				Reg				10
Second Wind	9644			HK	Wht.				Reg	Blk. number 5			20
Second Wind	9644			HK	Wht.				RL	Red number 5			30
Second Wind	9644			HK	Wht.				Reg	Red number 5			20
Second Wind	9644			MAL	Wht.				Reg				20
Second Wind	9644			MEX	Wht.				Reg	Blk. number 5			30
Shadow Jet	9590			MAL	Prp.	YT			Reg	Gr. & Yl. tr.	Yl. F3		5
Shadow Jet		Co. Rcr.		MAL	Maroon to Yl.				Reg				5
Shadow Jet		Getty		MAL	Blu.	CL			Reg	Yl., Red & Wht. tr.	Getty		5
Shadow Jet		Video Car		MAL	N. Pnk.	TNT			Reg				10
Shadow Jet	477			MAL	Gr.	DT			Reg	Gr. & Blu. tr.	Blu. F3		5
Shadow Jet	4699			MAL	Yl.	LT			Reg	Red & Prp. tr.	Purple F3		5
Shadow Jet	4699			MAL	Yl.	LT			Reg	Red & Blu. tr.	Blu. F3		5
Shadow Jet	4699			MAL	Yl.	DT			Reg	Red & Prp. tr.	Purple F3		5
Shadow Jet	9590			MAL	Prp.	YT			Reg	Yl. & Gr. tr.	Gr. F3		5
Shadow Jet	9590			MAL	Prp.	YT			Reg	Gr. & Yl. tr.	Yl. F3	Very small FWs	8
Shadow Jet II	11848		Plst.	MAL	Dk. Chr.				UH				3
Shadow Jet II	11848		Plst.	MAL	Chr.				UH				3
Sharkruiser		Co. Rcr.		MAL	Grey to Wht.				Reg				5
Sharkruiser	3286 Speed Demon			MAL	Grey				HO - Silver				4
Sharkruiser	3286 Speed Demon			MAL	Grey				UH				4
Shelf Shocker	2518			MAL	Tan								6
Shell Shocker	2518			MAL	Knk.					Bro. star & numbers			6
Sheriff Patrol	9526			HK	M. Blu./Wht.				Reg	Blk. & Yl. tr.	Sheriff 701		5
Sheriff Patrol	9526			MAL	M. Blu./Wht.				Reg	Blk. & Yl. tr.	Sheriff 701		5
Sheriff Patrol		Ralston		MAL	M. Blu./Wht.				Reg	Blk. & Yl. tr. & Wht.r doors	Sheriff		6
Sheriff Patrol		Ralston		MAL	M. Blu./Wht.				Reg	Blk. & Yl. tr. & not so Wht. doors	Sheriff		6
Sheriff Patrol	2019			HK	Blk./Wht.		Rsd. 1977		Reg	Yl. tr.	701 on roof & Sheriff on doors	Wht. rear doors	5
Sheriff Patrol	2019			MAL	Blk./Wht.		Inv. MAL cstg.		Reg	Yl. tr.	701 on roof & Sheriff on doors	Wht. rear doors	5
Sheriff Patrol	2019			MAL	Blk./Wht.		Rsd. 1977		Reg	Yl. tr.	701 on roof & Sheriff on doors	Wht. rear doors	5

Name	#	Category	Casting	Ctry.	Color	Win.	Base	Interior	Wheels	Paint	Logo	Other	$
Sheriff Patrol	2019			HK	Blk./Wht.		Flat 1977		Reg	Yl. tr.	701 on roof & Sheriff on doors	Wht. rear doors	5
Sheriff Patrol	2019			MAL	Blk./Wht.		Flat 1977		Reg		701 on roof & Sheriff on doors		5
Sheriff Patrol	2019			MAL	Blk./Wht.		1982, HW & Rsd. MAL		Reg	Yl. tr.	701 on roof & Sheriff on doors	Wht. rear doors	5
Sheriff Patrol		Co. Rcr.		MAL					Reg				5
Sheriff Patrol		Co. Rcr.		HK					Reg				5
Sheriff Patrol	4004			MAL	Blk./Wht.				Reg	Yl. & Wht. tr.	701 on roof & Sheriff on doors	Blk. rear doors	5
Sheriff Patrol	9526			MAL	M. Blu./Wht.		N&N		Reg	Wht. rear doors			5
Sheriff Patrol	9526			MAL	M. Blu./Wht.		Inv. MAL		Reg	Wht. rear doors	Sheriff 701		5
Sheriff Patrol	9526			MAL	M. Blu./Wht.				Reg	Wht. rear doors	Sheriff 701		5
Sheriff Patrol	9526			HK	M. Blu./Wht.		N&N		Reg	Wht. rear doors			5
Sheriff Patrol	9526			MAL	M. Blu.				Reg	Blu. rear doors			5
Sheriff Patrol	9526			HK	M. Blu./Wht.				Reg	Wht. rear doors	Sheriff 701		5
Sheriff Patrol	9526			MAL	M. Blu./Wht.		HW logo		Reg	Wht. rear doors			5
Sheriff Patrol	9526			HK	M. Blu./Wht.		HW logo		Reg	Whi. rear doors			5
Sheriff Patrol	9526			HK	M. Blu.				Reg	Blu. rear doors			5
Shock Factor	3164			MAL	Blk./Pnk.				4x4 SHb				4
Shock Factor	3164			MAL	Blk./N. Pnk.				4x4 SHb				4
Show Hoss II	9646			FRA	Yl.				Reg	Red, Wht. & Blk. tr.	Show Hoss		40
Show Hoss II	9646			FRA	Yl.				Reg		Ananas		40
Show Hoss II	9646			FRA	Dk. Blu.				Reg				40
Show Hoss II	9646			MEX	Dk. Blu.				Reg				40
Show Hoss II	9646			HK	Gr.				Reg		Mustang II		30
Show Hoss II	9646			HK	Yl.				Reg				35
Show Hoss II	9646			HK	Yl.				RL				200
Show Off	6982			HK	Red			Dk. Bro.	RL				120
Show Off	6982			HK	Pale Gr.			Pale Bro.	RL				120
Show Off	6982			HK	Gr.			Grey	RL				120
Show Off	6982			HK	Flr. Lime			Pale Bro.	RL				120
Show Off	6982			HK	Dk. Blu.			Grey	RL				120
Show Off	6982			HK	Gr.			Dk. Bro.	RL				120
Show Off	6982			HK	Pale Blu.			Pale Bro.	RL				120
Show Off	6982			HK	Pale Yl.			Blk.	RL				120
Show Off	6982			HK	Gr.			Pale Bro.	RL				120
Show Off	6982			HK	Dk. Blu.			Dk. Bro.	RL				120
Show Off	6982			HK	Dk. Blu.			Blk.	RL				120
Show Off	6982			HK	Pnk.			Blk.	RL				120
Show Off	6982			HK	Gr.			Blk.	RL				120
Show Off	6982			HK	Pnk.			Wht.	RL				120
Show Off	6982			HK	Dk. Yl.			Dk. Bro.	RL				120
Show Off	6982			HK	Plum			Dk. Bro.	RL				120
Show Off	6982			HK	Pale Gr.			Wht.	RL				120
Show Off	6982			HK	Pale Gr.			Blk.	RL				120
Show Off	6982			HK	Pale Gr.			Grey	RL				120
Show Off	6982			HK	Flr. Lime			Blk.	RL				120
Show Off	6982			HK	Flr. Lime			Wht.	RL				120
Show Off	6982			HK	Pale Gr.			Dk. Bro.	RL				120
Show Off	6982			HK	Flr. Lime			Dk. Bro.	RL				120

Name	#	Category	Casting	Ctry.	Color	Win.	Base	Interior	Wheels	Paint	Logo	Other	S
Show Off	6982			HK	Plum			Grey	RL				120
Show Off	6982			HK	Plum			Pale Bro.	RL				120
Show Off	6982			HK	Gr.			Wht.	RL				120
Show Off	6982			HK	Dk. Blu.			Pale Bro.	RL				120
Show Off	6982			HK	Flr. Lime			Grey	RL				120
Show Off	6982			HK	Pale Blu.			Dk. Bro.	RL				120
Show Off	6982			HK	Red			Blk.	RL				120
Show Off	6982			HK	Or.			Dk. Bro.	RL				120
Show Off	6982			HK	Pale Yl.			Wht.	RL				120
Show Off	6982			HK	Or.			Blk.	RL				120
Show Off	6982			HK	Red			Wht.	RL				120
Show Off	6982			HK	Pale Yl.			Dk. Bro.	RL				120
Show Off	6982			HK	Dk. Yl.			Pale Bro.	RL				120
Show Off	6982			HK	Or.			Grey	RL				120
Show Off	6982			HK	Red			Pale Bro.	RL				120
Show Off	6982			HK	Red			Grey	RL				120
Show Off	6982			HK	Or.			Wht.	RL				120
Show Off	6982			HK	Pale Yl.			Grey	RL				120
Show Off	6982			HK	Plum			Wht.	RL				120
Show Off	6982			HK	Pnk.			Pale Bro.	RL				120
Show Off	6982			HK	Dk. Yl.			Grey	RL				120
Show Off	6982			HK	Pale Blu.			Wht.	RL				120
Show Off	6982			HK	Dk. Yl.			Blk.	RL				120
Show Off	6982			HK	Dk. Yl.			Wht.	RL				120
Show Off	6982			HK	Pnk.			Dk. Bro.	RL				120
Show Off	6982			HK	Dk. Blu.			Wht.	RL				120
Show Off	6982			HK	Plum			Blk.	RL				120
Show Off	6982			HK	Pale Blu.			Grey	RL				120
Show Off	6982			HK	Pale Blu.			Blk.	RL				120
Show Off	6982			HK	Pale Yl.			Pale Bro.	RL				120
Show Off	6982			HK	Or.			Pale Bro.	RL				120
Show Off	6982			HK	Pnk.			Grey	RL				120
Silhouette	5715	25th Ann.		CHN	M. Turquoise				RL				4
Silhouette	5715	25th Ann.		CHN	M. Bro.				RL				4
Silhouette	5715	25th Ann.		CHN	M. Violet				RL				4
Silhouette	5715	25th Ann.		CHN	M. Pnk.				RL				4
Silhouette	5715	25th Ann.		CHN	M. Red				RL				4
Silhouette	5715	25th Ann.		CHN	M. Magenta				RL				4
Silhouette	5715	25th Ann.		CHN	M. Gr.				RL				4
Silhouette	5715	25th Ann.		CHN	M. Olive Gr.				RL				4
Silhouette	5715	25th Ann.		CHN	M. Or.				RL				4
Silhouette	5715	25th Ann.		CHN	M. Blu.				RL				4
Silhouette	5715	25th Ann.		CHN	M. Lime				RL				4
Silhouette	5715	25th Ann.		CHN	Navy Blu.				RL				4
Silhouette	5715	25th Ann.		CHN	Gold				RL				4
Silhouette	5715	Gold Ser.		CHN	M. Chestnut				RL - Gold			GEng - FAOSc	25
Silhouette	5715	Vintage		CHN	M. Royal Blu.				RL				4
Silhouette	5715	Vintage		CHN	Br. Red				RL				4
Silhouette	5715	Vintage		CHN	M. Dk. Bro.				RL				4
Silhouette	5715	Vintage		CHN	M. Electric Gr.				RL				4
Silhouette	5715	Vintage		CHN	M. Dk. Gr.				RL				4

Name	#	Category	Ctry.	Color	Win.	Base	Interior	Wheels	Paint	Logo	Other	$
Silhouette	5715	Vintage	CHN	M. Gold				RL				4
Silhouette	5715	Vintage	CHN	Maroon				RL				4
Silhouette	5715	Vintage	CHN	Gunmetal				RL				4
Silhouette	5715	Vintage	CHN	M. Prp.				RL				4
Silhouette	5715	Vintage	CHN	M. Br. Blu.				RL				4
Silhouette	5715	Vintage	CHN	Wht.				RL				4
Silhouette	5715	Vintage	CHN	M. Mauve				RL				4
Silhouette	5715	Vintage	CHN	M. Pale Pnk.				RL				4
Silhouette II	5267		MAL	M. Prp.		Chr.		UH				3
Silhouette II	5267		MAL	M. Prp.		Grey		UH				3
Silver Bullet		Co. Rcr.	MAL	Blu. to Wht.				Reg		15		5
Silver Bullet	9535	Ultra Hot	MAL	Grey MF.		HW across the width & N&N		UH	Red & Yl. lightning tr.	Ultra Hots		7
Silver Bullet	9535	Ultra Hot	MAL	Grey MF.		HW across the width		UH	Red & Yl. lightning tr.	Ultra Hots		7
Silver Bullet	9535	Ultra Hot	HK	Silver				UH	Red & Yl. lightning tr.	Ultra Hots		8
Silver Bullet	9535	Ultra Hot	MAL	Grey MF.		HW logo		UH	Red & Yl. lightning tr.	Ultra Hots		7
Silver Surfer	3300	Heroes	HK	Chr.				Reg				15
Silver Surfer	3300	Heroes	MAL	Chr.				Reg				15
Sir Rodney Roadster	8261		FRA	Gunmetal				Reg				35
Sir Rodney Roadster	8261		FRA	Silver				Reg				35
Sir Rodney Roadster	8261		FRA	Silver				Reg	Red flames			35
Sir Rodney Roadster	8261		HK	Gr.				RL				200
Sir Rodney Roadster	8261		MEX	Yl.				Reg	Red flames			40
Sir Rodney Roadster	8261		HK	Yl.				RL				40
Sir Rodney Roadster	8261		HK	Bro.				RL	Red flames			300
Sir Rodney Roadster	8261		MEX	Yl.		No MEX		Reg	Red flames			40
Snake	6969		HK	Wht.	NW			RL	Red flames			500
Snake	6969		HK	Yl.	NW			RL	Red flames			500
Snake	10497	Vintage	CHN	Yl.				RL				5
Snake	10497	Vintage	CHN	M. Gr.				RL				5
Snake	10497	Vintage	CHN	Yl. enamel				RL				5
Snake	10497	Vintage	CHN	Wht.				RL	Blu., Red & Yl. tr.			5
Snake	10497	Vintage	CHN	Gold				RL				5
Snake	10497	Vintage	CHN	M. Gold				RL				5
Snake	10497	Vintage	CHN	Wht.				RL	Gr., Yl. & Red tr.			5
Snake	10497	Vintage	CHN	M. Lime Gr.				RL				5
Snake Buster	9587		MEX	Silver MF.				HO - Gold				20
Snake Buster	9587		MAL	Silver MF.				UH				8
Snake Buster	9587		MAL	Silver				UH				10
Snake Buster	9587		MAL	Silver MF.				HO - Gold			Snake Mountain Challenge	10
Sol-Aire CX4	13578		MAL	Blu./Wht.	TNT	Wht.	Wht.	UH	Red & Yl. tr.	HW & 1		3
Sol-Aire CX4	13578		MAL	Blu./Wht.	CL	Wht.	Wht.	UH	Red & Yl. tr.	HW & 1		3
Sol-Aire CX4		25th Ann.	MAL	N. Or.				UH	Blu. geo. tr.	2		5
Sol-Aire CX4	2105	Cal Cus.	MAL	N. Blz.	YT	Flat MAL		Rtr - Chr.	Yl., Blu. & Pnk. geo. shps.	2		7
Sol-Aire CX4	2105	Cal Cus.	MAL	N. Blz.	YT	Rsd. MAL		Rtr - Chr.	Yl., Blu. & Pnk. geo. shps.	2		7
Sol-Aire CX4	2200	Park'n Plate	MAL	Yl.	Blk.			UH	Blu. & Red tr.	13		7
Sol-Aire CX4	2200	Park'n Plate	MAL	Yl.	BluT			UH	Blu. & Red tr.	13		7
Sol-Aire CX4		Revealer	MAL	M. Blu.				UH - N. Yl.	Red & Blu. playing card suit shps.			5

Name	#	Category	Casting	Ctry.	Color	Win.	Base	Interior	Wheels	Paint	Logo	Other	S
Sol-Aire CX4		Revealer		MAL	Ivory				UH - N. Gr.	Red & Blu. playing card suit shps.			5
Sol-Aire CX4		Revealer		MAL	N. Yl.				UH - N. Pnk.	Red & Blu. playing card suit shps.			5
Sol-Aire CX4	5902	Ultra Hot	OWng	MAL	Red	Blk.	Logo & No rsd. bar		UH	Blu., Yl. & Or. tr.	Ultrahots		5
Sol-Aire CX4	5902	Ultra Hot	OWng	MAL	Red	Blk.			UH	Blu., Yl. & Or. tr.	Ultrahots		5
Sol-Aire CX4	2200	Video Car		MAL	Red	Yl.			UH	Blk., Yl. & Or. tr.	13		5
Sol-Aire CX4	451			MAL	N. Blu.	CL	Plst.	Blk.	HO - Silver	Pnk., Prp. & Or. geo. tr.	2		5
Sol-Aire CX4	451			MAL	N. Blu.	CL	Plst.	Blk.	UH	Pnk., Prp. & Or. geo. tr.	2		5
Sol-Aire CX4	451	Set		MAL	N. Blu.	CL		Silver	UH	Pnk., Prp. & Or. geo. tr.	2		10
Sol-Aire CX4	1102	Set	CWng	HK	Red				UH	Wht., Blu. & Yl. stripes		Turbotrax Race	10
Sol-Aire CX4	1102	Set	CWng	MAL	Red				UH	Wht., Blu. & Yl. stripes		Turbotrax Race	10
Sol-Aire CX4	1494		CWng	MAL	Blk.	DT	HW logo		UH	Or., Yl. & Prp. tr.	33		5
Sol-Aire CX4	1494		CWng	MAL	Blk.	YT	HW		UH	Or., Yl. & Prp. tr.	33		5
Sol-Aire CX4	1494		OWng	MAL	Blk.	YT	HW logo		UH	Or., Yl. & Blu. tr.	33		5
Sol-Aire CX4	1494		CWng	MAL	Blk.	YT	HW logo		UH	Or., Yl. & Prp. tr.	33		5
Sol-Aire CX4	1494		OWng	MAL	Blk.	YT	HW		UH	Or., Yl. & Blu. tr.	33		5
Sol-Aire CX4	1494		CWng	MAL	Blk.	YT	HW logo		UH - Gold	Or., Yl. & Blu. tr.	33		5
Sol-Aire CX4	1494		CWng	MAL	Blk.	DT	HW		UH	Or., Yl. & Prp. tr.	33		5
Sol-Aire CX4	1494		OWng	MAL	Blk.	YT	Blk. Plst.		HO - Silver	Or., Yl. & Blu. tr.	33		5
Sol-Aire CX4	5902	Ultra Hot	CWng	MAL	Metal	Blk.			UH	Red, Or. & Yl. tr.	Ultrahots		5
Sol-Aire CX4	5902	Ultra Hot	CWng	HK	Metal	Blk.			UH	Red, Or. & Yl. tr.	Ultrahots		5
Sol-Aire CX4	9342	Ultra Hot	CWng	MAL	Silver				UH	Red, Or. & Yl. tr.	Ultrahots		5
Sol-Aire CX4	9342	Ultra Hot	CWng	MAL	Red	Blk.	No rsd. bar		UH	Or., Yl. & Prp. tr.	Ultrahots		7
Sol-Aire CX4	9342	Ultra Hot	CWng	HK	Silver				UH	Red, Or. & Yl. tr.	Ultrahots		7
Sol-Aire CX4	9342	Ultra Hot	CWng	MAL	Red	Blk.			UH	Or., Yl. & Prp. tr.	Ultrahots		7
Sol-Aire CX4	9342	Ultra Hot	CWng	MAL	Metal	Blk.	MAL smr.		UH	Red, Or. & Yl. tr.	Ultrahots		7
Sol-Aire CX4	9342	Ultra Hot	CWng	MAL	M. Red				UH	Blk., Wht. & Yl. tr.	Ultrahots	Stamper 3 Pack	12
Sol-Aire CX4	13578	Gold Medal Speed		MAL	Blu./Wht.	CL	Wht.	Wht.	UH - Gold	Red & Yl. tr.	HW & 1		3
Space Vehicle	2855			MEX	Silver				Reg				30
Space Vehicle	2855			MAL	Silver				Reg	Red & Wht. lightning tr.			20
Space Vehicle	2855			MEX	Silver				Reg	Red & Wht. lightning tr.			30
Space Vehicle	2855			HK	Silver				Reg	Red & Wht. lightning tr.			20
Space Van	2855	Scene Machine		HK	Grey/Wht.				Reg				40
Spacer Racer	2503			HK	Red				Reg				15
Spacer Racer	2503			MEX	Red				Reg				25
Spacer Racer	2503			MAL	M. Red				Reg				7
Spacer Racer	2503			MEX	Red				Reg			Larger wheels	25
Spacer Racer	2503			HK	M. Red				Reg				7
Spacer Racer	2503			MAL	Red				Reg				7
Speed Seeker		Co. Rcr.		MAL	Mauve to Pale Blu.				Reg				5
Speed Seeker	1512	Ultra Hot		HK	Wht.			Long strg. col.	UH				7
Speed Seeker	1512	Ultra Hot		HK	Wht.			Med. strg. col.	UH				7
Speed Seeker	1512	Ultra Hot		MAL	Wht.			Long strg. col.	UH				7
Speed Seeker	1512	Ultra Hot		MAL	Wht.			Med. strg. col.	UH				7
Speed Seeker	1512	Ultra Hot		MAL	Wht.			Short strg. col.	UH				7
Speed Seeker	1512	Ultra Hot		HK	Wht.			Short strg. col.	UH				7
Speed Seeker	7299	Ultra Hot		HK	M. Prp.				UH				7
Speed Seeker	7299	Ultra Hot		MAL	M. Prp.				UH				7

Name	#	Category	Casting	Ctry.	Color	Win.	Base	Interior	Wheels	Paint	Logo	Other	S
Speed Seeker	9348	Ultra Hot		MAL	Gold				UH				12
Speed Seeker	9348	Ultra Hot		HK	Gold				UH				12
Speed Shark	5640			MAL	Prp.				Reg				5
Speed Shark	5640			MAL	Maroon				Reg				25
Speed Shark		25th Ann.		MAL	Silver				Reg				5
Speed Shark		Video Car		MAL	Wht.				Reg				8
Spiderman	2852	Scene Machine		MAL	Wht.				Reg				35
Spiderman	2852	Scene Machine		HK	Wht.				Reg				35
Spiderman	2877			MEX	Blk.				Reg				20
Spiderman	2877	Heroes		HK	Blk.		No rsd. bar		Reg				10
Spiderman	2877	Heroes		HK	Blk.		Rsd. bar		Reg				10
Spiderman	2877	Heroes		MAL	Blk.		No rsd. bar		Reg				10
Spiderman	2877	Heroes		MAL	Blk.		Rsd. bar		Reg				10
Corvette Split Window	3092			MAL	N. Blu.		Chr. Plst.		Reg	Yl., Prp. & Bro. tr.			4
Corvette Split Window	3092			MAL	N. Blu.		Grey Plst.		WW	Yl., Prp. & Bro. tr.			3
Corvette Split Window	3092			MAL	N. Blue		Chr. Plst		WW	Yl., Prp. & Bro. tr.			4
Split Window '63	1486			MAL	Pale Gr.		Grey Plst.		Reg	Red, Yl. & Blu. lightning tr.			5
Split Window '63	4354			MAL	Blk.	YT	Grey Plst.		Reg	Yl. & Prp. flames			10
Split Window '63	4354			MAL	Pale Gr.		Grey Plst.		Reg	Red, Yl. & Mgta. lightning tr.			5
Split Window '63	4354			MAL	Blk.	DT	Grey Plst.		Reg	Yl. & Prp. flames			10
Split Window '63		25th Ann.		MAL	Crimson				WW	Blu., Yl. & Pnk. tr.			5
Split Window '63	9252	Billionth Car		MAL	Gold				Reg				10
Split Window '63	1305	Cal Cus.		MAL	N. Pnk.		Rsd. MAL		Reg	Blu. & neon blaze tr.		Freeway Frenzy Set	6
Split Window '63	1305	Cal Cus.		MAL	Prp. Chr.		Rsd. MAL		RR - N. Yl.	Blu. & neon blaze tr.			6
Split Window '63	1305	Cal Cus.		MAL	Prp. Chr.		Flat MAL		RR - N. Yl.	Blu. & neon blaze tr.			6
Split Window '63	1305	Cal Cus.		MAL	N. Pnk.		Flat MAL		Reg	Blu. & neon blaze tr.		Freeway Frenzy Set	6
Split Window '63	1305	Co. Rcr.		MAL	Gr. to Yl.				Reg	Yl. flames when Gr.	Corvette		5
Split Window '63		Getty		MAL	Blk.		Chr. Plst.		Reg	Red, Yl. & Wht. tr.	Getty		5
Split Window '63		Kool Aid		MAL	Ivory		Grey Plst.		Reg	Neon Pnk., neon Or. & neon Blu. tr.	Kool-Aid		8
Split Window '63		World Cup		MAL	M. Dk. Blu.				Reg	Wht., Bro., Blk., Blu. & Red soccer tr.	World Cup USA 94		5
Split Window '63	1136	Hiraker		HK	Yl.				Reg	Or., Prp. & Blu. tr.			10
Split Window '63	1136	Hiraker		HK	Grey				Reg	Red, Wht. & Blu. tr.	Chevrolet Corvette		8
Split Window '63	1136	Hiraker		MAL	Yl.				Reg	Or., Prp. & Blu. tr.			10
Split Window '63	1486			MAL	Maroon				Reg	Gr., Wht. & Yl. flames			5
Split Window '63	1486			MAL	Wht.				Reg	Red flames & Blu. & Yl. tr.	Corvette		10
Split Window '63	1486			HK	Magenta				Reg	Gr., Wht. & Yl. flames			10
Split Window '63	3983			HK	Blk.		Rsd. HK		Reg	Blu. flames & Or. & Yl. tr.			7
Split Window '63	3983			HK	Blk.				Reg	Blu. flames & Or. & Yl. tr.			7
Split Window '63	3984			HK	Silver		Flat HK		Reg	Red & Pnk. tr.			7
Split Window '63	3984			HK	Silver		Rsd. HK		Reg	Red & Pnk. tr.			7
Split Window '63	3984			MAL	Silver				Reg	Red & Pnk. tr.			7
Split Window '63	4354	Hiraker		MAL	Blk.		Rsd. MAL & bar over old cstg.		RR - Grey				15
Split Window '63	4354	Hiraker		MAL	Gold MF.		Flat MAL & bar over old cstg.		RR - Wht.	Or., Prp. & Blu. tr.			15
Split Window '63	4354	Hiraker		MAL	Blk.				RR - Grey	Yl., Blu. & Red tr.			15

Name	#	Category	Casting	Ctry.	Color	Win.	Base	Interior	Wheels	Paint	Logo	Other	$
Split Window '63		4354 Hiraker		MAL	Gold MF.				Reg	Or., Prp. & Blu. tr.			7
Split Window '63		4354 Hiraker		HK	Blk.				Reg	Yl., Blu. & Red tr.			10
Split Window '63		4354 Hiraker		MAL	Gold MF.		Rsd. MAL & bar over old cstg.		Reg	Or., Prp. & Blu. tr.			7
Split Window '63		4354 Hiraker		MAL	Gold MF.		Flat MAL & bar over old cstg.		Reg	Or., Prp. & Blu. tr.			7
Split Window '63		4354 Hiraker		HK	Gold MF.				Reg	Or., Prp. & Blu. tr.			7
Split Window '63		4354 Hiraker		HK	Blk.				RR - Wht.	Yl., Blu. & Red tr.			15
Split Window '63		4354 Hiraker		MAL	Blk.		Rsd. MAL & bar over old cstg.		RR - Wht.				15
Split Window '63		4354 Hiraker		MAL	Blk.		Rsd. MAL & bar over old cstg.		Reg				7
Split Window '63		4354 Hiraker		MAL	Gold MF.				RR - Wht.	Or., Prp. & Blu. tr.			20
Split Window '63		4354 Hiraker		MAL	Gold MF.		Rsd. MAL & bar over old cstg.		RR - Wht.	Or., Prp. & Blu. tr.			20
Split Window '63		4354 Hiraker		HK	Gold MF.				RR - Grey	Or., Prp. & Blu. tr.			20
Split Window '63		4354 Hiraker		MAL	Blk.				Reg	Yl., Blu. & Red tr.			7
Split Window '63		4354 Hiraker		MAL	Blk.				RR - Wht.	Yl., Blu. & Red tr.			15
Split Window '63		4354 Hiraker		HK	Blk.				RR - Grey	Yl., Blu. & Red tr.			15
Splittin' Image		5708 25th Ann.		CHN	M. Blu.				RL				4
Splittin' Image		5708 25th Ann.		CHN	M. Magenta				RL				4
Splittin' Image		5708 25th Ann.		CHN	M. Dk. Red				RL				4
Splittin' Image		5708 25th Ann.		CHN	M. Bro.				RL				4
Splittin' Image		5708 25th Ann.		CHN	M. Red				RL				4
Splittin' Image		5708 25th Ann.		CHN	Gold				RL				4
Splittin' Image		5708 25th Ann.		CHN	M. Lime				RL				4
Splittin' Image		5708 25th Ann.		CHN	M. Violet				RL				4
Splittin' Image		5708 25th Ann.		CHN	M. Pnk.				RL				4
Splittin' Image		5708 25th Ann.		CHN	M. Or.				RL				4
Splittin' Image		5708 25th Ann.		CHN	M. Br. Red				RL				4
Splittin' Image		5708 25th Ann.		CHN	M. Turquoise				RL				4
Splittin' Image		5708 25th Ann.		CHN	M. Olive Gr.				RL				4
Splittin' Image		5708 25th Ann.		CHN	M. Gr.				RL				4
Splittin' Image		5708 Gold Ser.		CHN	M. Br. Gr.				RL - Gold			GEng - FAOSc	25
Splittin' Image		5708 Vintage		CHN	Wht.				RL				4
Splittin' Image		5708 Vintage		CHN	M. Dk. Bro.				RL				4
Splittin' Image		5708 Vintage		CHN	M. Electric Gr.				RL				4
Splittin' Image		5708 Vintage		CHN	Gunmetal				RL				4
Splittin' Image		5708 Vintage		CHN	M. Gold				RL				4
Splittin' Image		5708 Vintage		CHN	M. Pale Pnk.				RL				4
Splittin' Image		5708 Vintage		CHN	M. Dk. Gr.				RL				4
Splittin' Image		5708 Vintage		CHN	M. Prp.				RL				4
Splittin' Image		5708 Vintage		CHN	M. Br. Gr.				RL				4
Splittin' Image		5708 Vintage		CHN	M. Royal Blu.				RL				4
Splittin' Image		5708 Vintage		CHN	Br. Red				RL				4
Splittin' Image		5708 Vintage		CHN	M. Br. Blu.				RL				4
Splittin' Image		5708 Vintage		CHN	Maroon				RL				4

Name	#	Category	Casting	Ctry.	Color	Win.	Base	Interior	Wheels	Paint	Logo	Other	$
Splittin' Image II	11850			MAL	M. Violet				UH - Pink		Wht.		3
Splittin' Image II	11850			MAL	M. Violet				UH		Wht.		3
Splittin' Image II	11850			MAL	M. Violet				UH - Pink		Red & Wht.		3
Spoiler Sport	9641		1 lg. r.wndw	MEX	Pnk.				Reg				100
Spoiler Sport	9641		1 lg. r.wndw	FRA	Gr.				Reg				20
Spoiler Sport		Pre-Pro	2 sm. r.wndws	HK	Pnk.								
Spoiler Sport		Pre-Pro	2 sm. r.wndws	HK	M. Gr.								
Spoiler Sport	9641		2 sm. r.wndws	HK	Gold				Reg				20
Spoiler Sport	9641		1 lg. r.wndw	HK	Wht.				Reg				7
Spoiler Sport	9641		1 lg. r.wndw	HK	Gr.				Reg				12
Spoiler Sport	9641		2 sm. r.wndws	HK	Gr.				Reg				12
Spoiler Sport	9641		1 lg. r.wndw	MAL	Wht.				Reg				7
Spoiler Sport	9641		2 sm. r.wndws	HK	Gr.				RL				25
Spoiler Sport	9641		1 lg. r.wndw	HK	Gold				Reg				20
Staff Car	9521		Cast roof sign	HK	Khk.				Reg				500
Staff Car	9521		Cast roof sign	HK	Khk.				RL				500
Stagefright	2020			MAL	Bro.				Reg				8
Stagefright	2020			HK	Bro.				Reg				8
Stagefright	2020			MEX	Bro.				Reg				40
Steadly Tudor		LE		MAL	Ivory				Dsh - Grey RL				15
Steam Roller	8260			HK	Yl.		Blk. Plst.		Reg	Red & Prp. tr.			15
Steam Roller	8260			HK	Wht.		Plst.		Reg	Red & Blu. tr. w/ 3 stars			20
Steam Roller	8260			HK	Wht.				RL	Red & Blu. tr. w/ 3 stars			40
Steam Roller	8260			HK	Wht.		Blk. Plst.		RL	Red & Blu. tr. w/ 7 stars			150
Steam Roller	9208 Super Chr.			HK	Chr.		Blk. Plst.		RL	Blu. & Yl. tr. w/ 3 stars			30
Steam Roller	9208 Super Chr.			HK	Chr.		Blk. Plst.		RL	Red & Prp. tr.			30
Steam Roller	9208 Super Chr.			HK	Chr.		Blk. Plst.		Reg	Blu. & Yl. tr. w/ 7 stars			120
Steam Roller	9208 Super Chr.			HK	Chr.		Blk. Plst.		Reg	Blu. & Yl. tr. w/ 3 stars			30
Sting Rod	5025			MAL	Des. Cmflg.				4x4 LHb - Blk.				8
Sting Rod	5025			MAL	Khk. Cmflg.				4x4 SHb - Blk.				7
Sting Rod	5025			MAL	Des. Cmflg.				4x4 SHb - Blk.				8
Stock Rocket	2522		No LUFV	HK	Red				Reg				25
Stock Rocket	2522		LUFV	MAL	Red				Reg				25
Stock Rocket	2522		No LUFV	MAL	Red				HO - Gold				25
Stock Rocket	2522		No LUFV	HK	Red				HO - Gold				25
Street Beast	5637			MAL	Wht./Aq.				WW				3
Street Beast	3975		LUFV	HK	Red				Reg	Yl., Blu. & Blk. tr.	308 on side & logo on hood		6
Street Beast	3975		LUFV	MAL	Red				Reg	Yl., Blu. & Blk. tr.	308 on side & logo on hood		6
Street Beast	3975		No LUFV	MAL	Red				Reg	Yl., Blu. & Blk. tr.	308 on side & logo on hood		6
Street Beast	3975		No LUFV	HK	Red		Rsd. HK		Reg - Gold	Yl., Blu. & Blk. tr.	308		6
Street Beast	3975		LUFV	HK	Red		Rsd. HK		Reg - Gold	Yl., Blu. & Blk. tr.	308		6
Street Beast	3975		LUFV	MAL	Red				Reg - Gold	Yl., Blu. & Blk. tr.	308		6
Street Beast	3975		No LUFV	HK	Red				Reg - Gold	Yl., Blu. & Blk. tr.	308		6
Street Beast	3975		No LUFV	MAL	Red				Reg - Gold	Yl., Blu. & Blk. tr.	308		6
Street Beast	3975		No LUFV	HK	Red		Rsd. HK		Reg	Yl., Blu. & Blk. tr.	308 on side & logo on hood		6
Street Beast	3975		No LUFV	HK	Red				Reg	Yl., Blu. & Blk. tr.	308 on side & logo on hood		6

Name	#	Category	Casting	Ctry.	Color	Win.	Base	Interior	Wheels	Paint	Logo	Other	$
Street Beast	3975		LUFV	HK	Red				Reg - Gold	Yl., Blu. & Blk. tr.	308		6
Street Beast	3975		LUFV	HK	Red		Rsd. HK		Reg	Yl., Blu. & Blk. tr.	308	308 on side & logo on hood	6
Street Beast	3976		No LUFV	HK	Silver		Rsd. HK		Reg	Red, Yl. & Blk. tr.	308		6
Street Beast	3976		LUFV	HK	Silver		Rsd. HK		Reg	Red, Yl. & Blk. tr.	308		6
Street Beast	3976		No LUFV	HK	Silver				Reg	Red, Yl. & Blk. tr.	308		6
Street Beast	3976		LUFV	MAL	Silver				Reg	Red, Yl. & Blk. tr.	308		6
Street Beast	3976		LUFV	HK	Silver				Reg	Red, Yl. & Blk. tr.	308		6
Street Beast	3976		No LUFV	MAL	Silver				Reg	Red, Yl. & Blk. tr.	308		6
Street Beast	9538	Ultra Hot	No LUFV	HK	M. Blu.				UH				6
Street Beast	9538	Ultra Hot	LUFV	MAL	M. Blu.				HO - Gold				6
Street Beast	9538	Ultra Hot	LUFV	HK	M. Blu.				HO - Gold				6
Street Beast	9538	Ultra Hot	LUFV	HK	M. Blu.				UH				6
Street Beast	9538	Ultra Hot	No LUFV	MAL	M. Blu.				HO - Gold				6
Street Beast	9538	Ultra Hot	No LUFV	MAL	M. Blu.				UH				6
Street Beast	9538	Ultra Hot	LUFV	MAL	M. Blu.				Reg - Gold				6
Street Beast	9538	Ultra Hot	LUFV	MAL	M. Blu.				UH				6
Street Beast	9538	Ultra Hot	No LUFV	HK	M. Blu.				HO - Gold				6
Street Beast	9538	Ultra Hot	LUFV	HK	M. Blu.				Reg - Gold				6
Street Eater	7669		Headlight	HK	Yl.				4x4 SHb				75
Street Roader	1470			MAL	M. Gr.				4x4 LHb				3
Street Roader	1287	Cal Cus.		MAL	N. Or./N. Blz.			Pnk.	4x4 LHb				7
Street Roader	1287	Cal Cus.		MAL	N. Or./N. Blz.			Red	4x4 LHb				7
Street Roader	1287	Cal Cus.		MAL	N. Or./N. Blz.			Red	4x4 SHb				7
Street Roader	1287	Cal Cus.		MAL	Wht./N. Blu.			Red	4x4 LHb				7
Street Roader	1287	Cal Cus.		MAL	N. Or.				4x4 LHb				7
Street Roader	1287	Cal Cus.		MAL	Wht./N. Blu.			Pnk.	4x4 LHb				7
Street Roader	1287	Cal Cus.		MAL	N. Or./N. Blz				4x4 SHb - Or.				7
Street Roader	1287	Cal Cus.		MAL	Wht./N. Blu.			Or.	4x4 SHb				7
Street Roader	1287	Cal Cus.		MAL	Wht./N. Blu.			Or.	4x4 SHb - Or.				7
Street Roader	1287	Cal Cus.		MAL	Wht./N. Blu.			Pnk.	4x4 SHb - Or.				7
Street Roader	1287	Cal Cus.		MAL	Wht./N. Blu.			Red	4x4 SHb				7
Street Roader		Co. Rcr.		MAL	Gr. to Yl.				4x4 LHb				5
Street Roader		Co. Rcr.		MAL	Prp. to Wht.				4x4 LHb				5
Street Roader		Video Car		MAL	N. Yl.			Pnk.	4x4 SHb	Prp., Pnk. & Wht. tr.			5
Street Roader	1470			MAL	Wht.				4x4 SHb	Red, Pnk. & Blu. tr.			8
Street Roader	1470			MAL	Wht.				4x4 SHb	Red, Prp. & Blu. tr.			5
Street Roader	1470			MAL	Wht.				4x4 LHb	Red, Blk. & Blu. tr.			8
Street Roader	1470			MAL	Wht.				4x4 LHb	Red, Pnk. & Blu. tr.			8
Street Roader	1470			MAL	Wht.				4x4 SHb - Yl.	Red, Prp. & Blu. tr.			5
Street Roader	1470			MAL	Wht.				4x4 LHb	Red, Prp. & Blu. tr.			5
Street Roader	1470			MAL	Wht.				4x4 SHb	Red, Blk. & Blu. tr.			8
Street Roader	1470			MAL	Wht.				4x4 LHb	Red, Blk. & Blu. tr.			8
Street Roader	4373			MAL	Wht.		MAL cast differently		Reg	Red & Yl. flames			15
Street Rodder	9242			HK	Blk.				RL	Red & Yl. flames			40
Street Rodder	9242			MAL	Wht.				Reg	Red & Yl. flames			15
Street Rodder	9242			HK	Wht.				Reg	Red & Yl. flames			15
Street Rodder	9242			MEX	Wht.				Reg	Red & Yl. flames			15
Street Rodder	9242			HK	Wht.				RR - Grey	Red & Yl. flames			15

Name	#	Category	Casting	Ctry.	Color	Win.	Base	Interior	Wheels	Paint	Logo	Other	S
Street Rodder	9242			MAL	Wht.				RR - Grey	Red & Yl. flames			15
Street Scorcher	9536		1 lg. r.wndw	MEX	Chestnut				UH	Or., Yl. & Wht. tr.			20
Street Scorcher	9536 Ultra Hot		1 lg. r.wndw	HK	M. Red				UH	Or., Yl. & Wht. tr.			12
Street Scorcher	9536 Ultra Hot		1 lg. r.wndw	MAL	M. Red				UH	Or., Yl. & Wht. tr.			12
Street Shocker		McD's	Plst.	CHN	Gr.				Uniq.				5
Street Snorter	6971			HK	Pale Gr.			Wht.	RL			No wing	175
Street Snorter	6971			HK	Red			Grey	RL			No wing	175
Street Snorter	6971			HK	Pnk.			Grey	RL			No wing	200
Street Snorter	6971			HK	Pnk.			Wht.	RL			No wing	200
Street Snorter	6971			HK	Flr. Lime			Blk.	RL			No wing	175
Street Snorter	6971			HK	Gr.			Grey	RL			No wing	175
Street Snorter	6971			HK	Dk. Yl.			Blk.	RL			No wing	175
Street Snorter	6971			HK	Dk. Blu.			Wht.	RL			No wing	175
Street Snorter	6971			HK	Dk. Yl.			Wht.	RL			No wing	175
Street Snorter	6971			HK	Plum			Blk.	RL			No wing	175
Street Snorter	6971			HK	Or.			Wht.	RL			No wing	175
Street Snorter	6971			HK	Red			Blk.	RL			No wing	175
Street Snorter	6971			HK	Red			Wht.	RL			No wing	175
Street Snorter	6971			HK	Pale Yl.			Blk.	RL			No wing	175
Street Snorter	6971			HK	Plum			Wht.	RL			No wing	175
Street Snorter	6971			HK	Pale Blu.			Blk.	RL			No wing	175
Street Snorter	6971			HK	Pale Yl.			Wht.	RL			No wing	175
Street Snorter	6971			HK	Flr. Lime			Grey	RL			No wing	175
Street Snorter	6971			HK	Dk. Blu.			Grey	RL			No wing	175
Street Snorter	6971			HK	Dk. Blu.			Blk.	RL			No wing	175
Street Snorter	6971			HK	Pale Blu.			Wht.	RL			No wing	175
Street Snorter	6971			HK	Pale Gr.			Grey	RL			No wing	175
Street Snorter	6971			HK	Pale Yl.			Grey	RL			No wing	175
Street Snorter	6971			HK	Or.			Blk.	RL			No wing	175
Street Snorter	6971			HK	Gr.			Wht.	RL			No wing	175
Street Snorter	6971			HK	Plum			Grey	RL			No wing	175
Street Snorter	6971			HK	Pnk.			Blk.	RL			No wing	200
Street Snorter	6971			HK	Pale Blu.			Grey	RL			No wing	175
Street Snorter	6971			HK	Flr. Lime			Wht.	RL			No wing	175
Street Snorter	6971			HK	Dk. Yl.			Grey	RL			No wing	175
Street Snorter	6971			HK	Pale Gr.			Blk.	RL			No wing	175
Street Snorter	6971			HK	Gr.			Blk.	RL			No wing	175
Street Snorter	6971			HK	Or.			Grey	RL			No wing	175
Stutz Blk.hawk	1126			FRA	Grey				Reg				20
Stutz Blk.hawk	2106 Cal Cus			MAL	N. Blz.				Rtr - N. Yl.				20
Stutz Blk.hawk	1126			MAL	Blk.				Reg	Red & Blu. stripes			8
Stutz Blk.hawk	1126			HK	Grey				Reg				8
Stutz Blk.hawk	1126			MAL	Dk. Bro. MF.				Reg	Red & Yl. stripes			15
Stutz Blk.hawk	1126			MAL	Grey				Reg	Blu., Wht. & Yl. tr.	Stutz		8
Stutz Blk.hawk	1126			HK	Dk. Bro. MF.				Reg	Red, Yl. & grey stripes			15
Stutz Blk.hawk	1126			MAL	Grey				Reg				8
Stutz Blk.hawk	1126			MAL	Dk. Bro. MF.				Reg	Red, Yl. & grey stripes			15
Stutz Blk.hawk	1126			HK	Dk. Bro. MF.				Reg	Red & Yl. stripes			15
Stutz Blk.hawk	1126			HK	Blk.				Reg	Red, Blu & grey stripes			8
Stutz Blk.hawk	1126			MEX	Dk. Bro. MF.				Reg	Red, Yl. & grey stripes			20
Stutz Blk.hawk	1126			HK	Grey				Reg	Blu. Wht. & Yl. tr.	Stutz		8

Name	#	Category	Casting	Ctry.	Color	Win.	Base	Interior	Wheels	Paint	Logo	Other	$
Sunagon	3251			IND	Prp.				Reg	Grey & Wht. tr.	VW		10
Sunagon	3251			MAL	Pale Or.				Reg				7
Sunagon	3251			MAL	Dk. Or./Tan				Reg				7
Sunagon	3251			HK	Pale Or.				Reg				7
Sunagon	3251			HK	Dk. Or./Tan				Reg				7
Sunagon	4340			MEX	Dk. Blu.	BluT			Reg				25
Sunagon	4340			MEX	Dk. Blu.	CL			Reg				25
Sunagon	4340			MEX	Blu. MF.				Reg				25
Sunagon	4340			MAL	Dk. Blu.	CL			Reg				7
Sunagon	4340			MAL	Blu. MF.				Reg				7
Super Cannon	9373			MAL	Jungle Cmflg.				Reg - Blk.				12
Super Cannon	9373			MAL	Khk. Cmflg.				Reg - Wht.				6
Super Cannon	9373			MAL	Khk. Cmflg.			1981	Reg				6
Super Cannon	9373			MAL	Des. Cmflg.				Reg				8
Super Cannon	9373			MAL	Khk. Cmflg.			1982	Reg				6
Super Scraper	1129			HK	Yl.			No TB	Reg	Or., Gr. & Blk. tr.	Speedy Removal		8
Super Scraper	1129			MAL	Yl.			No TB	Reg	Or., Gr. & Blk. tr.	Speedy Removal		8
Super Scraper	4350			HK	Blk.			No TB	RR - Grey	Yl., Or. & Red tr.	Henry's Hauling		15
Super Scraper	4350			MAL	Blk.		MAL cast flat	No TB	RR - Wht.	Yl., Or. & Red tr.	Henry's Hauling		15
Super Scraper	4350			MAL	Blk.		MAL cast flat	No TB	RR - Grey	Yl., Or. & Red tr.	Henry's Hauling		15
Super Scraper	4350			MAL	Blk.			No TB	Reg	Yl., Or. & Red tr.	Henry's Hauling		7
Super Scraper	4350			MAL	Blk.			No TB	Reg	Yl., Or. & Red tr.	Henry's Hauling		7
Super Scraper	4350			HK	Blk.			No TB	RR - Grey	Yl., Or. & Red tr.	Henry's Hauling		7
Super Scraper	4350			MAL	Blk.		MAL cast flat	No TB	RR - Grey	Yl., Or. & Red tr.	Henry's Hauling		7
Super Scraper	4350			MAL	Blk.			No TB	RR - Wht.	Yl., Or. & Red tr.	Henry's Hauling		7
Super Scraper	4350			HK	Blk.			TB	Reg	Yl., Or. & Red tr.	Henry's Hauling		7
Super Scraper	4350			MAL	Blk.		MAL cast flat	TB	RR - Grey	Yl., Or. & Red tr.	Henry's Hauling		7
Super Scraper	4350			HK	Blk.			No TB	RR - Wht.	Yl., Or. & Red tr.	Henry's Hauling		7
Super Scraper	4350			MAL	Blk.			TB	RR - Grey	Yl., Or. & Red tr.	Henry's Hauling		7
Super Scraper	4350			MAL	Blk.			TB	RR - Grey	Yl., Or. & Red tr.	Henry's Hauling		7
Super Scraper	4350			HK	Blk.			TB	RR - Grey	Yl., Or. & Red tr.	Henry's Hauling		7
Super Van	9205			MAL	Blk.				Reg	Red tr.			6
Super Van	2125	Kelloggs		MAL	Blu.				Reg	Yl. & Wht. flames	Super Van		15
Super Van	7649			HK	Blu.	BluT			RL	Red & Yl. flames			500
Super Van	7649			HK	Blk.	GT	Metal		RL	Red & Yl. flames			30
Super Van	7649			HK	Blk.	GT			RL	Red & Yl. flames			30
Super Van	7649			HK	Blk.	BluT			RL	Red & Yl. flames			30
Super Van	7649			MAL	Wht.				Reg	Red Flames			8
Super Van	7649			HK	Magenta	GT			RL	Or., Blu. & Yl. motorcycle			75
Super Van	7649			HK	Magenta	BluT			RL	Or., Blu. & Yl. motorcycle			75
Super Van	7649			HK	Blk.	GT			Reg	Red & Yl. flames			10
Super Van	7649			HK	Wht.				Reg	Red Flames			8
Super Van	7649 Toy Fair			HK	Gold				RL	Red, Yl. & Blk. tr.	Toy Fair 1975 Mattel		600
Super Van	7649 Toy Fair			HK	Chr.				RL	Red, Yl. & Blk. tr.	Toy Fair 1975 Mattel		600
Super Van	7649 Toy Fair			HK	Wht.				RL	Red, Yl. & Blk. tr.	Toy Fair 1975 Mattel		600
Super Van	9205			MAL	Silver				Reg	Red, Yl. & Blk. tr.	California Cruisin'		15

Name	#	Category	Casting	Ctry.	Color	Win.	Base	Interior	Wheels	Paint	Logo	Other	S
Super Van	9205	Super Chr.		HK	Chr.				Reg	Red, Yl. & Blk. tr. & silver sparkles	California Cruisin'		15
Super Van	9205	Super Chr.		HK	Chr.		Chr. Plst.		RL	Red & Yl. flames			30
Super Van	9205	Super Chr.		HK	Chr.		Blk. Plst.		RL	Red & Yl. flames			30
Super Van	9205	Super Chr.		HK	Chr.				Reg	Red, Yl. & Blk. tr.	California Cruisin'		15
Super Van	9205	Super Chr.		HK	Chr.				Reg	Red & Yl. flames			25
Super Van	9205	Super Chr.		HK	Chr.				RL	Red & Yl. flames			30
Superfine Turbine	6004			HK	Dk. Blu.				RL				225
Superfine Turbine	6004			HK	Flr. Lime				RL				225
Superfine Turbine	6004			HK	Pale Blu.				RL				225
Superfine Turbine	6004			HK	Dk. Yl.				RL				225
Superfine Turbine	6004			HK	Gr.				RL				225
Superfine Turbine	6004			HK	Pale Gr.				RL				225
Superfine Turbine	6004			HK	Plum				RL				225
Superfine Turbine	6004			HK	Pale Yl.				RL				225
Superfine Turbine	6004			HK	Red				RL				225
Superfine Turbine	6004			HK	Pnk.				RL				250
Superfine Turbine	6004			HK	Or.				RL				225
Surf Patrol		Aqua Fresh		MAL	M. Blu.				4x4 SHb	Yl. & Wht. tr.			5
Surf Patrol	5145			MAL	Yl.				4x4 SHb	Red tr.			5
Suzuki Quadracer	479			MAL	Pnk.		20.s		4x4 SHb				5
Suzuki Quadracer	9582			MAL	Wht.		20.s		4x4 SHb - Yl.				5
Suzuki Quadracer		Pre-Pro		MAL	Bro.				Reg				4
Suzuki Quadracer	429			MAL	Pnk.		20.s		4x4 SHb				5
Suzuki Quadracer	9582			MAL	Wht.		20.s		4x4 SHb				10
Suzuki Quadracer		Kool Aid		MAL	Aq.		20.s		4x4 SHb				5
Suzuki Quadracer	3209			MAL	Yl.				4x4 SHb				5
Suzuki Quadracer	3209			MAL	Yl.		20.s		4x4 LHb - Yl.				5
Suzuki Quadracer	3209			MAL	Yl.		20.s		4x4 SHb				5
Suzuki Quadracer	3209			MAL	Yl.		20.s		4x4 SHb - Yl.				5
Sweet 16	6007			HK	Pale Gr.				RL				150
Sweet 16	6007			HK	Pale Yl.				RL				150
Sweet 16	6007			HK	Gr.				RL				150
Sweet 16	6007			HK	Flr. Lime				RL				150
Sweet 16	6007			HK	Pnk.				RL				160
Sweet 16	6007			HK	Dk. Blu.				RL				150
Sweet 16	6007			HK	Dk. Yl.				RL				150
Sweet 16	6007			HK	Pale Blu.				RL				150
Sweet 16	6007			HK	Or.				RL				150
Sweet 16	6007			HK	Red				RL				150
Sweet 16	6007			HK	Plum				RL				150
Swingfire	4312			MAL	M. Blu./Wht.				WW				4
Swingfire		Gold Ser.		MAL	M. Blu./Wht.				P-C - Gold			FAOSc	25
Swingfire	4312			MAL	M. Blu./Wht.				WW				4
Tac-Com	5273	Mega Force		MAL	Tan				Reg				20
Tail Gunner	4059			MAL	Arctic Cmflg.				4x4 SHb - Blk.				6
Tail Gunner	4059			MAL	Des. Cmflg.				4x4 SHb - Blk.				6
Tail Gunner	4059			MAL	Des. Cmflg.				4x4 LHb - Blk.				6
Tail Gunner	4059			MAL	Khk. Cmflg.				4x4 SHb - Blk.				6
Talbot Lago	4741			MAL	Glt. Maroon				WW				5
Talbot Lago	4741			MAL	Blk.				WW				5

Name	#	Category	Casting	Ctry.	Color	Win.	Base	Interior	Wheels	Paint	Logo	Other	$
Talbot Lago		Co. Rcr.		MAL	Prp. to Or.				WW				5
Talbot Lago		Gold Ser.		MAL	Ivory				SS - Gold			FAOSc	25
Talbot Lago	4741			MAL	Maroon				WW				8
Talbot Lago	4741			MAL	Wht.				WW				4
Tall Ryder		20th Ann.		MAL	Silver				4x4 SHb				8
Tall Ryder		20th Ann.		HK	Silver				4x4 SHb				8
Tall Ryder		Co. Rcr.		MAL	Yl. to Gr.				4x4 SHb				5
Tall Ryder	7530			HK	M. Grey				4x4 SHb	Red, Yl. & Prp. tr.			5
Tall Ryder	7530			HK	M. Grey				4x4 LHb	Red, Yl. & Blu. tr.			5
Tall Ryder	7530			HK	Grey				4x4 SHb	Red, Yl. & Prp. tr.			5
Tall Ryder	7530			HK	Grey				4x4 LHb	Red, Yl. & Prp. tr.			5
Tall Ryder	7530			HK	M. Grey				4x4 SHb	Red, Yl. & Blu. tr.			5
Tall Ryder	7530			HK	Grey				4x4 SHb	Red, Yl. & Prp. tr.			5
Tall Ryder	7530			MAL	M. Grey				4x4 LHb	Red, Yl. & Prp. tr.			5
Tall Ryder	7530			MAL	M. Grey				4x4 SHb	Red, Yl. & Prp. tr.			5
Tall Ryder	7530			HK	M. Grey				4x4 LHb	Red, Yl. & Prp. tr.			5
Tall Ryder	7530			MAL	M. Grey				4x4 SHb	Red, Yl. & Blu. tr.			5
Tall Ryder	7530			HK	M. Grey				4x4 LHb	Red, Yl. & Blu. tr.			5
Tall Ryder	7530			MAL	Grey				4x4 LHb	Red, Yl. & Prp. tr.			5
Tank Gunner	9374			MAL	Khk. Cmflg.				Reg - Wht.				7
Tank Gunner	9374			MAL	Des. Scrub		Holes		Reg - Blk.				7
Tank Gunner	9374			MAL	Des. Scrub		No holes		Reg - Blk.				7
Tank Gunner	9374			MAL	Des. Cmflg.				Reg				7
Tank Gunner	9374			MAL	Khk. Cmflg.		No holes		Reg				7
Tank Gunner	9374			HK	Khk. Cmflg.		No holes		Reg				7
Tank Gunner	9374			HK	Des. Cmflg.				Reg				7
Tank Gunner	9374			HK	Khk. Cmflg.		Holes		Reg				7
Tank Gunner	9374			MAL	Khk. Cmflg.		Holes		Reg				7
Tank Truck		Unocal 76		MAL	Or./Grey				Reg	Blu. tr.	Unocal 76		5
Tank Truck		Gulf		MAL	Or./Grey				Reg	Or., Wht. & Blk. tr.	Gulf		5
Tank Truck		Pre-Pro		MAL	Red/Chr.	Chr.			Reg	Red, Blk. & Wht.	Texaco		
Tank Truck		Pre-Pro		MAL	Red/Chr.	Blk.			Reg	Red, Blk. & Wht.	Texaco		
Tank Truck	2076			MAL	Red/Chr.				Reg	Blu. & Or. tr.	Unocal		4
Taxi	5181			FRA	Yl.				HO - Gold				15
Taxi	5181			MAL	Yl.				HO - Gold				7
Taxi	5181			HK	Yl.				HO - Gold				7
Thunderbird Stocker				MAL	Blk.				UH	Red, Yl. & Wht. tr.	Havoline 28		75
Thunderbird Stocker	4916		Plst.	MAL	Red				UH	Wht. & Blu. tr.	Ford #11		7
Thunderbird Stocker	5298			MAL	Wht./Blk.				UH	Red, Yl. & Blu. tr.	Havoline 28		7
Thunderbird Stocker				MAL	Or.				Reg	Blu. & Wht. tr.	76		5
Thunderbird Stocker		Auto Palace		CHN	Blu./Wht.				P-C - Blu.	Red & Blk. tr.	AC Delco 9		15
Thunderbird Stocker		McD's		CHN	Gr.				Uniq.	Wht. tr.	Quaker State 62		5
Thunderbird Stocker		McD's		CHN	Red				Uniq.	Yl. tr.	McDonalds 27		5
Thunderbird Stocker		Pre-Pro	Plst.	MAL	Red				Reg	Wht. & Blu. tr.	Ford #11		
Thunderbird Stocker	2568	Pro-Circuit		CHN	Wht./Red				P-C - Grey	Blk., Blu. & Or. tr.	Citgo 21, GE & Morgan Shephard		8
Thunderbird Stocker	2568	Pro-Circuit		CHN	Wht./Red				P-C - Grey	Blk., Blu. & Or. tr.	Citgo 21, GE & Morgan Shepherd		5
Thunderbird Stocker	2456	Pro-Circuit		CHN	Gr./Wht.				P-C - Chr.	Blk. & Red tr.	Elmo 64		15
Thunderbird Stocker	2565	Pro-Circuit		CHN	Wht./Red/Blu.			Pale grey	P-C - Grey	Pale Blu. tr.	Valvoline 6	No logos behind FWs	5

Name	#	Category	Casting	Ctry.	Color	Win.	Base	Interior	Wheels	Paint	Logo	Other	$
Thunderbird Stocker	2568	Pro-Circuit		CHN	Wht./Red				P-C - Grey	Blk., Blu. & Or. tr.	Citgo 21, GE & Morgan Shepherd	Large Ford logo	5
Thunderbird Stocker	2567	Pro-Circuit		CHN	Gr.				P-C - Grey	Wht., Blk. & Blu. tr.	Quaker State 26		7
Thunderbird Stocker	2565	Pro-Circuit		CHN	Wht./Red/Blu.			Silver	P-C - Grey	Pale Blu. tr.	Valvoline 6	No logos behind FWs	5
Thunderbird Stocker	2565	Pro-Circuit		CHN	Wht./Red/Blu.			Silver	P-C - Grey	Pale Blu. tr.	Valvoline 6	Logos behind FWs	5
Thunderbird Stocker	2568	Pro-Circuit		CHN	Wht./Red				P-C - Grey	Blk., Blu. & Or. tr.	Citgo 21 & Morgan Shephard		5
Thunderbird Stocker	4916			MAL	Red				Reg	Wht. & Blu. tr.	Motorcraft	Large RWs	8
Thunderbird Stocker	4916			MAL	Red				Reg	Wht. & Blu. tr.	Motorcraft	Small RWs	8
T-Bucket		Video Car		MAL	N. Yl.			Pnk.	Reg	Red & Prp. flames			10
T-Bucket		Video Car		MAL	Lime Gr.				Reg				10
T-Bucket	7672			MAL	Yl.				Reg	Red & Blu. flames			4
T-Bucket	7672			MAL	Or.				Reg	Red & Blu. flames			7
T-Bucket	9402 LE			MAL	Blk.				Dsh - Grey	Red & Yl. flames			15
The Demon	5730	25th Ann.		CHN	M. Olive Gr.			Blk.	RL				4
The Demon	5730	25th Ann.		CHN	M. Bro.			Blk.	RL				4
The Demon	5730	25th Ann.		CHN	M. Red			Blk.	RL				4
The Demon	5730	25th Ann.		CHN	M. Blu.			Blk.	RL				4
The Demon	5730	25th Ann.		CHN	M. Violet			Blk.	RL				4
The Demon	5730	25th Ann.		CHN	M. Turquoise			Blk.	RL				4
The Demon	5730	25th Ann		CHN	M. Pnk.			Blk.	RL				4
The Demon	5730	25th Ann		CHN	M. Gr.			Blk.	RL				4
The Demon	5730	25th Ann		CHN	M. Lime			Blk.	RL				4
The Demon	5730	25th Ann.		CHN	Gold			Blk.	RL				4
The Demon	5730	25th Ann.		CHN	M. Magenta			Blk.	RL				4
The Demon	5730	25th Ann.		CHN	M. Or.			Blk.	RL				4
The Demon	5730	25th Ann.		CHN	Navy Blu.			Blk.	RL				4
The Demon	5730	Gold Ser.		CHN	M. Prp.			Blk.	RL - Gold			GEng - FAOSc	25
The Demon	5730	Toy Fair		CHN	M. Dk. Blu.			Blk.	RL		New York Toy Fair		150
The Demon	5730	Vintage		CHN	Wht.			Blk.	RL				4
The Demon	5730	Vintage		CHN	M. Chestnut			Blk.	RL				4
The Demon	5730	Vintage		CHN	M. Prp.			Blk.	RL				4
The Demon	5730	Vintage		CHN	M. Gold			Blk.	RL				4
The Demon	5730	Vintage		CHN	Gunmetal			Blk.	RL				4
The Demon	5730	Vintage		CHN	M. Br. Blu.			Blk.	RL				4
The Demon	5730	Vintage		CHN	M. Dk. Bro.			Blk.	RL				4
The Demon	5730	Vintage		CHN	M. Dk. Gr.			Blk.	RL				4
The Demon	5730	Vintage		CHN	Maroon			Blk.	RL				4
The Demon	5730	Vintage		CHN	M. Royal Blu.			Blk.	RL				4
The Demon	5730	Vintage		CHN	Br. Red			Blk.	RL				4
The Demon	5730	Vintage		CHN	M. Pale Pnk.			Blk.	RL				4
The Demon	5730	Vintage		CHN	M. Electric Gr.			Blk.	RL				4
The Incredible Hulk	2850	Scene Machine		HK	Wht.				Reg				40
The Incredible Hulk	2878	Heroes	1 lg. r.wndw	HK	Yl.				Reg				15
The Incredible Hulk	2878	Heroes	2 sm. r.wndws	HK	Yl.				Reg				15
The Incredible Hulk	2878	Heroes	1 lg. r.wndw	MAL	Yl.				Reg				15
The Incredible Hulk	2878	Heroes	2 sm. r.wndws	MAL	Yl.				Reg				15
The Thing	2882	Heroes		MAL	Blu.				Reg				15
The Thing	2882	Heroes		HK	Blu.				Reg				15
Thor	2880	Heroes		HK	Yl.				Reg				12

Name	#	Category	Casting	Ctry.	Color	Win.	Base	Interior	Wheels	Paint	Logo	Other	S
Thunder Roller	3924			HK	Yl.		No holes		Reg				6
Thunder Roller	3924			MAL	Yl.				Reg				6
Thunder Roller	3924			HK	Yl.				Reg				6
Thunder Roller	3924			MAL	Yl.		No holes		Reg				6
Thunder Roller	3924		7 ribs on roof	MAL	Yl.		No holes		Reg				6
Thunder Roller	3924			HK	Yl.		Rsd. HK		Reg				6
Thunder Roller	3924		7 ribs on roof	MAL	Yl.		N&N & no holes		Reg				6
Thunder Roller	3924		7 ribs on roof	HK	Yl.		N&N & no holes		Reg				6
Thunder Roller	3924		7 ribs on roof	HK	Yl.		No holes		Reg				6
Thunderbird Stocker	5900			MAL	Wht.				Reg	Blu. & Red tr.	Valvoline		30
Thunderbird Stocker	5900			HK	Wht.				Reg	Blu. & Red tr.	Valvoline		30
Thunderburner	5139		T-Bird cast on rear licence plate	MAL	Wht./Blu.				HO - Gold	Blu. & Red tr.	Valvoline		8
Thunderburner	5139			MAL	Wht./Dk. Blu.				HO - Gold	Blu. & Red tr.	Valvoline		8
Thunde-burner	5139		T-Bird cast on rear licence plate	MAL	Wht./Dk. Blu.				HO - Gold	Blu. & Red tr.	Valvoline		8
Thunderburner	5139			MAL	Wht./Blu.				HO - Gold	Blu. & Red tr.	Valvoline		8
Thunderburner		Co. Rcr.		MAL	Dk. Gr. to Or.				Reg				5
Thunderburner		Getty		MAL	Yl.				Reg	Prp. flames & Red & Wht. tr.	Getty		6
Thunderburner		Ralston	T-Bird cast on rear licence plate	MAL	Blu.		HW logo		HO - Gold	Red, Wht. & Yl. tr.	The Blk. Knight		5
Thunderburner		Ralston	T-Bird cast on rear licence plate	MAL	Blu.		Name		HO - Gold	Red, Wht. & Yl. tr.	The Blk. Knight		5
Thunderburner		Ralston		MAL	Blu.		HW logo		HO - Gold	Red, Wht. & Yl. tr.	The Blk. Knight		5
Thunderburner		Ralston		MAL	Blu.		Name		HO - Gold	Red, Wht. & Yl. tr.	The Blk. Knight		5
Thunderburner	1456			MAL	Blk.		No Thunder Stocker		HO - Gold	Yl. tr.	The Blk. Knight		5
Thunderburner	1456			MAL	Blk.		No Thunder Stocker		Reg	Yl. tr.	The Blk. Knight		5
Thunderburner	1456			MAL	Blk.		N&N		Reg	Yl. tr.	The Blk. Knight		5
Thunderburner	1456			MAL	Blk.		N&N		HO - Gold	Yl. tr.	The Blk. Knight		5
Thunderburner	1456			MAL	Blk.		Thunder Stocker		HO - Gold	Yl. tr.	The Blk. Knight		5
Thunderburner	1456			MAL	Blk.		Thunder Stocker		Reg	Yl. tr.	The Blk. Knight		5
Thunderburner	5139		T-Bird cast on rear licence plate	MAL	Wht.				UH	Red, Blk. & Blu. stripes	HW logo & 1		8
Thunderburner	5139			MAL	Wht.				HO - Gold	Red, Blk. & Blu. stripes	HW logo & 1		8
Thunderburner	5139			MAL	Wht.				UH	Red, Blk. & Blu. stripes	HW logo & 1		8
Thunderburner	5139		T-Bird cast on rear licence plate	MAL	Wht.				HO - Gold	Red, Blk. & Blu. stripes	HW logo & 1		8
Thunderburner	7904 Set			MAL	Blk.				UH	Prp., Yl. & Gr. tr.	4	Crashpile Set	12
Thunderstreak	4835		Short rear wing	MAL	Blu./Gr.		HW		Reg	Red & Wht. tr.	HW logo		10
Thunderstreak	9545		Long rear wing	MAL	Yl.				Reg	Red & Blk. tr.	Pennzoil 4		5
Thunderstreak	4835		Short rear wing	MAL	Blu./Gr.		HW		Reg	Red & Whi. tr.	1 & HW logo		10
Thunderstreak		Aqua Fresh	Long rear wing	MAL	Turquoise				Reg		WaterPik on rear wing		10

Name	#	Category	Casting	Ctry.	Color	Win.	Base	Interior	Wheels	Paint	Logo	Other	S
Thunderstreak		Aqua Fresh	Long rear wing	MAL	Turquoise				Reg		aq.fresh on rear wing		5
Thunderstreak		Corgi	Long rear wing	CHN	Wht./Gr.				6 Spoke - Chr.	Red & Blk. tr.	Fuji Film 2	Model packaged as Corgi toy	100
Thunderstreak		Pre-Pro	Long rear wing	CHN	Yl.				6 Spoke - Chr.	Red & Blk. tr.	Penzzoil 4		8
Thunderstreak		Pre-Pro	Long rear wing	CHN	Blk./Yl.				6 Spoke - Grey	Wht. tr.	Rahal 12		5
Thunderstreak		Pre-Pro	Long rear wing	CHN	Red/Wht.				6 Spoke - Grey	Blk. tr.	Truesports 10		5
Penske #5	2694	Pro-Circuit	Long rear wing	CHN	Wht./N. Or.				6 Spoke - Chr.	Blk. & Red tr.	Penske 5	Blu. helmet	8
Quaker State Car #26	2567	Pro-Circuit	Long rear wing	CHN	Gr./Wht.				6 Spoke - Chr.	Wht. tr.	Quaker State 26		5
Texaco #1	2638	Pro-Circuit	Long rear wing	CHN	Wht./Blk.				6 Spoke - Grey	Blk. & Red tr.	Kmart 1	Wht. RB	5
Texaco #2	2677	Pro-Circuit	Long rear wing	CHN	Wht./Blk.				Ribbon - Grey	Blk. & Red tr.	Kmart 2	Red RB	5
Penske #5	2694	Pro-Circuit	Long rear wing	CHN	Wht./N. Or.				6 Spoke - Chr.	Blk. & Red tr.	Penske 4	Wht. helmet	5
Texaco #1	2638	Pro-Circuit	Long rear wing	CHN	Wht./Blk.				Ribbon - Grey	Blk. & Red tr.	Kmart 1	Wht. RB	5
Texaco #2	2677	Pro-Circuit	Long rear wing	CHN	Wht./Blk.				6 Spoke - Grey	Blk. & Red tr.	Kmart 2	Red RB	5
Valvoline #3	2690	Pro-Circuit	Long rear wing	CHN	Wht./Blu.				6 Spoke - Chr.	Red, Blu. & Blk. tr.	Valvoline 3		7
Thunderstreak	1491		Short rear wing	MAL	Brg./Prp.				Reg	Or., Wht. & Yl. tr.	8		7
Thunderstreak	1491		Short rear wing	MAL	Blu./Yl.		HW		Reg		Kraco STP logo		7
Thunderstreak	1491		Short rear wing	MAL	Brg./Prp.		HW		RR - Grey	Or., Wht. & Yl. tr.	8		7
Thunderstreak	1491		Short rear wing	MAL	Blu./Yl.		HW		RR - Grey		Kraco		7
Thunderstreak	2540		Short rear wing	MAL	Red/Brg.				RR - Grey				12
Thunderstreak	2540		Short rear wing	MAL	Red/Brg.				Reg				7
Thunderstreak	3998		Short rear wing	MAL	Brg./Prp.		HW		Reg	Or. & Wht. tr.			7
Thunderstreak	3998		Short rear wing	MAL	Brg./Prp.		HW logo		Reg	Or. & Wht. tr.			7
Thunderstreak	3999		Short rear wing	MAL	Blu./Yl.		HW logo		Reg	Yl., Or. & Wht. tr.	Kraco		6
Thunderstreak	3999		Short rear wing	MAL	Blu./Yl.		HW logo		Reg	Yl., Or. & Wht. tr.	Kraco STP logo		6
Thunderstreak	9545		Short rear wing	MAL	Red/Wht.				RR - Grey		Or. 8 on nose		12
Thunderstreak	9545		Short rear wing	MAL	Red/Wht.				RR - Grey		Yl. 8 on nose		12
Thunderstreak	9545		Short rear wing	MAL	Red/Wht.				Reg				7
Top Eliminator	7630			FRA	Red			Red	Reg	Racer tr.	Radical Racer 301		25
Top Eliminator	7630			FRA	Blu.				Reg	Gr., Or. & Yl. tr.	HW Flying Colors		25
Top Eliminator	7630			FRA	Wht.				Reg	Red flames			35
Top Eliminator	7630			HK	Blu.				RL	Gr., Or. & Yl. tr.	HW Flying Colors		50
Top Eliminator	7630			HK	Gold				RL	Blu., Or. & Mgta. tr.	Hemi Hauler & Blu. A/C		40
Top Eliminator	7630			MAL	Red			Tan	Reg	Racer tr.	Radical Racer 301		15
Top Eliminator	7630			HK	Gold				Reg	Blu., Or. & Mgta. tr.	Hemi Hauler & Blu. A/C		20
Top Eliminator	7630			HK	Gold				Reg	Blu., Or. & Mgta. tr.	Hemi Hauler & Or. A/C		20
Thrill Drivers Torino	9793			MEX	Red				Reg	Or., Yl. & Blu. tr.	Thrill Drivers		75
Torino Stocker	7191			MEX	Wht.				Reg	Red & Yl. flames			40
Torino Stocker	7647			MAL	Blk.				Reg	Or., Yl. & Wht. tr.	3		18
Torino Stocker	7647			HK	Red				RL	Blu., Wht. & Yl. tr.	23		45
Torino Stocker	7647			MAL	Red				Reg	Blu., Wht. & Yl. tr.	23		30
Torino Stocker	7647			HK	Blk.				Reg	Or., Yl. & Wht. tr.	3		18
Torino Stocker	7647			MEX	Blk.				HO - Gold	Or., Yl. & Wht. tr.	3		25
Torino Stocker	7647			HK	Red				Reg	Blu., Wht. & Yl. tr.	23		30
Torino Stocker	7647			MAL	Blk.				HO - Gold	Or., Yl. & Wht. tr.	3		20
Torino Stocker	7647			MEX	Blk.				Reg	Or., Yl. & Wht. tr.	3		25
Torino Stocker	7647			HK	Blk.				HO - Gold	Or., Yl. & Wht. tr.	3		20
Thrill Drivers Torino	9793			HK	Red				Reg	Red, Yl. & Blu. tr.	Thrill Drivers		100

Name	#	Category	Casting	Ctry.	Color	Win.	Base	Interior	Wheels	Paint	Logo	Other	S
Torino Stocker	9793			MAL	Wht.				Reg	Red, Yl. & Blu. tr.	Thrill Drivers		75
Torino Stocker	9793			HK	Wht.				Reg	Red, Yl. & Blu. tr.	Thrill Drivers		75
Torino Stocker	9793			MAL	Red				Reg	Red, Yl. & Blu. tr.	Thrill Drivers		100
Torino Tornado	9533			MAL	Yl.				HO - Gold	Blu., Red & Wht. tr.	17 HW		12
Torino Tornado	9533			MEX	Yl.				HO - Gold	Blu., Red & Wht. tr.			25
Torino Tornado	9533			HK	Yl.				Reg	Blu., Red & Wht. tr.			12
Torino Tornado	9533			HK	Yl.				HO - Gold	Blu., Red & Wht. tr.	17 HW		12
Torino Tornado	9533			MEX	Yl.				HO - Gold				30
Torino Tornado	9533			MAL	Yl.				Reg	Blu., Red & Wht. tr.			12
Tough Customer	7655			HK	Khk.		No Tough Customer						35
Tough Customer	7655			HK	Khk. Cmflg.		No Tough Customer						35
Tough Customer	7655			HK	Khk.		Tough Customer						35
Tough Customer	7655			HK	Khk.		No Tough Customer			Wht. star			35
Tough Customer	7655			HK	Khk.		Tough Customer			Wht. star			35
Tough Customer	7655			HK	Khk. Cmflg.		No Tough Customer & Lrg. Rsd. rectangle						35
Toyota MR2 Rallye	4609	Aqua Fresh		MAL	N. Pnk.				UH	Wht., tan & Yl. tr.	Toyota MR2	Chr. spot lights	10
Toyota MR2 Rallye	5660	Aqua Fresh		MAL	Red				UH	Wht., Blk. & Yl. tr.	Toyota MR2	Chr. spot lights	6
Toyota MR2 Rallye	5660	Getty		MAL	Blu.				UH	Red, Wht. & Yl. tr.	Getty	Blk. spot lights	5
Toyota MR2 Rallye	5660	Set		MAL	N. Pnk.				UH	Wht., tan & Red tr.		Chr. lights - Criss Cross Set	10
Toyota MR2 Rallye	4609			MAL	Wht.				UH	Red, Pnk. & Prp. tr.	Europe/Asia 34	Chr. spot lights	4
Toyota MR2 Rallye	5660			MAL	Wht.				UH	Red, Yl. & Or. tr.	Toyota MR2	Chr. spot lights	4
Toyota MR2 Rallye	5660			MAL	Wht.				HO - Silver	Red, Yl. & Or. tr.	Toyota MR2	Chr. spot lights	4
Toyota MR2 Rallye	5660			MAL	Wht.				UH	Red, Yl. & Or. tr.	Toyota MR2	Blk. spot lights	10
Tractor	2075			MAL	Red				4x4				5
Tractor	2075			MAL	Yl.				4x4 SHb - Yl.				5
Trailbuster	5636			MAL	Aq.				4x4 SHb	Blk., Yl. & Dk. Pnk.			10
Trailbuster	5636			MAL	Aq.				4x4 SHb	Dk. Blu., Yl. & pale Pnk.			4
Trailbuster	5636			MAL	Aq.				4x4 SHb	Pale Blu., Yl. & Dk. Pnk.			4
Trailbuster			Plst.	MAL	Chr.			N. Gr.	4x4 SHb				5
Trailbuster		Chuck E Cheese		MAL	Wht.			Or.	4x4 SHb		Chuck E Cheese		10
Trailbuster		Kool Aid		MAL	Prp.				4x4 SHb	Or., Yl. & Blu. flames	Kool Aid		10
Trash Truck	3912			MAL	Or.				Reg	Gr., Blk. & Red tr.			12
Trash Truck	3912			HK	Or.				Reg	Gr., Blk. & Red tr.			12
Trash Truck	3912			MEX	Or.		Blk. Plst.		Reg	Blk. & Yl. tr.			30
Trash Truck	3912			MEX	Or.		Chr. Plst.		Reg	Gr., Blk. & Red tr.			30
Treadator	3025			MAL	Red								3
Tri-car X8		Ralston		MAL	Pale Blu.	DC	Red		Reg	Blk., Yl. & Wht. tr.			20
Tri-car X8	1130			MAL	Red		Sm. typeface		Reg	Wht. & Yl. flames			5
Tri-car X8	1130			MAL	Red		Lrg. typeface		Reg	Wht. & Yl. flames			5
Tri-car X8	1130			HK	Wht.		Lrg. typeface		Reg	US Flag tr.		Hard nose	6
Tri-car X8	1130			MAL	Wht.		Lrg. typeface		Reg	US Flag tr.		Hard nose	6
Tri-car X8	1130			HK	Wht.		Sm. typeface		Reg	US Flag tr.		Soft nose	6

Name	#	Category	Casting	Ctry.	Color	Win.	Base	Interior	Wheels	Paint	Logo	Other	S
Tri-car X8	1130			MAL	Wht.		Sm. typeface		Reg	US Flag tr.		Soft nose	6
Tri-car X8	2525			MAL	Silver		Sm. typeface		Reg	Or., Mgta. & Yl. tr.	X8		7
Tri-car X8	2525			MAL	Silver		Lrg. typeface		Reg	Or., Mgta. & Yl. tr.	X8		7
Tri-car X8		Kelloggs		MAL	Red		Lrg. typeface		Reg	Blu. & Wht. stars & stripes			8
Tri-car X8	5112			MAL	Yl.	LC	Red		Reg	Red, Wht. & Prp. tr.			5
Tri-car X8	5112			MAL	Yl.	LC	Red w/ N&N		Reg	Red, Wht. & Prp. tr.			5
Tri-car X8	5112			MAL	Yl.	DC	Yl.		Reg	Red, Wht. & Prp. tr.			30
Tri-car X8	5112			MAL	Yl.	DC	Yl. w/ N&N		Reg	Red, Wht. & Prp. tr.			30
Tri-car X8	5112			MAL	Yl.	DC	Red		Reg	Red, Wht. & Prp. tr.			5
Tri-car X8	5112			MAL	Yl.	DC	Red w/ N&N		Reg	Red, Wht. & Prp. tr.			5
Troop Carrier	4921			MAL	Khk. Cmflg.				Reg				5
Troop Carrier	4921			MAL	Des.				Reg - Blk.				5
Troop Carrier	4921			HK	Khk. Cmflg.				Reg				5
Troop Carrier	4921			HK	Des.				Reg - Tan				5
Troop Convoy	4921			MAL	Khk./Des.				Reg - Wht.		US Army		5
Troop Convoy	9379			MAL	Khk. Cmflg.				Reg - Blk.				5
Troop Convoy	9379			HK	Des. Cmflg.				Reg - Blk.				5
Troop Convoy	9379			MAL	Des. Cmflg.				Reg - Blk.				5
Troop Convoy	9379			HK	Khk. Cmflg.				Reg - Blk.				5
T-Totaller	9648			HK	Bro.				Reg				15
T-Totaller	9648			MEX	Dk. Bro.				HO - Gold				30
T-Totaller	9648			MAL	Bro.				Reg				15
T-Totaller	9648			MAL	Red				Reg				7
T-Totaller	9648			HK	Red				Reg				7
T-Totaller	9648			MAL	Blk.				Reg				15
T-Totaller	9648			HK	Blk.				Reg				15
T-Totaller	9648			MAL	Dk. Bro.				HO - Gold				15
T-Totaller	9648			HK	Blk.				RL				400
T-Totaller	9648			MEX	Dk. Bro.				Reg				30
Turbine 4-2		McD's		CHN	Blu.				Uniq.				5
Turbo Heater	5911			HK	Magenta	BluT			Reg				6
Turbo Heater	5911			MAL	Magenta	CL			Reg				6
Turbo Heater	9524			MAL	M. Blu.				HO - Gold				6
Turbo Heater	9524			MAL	M. Blu.				Reg				6
Turbo Mustang	1135			IND	Aq.				Reg	Maroon & Blu. tr.	Cobra		10
Turbo Mustang	1135			IND	Blu.				Reg	Wht. & Yl. tr.	Cobra		10
Turbo Mustang		Co. Rcr.		MAL	Prp. to Pnk.				Reg				5
Turbo Mustang		Pre-Pro		HK	Silver				Reg	Or. & Blk. tr., starburst on rf.			
Turbo Mustang	1125			HK	Yl.				Reg	Red & Blk. tr., starburst on rf.			6
Turbo Mustang	1125			HK	Wht.		Yl.		HO - Gold	Red, Yl. & Blk. tr.	31		6
Turbo Mustang	1125			MEX	Red				HO - Gold	Blk. & Yl. tr.			75
Turbo Mustang	1125			HK	Or.				Reg	Blk., Red & Yl. tr.	Cobra		10
Turbo Mustang	1125			HK	Red				HO - Gold	Blk. & Yl. tr.	Cobra		7
Turbo Mustang	1125			MAL	Wht.		Yl.		HO - Gold	Red, Yl. & Blk. tr.	31		6
Turbo Mustang	1125			HK	M. Blu.				HO - Gold	Yl., Blk & Blu. tr.	Cobra		50
Turbo Mustang	1125			HK	Yl.				HO - Gold	Red & Blk. tr., starburst on rf.	Cobra		6
Turbo Mustang	1125			HK	Red				HO - Gold	Blk, Yl. & Blu. tr.	Cobra		15
Turbo Mustang	1125			HK	Red				Reg	Yl., Blk. & Blu. tr.			7

Name	#	Category	Casting	Ctry.	Color	Win.	Base	Interior	Wheels	Paint	Logo	Other	$
Turbo Mustang	1125			MAL	Red				Reg	Yl., Blk. & Blu. tr.			7
Turbo Mustang	1125			MEX	Red				HO - Gold				40
Turbo Mustang	1125			HK	M. Red				Reg	Blk. & Yl. tr.	Cobra		6
Turbo Streak	1125	20th Ann.		MAL	Wht.				Reg	Blu., Red & Yl. tr. w/ large logo	20th Anniversary		25
Turbo Streak		20th Ann.		MAL	Wht.				Reg	Blu., Red & Yl. tr. w/ small logo	20th Anniversary		25
Turbo Streak		Gulf		MAL	Or.				Reg	Blk. & Wht. tr.	Gulf		4
Turbo Streak		Mail Tour		MAL	Wht.				Reg	Red & Yl. tr.	Indy 500		75
Turbo Streak		Shell		MAL	Yl.				Reg	Red, Blk. & Wht. shell tr.	Formula Shell		4
Turbo Streak		Shell		MAL	Yl.				Reg	Red Shell tr.			6
Turbo Streak		Video Car		MAL	Wht.				Reg				10
Turbo Streak	4365			HK	Yl.				RR - Wht.		No Michelin & Elf on side		12
Turbo Streak	4365			HK	Yl.				RR - Grey		No Michelin & Elf on side		12
Turbo Streak	4365			MAL	Yl.				RR - Wht.		No Michelin & Elf on side		12
Turbo Streak	4365			MAL	Yl.				Reg		No Michelin & Elf on side		5
Turbo Streak	4365			HK	Yl.				Reg		Michelin & Elf on side		5
Turbo Streak	4365			HK	Yl.				Reg		No Michelin & Elf on side		5
Turbo Streak	4365			HK	Yl.				RR - Grey		Michelin & Elf on side		12
Turbo Streak	4365			MAL	Yl.				Reg		Michelin & Elf on side		5
Turbo Streak	4365			MAL	Yl.				RR - Grey		Michelin & Elf on side		12
Turbo Streak	4365			MAL	Yl.				RR - Grey		No Michelin & Elf on side		12
Turbo Streak	4639			MAL	N. Blz.				Reg	Painted wings	Tuneup Masters & logo		35
Turbo Streak	4639			MAL	N. Blz.				Reg	Painted wings	Tuneup Masters & no logo		35
Turbo Streak	4639			MAL	N. Yl.				Reg	Unpainted wings	Tuneup Masters & no logo		4
Turbo Streak	4639			MAL	N. Blz.				Reg	Unpainted wings	Tuneup Masters & no logo		4
Turbo Streak	4639			MAL	N. Blz.				Reg	Unpainted wings	Tuneup Masters & logo		4
Turbo Wedge		Pre-Pro		MAL	Or. MF.		RWJU		Reg				
Turbo Wedge	1134	Hiraker		HK	Or.		RWJU		Reg				6
Turbo Wedge	1134	Hiraker		MAL	Or.		RWJU		Reg				6
Turbo Wedge	1134	Hiraker		HK	Gr.		RWJU		Reg				6
Turboa	2061	Speed Demon		HK	Yl.				UH				6
Turboa	2061	Speed Demon		MAL	Yl.				UH				6
Turboa	2061	Speed Demon		MAL	Yl.				HO - Silver				6
Turismo	1694			FRA	Plum				Reg	Wht. tr.			25
Turismo	1694			FRA	Yl.				Reg	Red & Blk. tr.			25
Turismo	1694			HK	Red				Reg			Tan bmp	8

Name	#	Category	Casting	Ctry.	Color	Win.	Base	Interior	Wheels	Paint	Logo	Other	S
Turismo	1694			MAL	Yl.	BluT			Reg	Prp., Or. & Blk. tr.		Blk. bmp	8
Turismo	1694			MAL	Yl.				Reg	Prp., Or. & Blk. tr.		Prp. bmp	8
Turismo	1694			MAL	Red				Reg			Blk. bmp	8
Turismo	1694			MAL	Yl.				Reg	Prp., Or. & Blk. tr.		Tan bmp	8
Turismo	1694			MAL	Yl.	DT			Reg	Prp., Or. & Blk. tr.		Blk. bmp	8
Twin Mill II	5266			MAL	N. Yl.		Blk.		UH				3
Twin Mill II	5266			MAL	N. *Yl.		Grey		UH				3
Twin Mill II	5266			MAL	N. Yl.		Chr.		UH				3
Twinmill		5709 25th Ann.		CHN	M. Violet				RL				4
Twinmill		5709 25th Ann.		CHN	M. Turquoise				RL				4
Twinmill		5709 25th Ann.		CHN	M. Bro.				RL				4
Twinmill		5709 25th Ann.		CHN	M. Magenta				RL				4
Twinmill		5709 25th Ann.		CHN	M. Pnk.				RL				4
Twinmill		5709 25th Ann.		CHN	M. Lime				RL				4
Twinmill		5709 25th Ann.		CHN	M. Or.				RL				4
Twinmill		5709 25th Ann.		CHN	M. Red				RL				4
Twinmill		5709 25th Ann.		CHN	Gold				RL				4
Twinmill		5709 25th Ann		CHN	M. Blu.				RL				4
Twinmill		5709 25th Ann.		CHN	M. Olive Gr.				RL				4
Twinmill		5709 25th Ann		CHN	M. Br. Red				RL				4
Twinmill		5709 25th Ann.		CHN	M. Gr.				RL				4
Twinmill		5709 Gold Ser.		CHN	M. Grey				RL - Gold			GEngs - FAOSc	25
Twinmill		5709 Vintage		CHN	M. Dk. Gr.				RL				4
Twinmill		5709 Vintage		CHN	M. Br. Gr.				RL				4
Twinmill		5709 Vintage		CHN	M. Br. Blu.				RL				4
Twinmill		5709 Vintage		CHN	M. Electric Gr.				RL				4
Twinmill		5709 Vintage		CHN	Maroon				RL				4
Twinmill		5709 Vintage		CHN	M. Royal Blu.				RL				4
Twinmill		5709 Vintage		CHN	Br. Red				RL				4
Twinmill		5709 Vintage		CHN	M. Dk. Bro.				RL				4
Twinmill		5709 Vintage		CHN	M. Gold				RL				4
Twinmill		5709 Vintage		CHN	M. Prp.				RL				4
Twinmill		5709 Vintage		CHN	M. Pale Pnk.				RL				4
Twinmill		5709 Vintage		CHN	Wht.				RL				4
Twinmill		5709 Vintage		CHN	Gunmetal				RL				4
Twinmill II		8240		HK	Or.				RL	Red, Wht. & Blu. tr.			25
Twinmill II		9509 Super Chr.		HK	Chr.				Reg				20
Twinmill II		9509 Super Chr.		HK	Chr.				RL				35
Unimog		5673		MAL	Wht.				4x4 SHb				5
Unimog		4643		MAL	Des. Cmflg.				4x4 SHb				4
Unimog		4643		MAL	Des. Cmflg.				4x4 SHb - Blk.				4
Unimog		4643		MAL	Des. Cmflg.				4x4 SHb - Wht.				4
Upfront 924		2500		FRA	Wht.		Blk. Plst.		Reg			RRR	20
Upfront 924		2500		FRA	Or.		Blk. Plst.		Reg				20
Upfront 924		2500		FRA	Wht.		Blk. Plst.		Reg				20
Upfront 924		2500		MAL	Or.				Reg				7
Upfront 924		2500		HK	Or.				Reg				7
Upfront 924		2500		MAL	Blk.				Reg	Red & Yl. stripes	Turbo 924		7
Upfront 924		2500		HK	Yl.				Reg				8
Upfront 924		4339		MAL	Gold MF.		Silver		Reg	Red, Blk. & Wht. stripes		RRR	6
Upfront 924		4339		MEX	Gold MF.		Silver		Reg				30

Name	#	Category	Casting	Ctry.	Color	Win.	Base	Interior	Wheels	Paint	Logo	Other	S
Upfront 924	4339			MAL	Gold MF.		Gold MF.		Reg	Red, Blk. & Wht. stripes		RRR	6
Upfront 924	4339			MEX	Gold MF.		Silver		WW				40
Upfront 924	4339			MEX	Gold MF.		Wht.		Reg	Red, Blk. & Wht. stripes			30
Upfront 924	4339			MEX	Gold MF.		Wht.		WW	Red, Blk. & Wht. stripes			40
Upfront 924	4339			MEX	Gold MF.		Wht.		Reg	Red, Blk. & Wht. stripes		RRR	30
Vampyra		Speed Demon		MAL	Wht.				UH				5
Vampyra	2060	Speed Demon		MAL	Prp.				UH				5
Vampyra	444	Speed Demon		MAL	Blk.				Reg	Yl., Gr. & Prp. tr.		Yl. & Gr. eyes	6
Vampyra	2060	Speed Demon		HK	Prp.				UH				5
Vampyra	444	Speed Demon		MAL	Blk.				HO - Silver	Yl., Gr. & Prp. tr.		Yl. & Gr. eyes	4
Vampyra	444	Speed Demon		MAL	Blk.				UH	Yl., Gr. & Prp. tr.		Yl. & Gr. eyes	4
Vampyra	444	Speed Demon		MAL	Blk.				Reg	Prp., Gr. & Yl. tr.		Prp. & Gr. eyes	4
Vampyra	2060	Speed Demon		MAL	Dk. Prp.				Reg				5
Vampyra	2060	Speed Demon		MAL	Dk. Prp.				UH				5
Vector Avtech WX-3	3050			MAL	Silver				UH				3
Vector Avtech WX-3	3050			MAL	Prp.				UH	Body colored top			3
Vector Avtech WX-3	3050			MAL	Prp.				UH	Pale top			3
Vega Bomb	7658			FRA	Or.				Reg				30
Vega Bomb	7658			FRA	Magenta				Reg				40
Vega Bomb	7658			FRA	Maroon			Bro.	Reg				30
Vega Bomb	7658			FRA	Maroon			Or.	Reg				30
Vega Bomb	7658			HK	Or.				RL				40
Vega Bomb	7658			HK	Pale Gr.				RL				400
Vega Bomb	7658			HK	Or.				Reg				40
Vette Van	1135	Hiraker		MAL	Red		RWJU	Tan	Reg	Wht., Blu. & Yl. stripes			12
Vette Van	1135	Hiraker		MAL	Blk.		RWJU	Tan	Reg	Wht., Red & Yl. stripes			12
Vette Van	1135	Hiraker		HK	Blk.		RWJU	Tan	Reg	Wht., Red & Yl. stripes			12
Vette Van	1135	Hiraker		HK	Blk.		RWJU & Rsd. MAL	Tan	Reg	Wht., Red & Yl. stripes			12
Vette Van	1135	Hiraker		HK	Red		RWJU	Tan	Reg	Wht., Blu. & Yl. stripes			12
Vette Van	1135	Hiraker		HK	Red		RWJU & Rsd. MAL	Tan	Reg	Wht., Blu. & Yl. stripes			12
Vetty Funny	2508			MAL	Wht.		ROA		Reg	Red, Yl. & Prp. tr.	Corvette Fever		15
Vetty Funny	2508			HK	Grey		No rivet		Reg	Red, Yl. & Blk. tr.	Tom McEwen & English Leather		18
Vetty Funny	2508			HK	Grey		RAF		Reg	Red, Yl. & Blk. tr.	Tom McEwen & English Leather		18
Vetty Funny	2508			HK	Grey		No rivet		Reg	Wht., Yl. & Blk. tr.	Tom McEwen & English Leather		200
Vetty Funny	2508			MAL	Grey		ROA		Reg	Red, Yl. & Blk. tr.	Tom McEwen & English Leather		18
Vetty Funny	2508			HK	Grey		RAF		Reg	Wht., Yl. & Blk. tr.	Tom McEwen & English Leather		18
Vetty Funny	2508			MAL	Wht.		RAF & SIS		Reg	Red, Yl. & Prp. tr.	Corvette Fever		15
Vetty Funny	2508			MAL	Grey		RAF & SIS		Reg	Red, Yl. & Blk. tr.	Tom McEwen & English Leather		18
Vetty Funny	2508			MAL	Grey		RAF & no SIS		Reg	Red, Yl. & Blk. tr.	Tom McEwen & English Leather		18
Vetty Funny	2508			MAL	Wht.		RAF & no SIS		Reg	Red, Yl. & Prp. tr.	Corvette Fever		15
VW Bug	453			MAL	Prp.				Reg	Gr., Yl. & Or. geo. shps.			3
Volkswagen		Co. Rcr.		MAL	Prp. to Pnk.				Reg	Prp., Pnk. & Wht. tr.			5

Name	#	Category	Casting	Ctry.	Color	Win.	Base	Interior	Wheels	Paint	Logo	Other	S
Volkswagen		Getty		MAL	Gr.				Reg	Red, Yl. & Wht. tr.	Getty		5
Volkswagen	9225 Park'n Plate			MAL	Yl.				Reg	Blu., Gr. & Or. tr.			15
Volkswagen		Randy's		MAL	Prp.				Dsh - Grey	Blk. & Wht. tr.	Randy's Stuff		15
Volkswagen		Randy's		MAL	N. Pnk.				Dsh - Grey	Blk. & Wht. tr.	Randy's Stuff		15
Volkswagen		Sema		MAL	Blk. MF.				Dsh - Grey				100
Volkswagen	2149			MAL	Red				Reg	Gr., Yl. & Wht. flames			4
Volkswagen	2149			MAL	Red				Reg	Blu., Yl. & Wht. flames			4
Volkswagen	7620		No sun roof	HK	Or.				RL	Beetle on rf.			50
Volkswagen	7620		No sun roof	HK	Or.				RL	Yl., Wht. & Blk. stripes			200
Volkswagen	7620 Herfy's		No sun roof	HK	Or.				RL	Beetle on rf.	Herfy's		100
Volkswagen	7620 Wisconsin Toy Co	No sun roof		HK	Or.		Plst.		RL	Beetle on rf.			10
Volkswagen	7671			MAL	Aq.				Reg	Yl., Or. & Blu. tr.			5
Volkswagen	7671			MAL	Aq.				Reg	Yl., Or. & Prp. tr.			5
Volkswagen Golf	9557			MAL	Wht.		Pnk. Plst.		Reg	Gr., Pnk. & Blu. tr.	VW		35
Volkswagen Golf	487			MAL	Glt. Gr.				Reg				15
Volkswagen Golf		Getty		MAL	Silver				Reg		Getty		4
Volkswagen Golf	487			MAL	Glt. Pnk.		Silver		Reg				5
Volkswagen Golf	487			MAL	Glt. Pnk.		Blk.		Reg				5
Volkswagen Golf	9714			MAL	Red				Reg				5
Hiway Hauler		Wal-Mart	DRA	HK	Wht.				Reg		Wal-Mart		15
Warpath	7654			FRA	Blu.				Reg				40
Warpath	7654			FRA	Pale Blu.				Reg				40
Warpath	7654			HK	Wht.		Plst.		RL				40
Warpath	7654			MEX	Wht.				Reg				30
Warpath	7654			HK	Wht.		US & Canada		RL				45
Warpath	7654 Wisconsin Toy Co			HK	Red		Plst.		RL				10
Warpath	9114 Herfy's			HK	Wht.				RL		Herfy's		120
Westin Bus				IND	Khk.				Reg	Wht. & Yl. tr.	Westin Hotels & Resorts		12
Westin Bus				IND	Blu.				Reg	Blk. & Yl. tr.	Westin Hotels & Resorts		12
Westin Bus				IND	Blu.				Reg	Wht. & Yl. tr.	Westin Hotels & Resorts		12
Westin Bus				IND	Red				Reg	Wht. & Yl. tr.	Westin Hotels & Resorts		12
Whip Creamer	11523 Vintage			CHN	M. Aq.				RL				5
Whip Creamer	11523 Vintage			CHN	M. Magenta				RL				5
Whip Creamer	11523 Vintage			CHN	M. Gr.				RL				5
Whip Creamer	11523 Vintage			CHN	M. Pale Blu.				RL				5
Whip Creamer	11523 Vintage			CHN	M. Or.				RL				5
Whip Creamer	11523 Vintage			CHN	M. Red				RL				5
Wind Splitter	1100 Video Car			HK	Yl.				UH				10
Wind Splitter	1100 Video Car			MAL	Yl.				UH				10
Wind Splitter	7296 Ultra Hot			HK	M. Blu.				UH				7
Wind Splitter	7296 Ultra Hot			MAL	M. Blu.				UH				7
Winnipeg	7618			HK	Yl.				RL	Or. & Blu. tr.			100
X21J Cruiser		McD's		CHN	Blu.				Uniq.				5
Xploder	6977			HK	Pale Gr.			Blk.	RL				150
Xploder	6977			HK	Pale Blu.			Blk.	RL				150
Xploder	6977			HK	Pale Yl.			Blk.	RL				150
Xploder	6977			HK	Dk. Yl.			Blk.	RL				150

Name	#	Category	Casting	Ctry.	Color	Win.	Base	Interior	Wheels	Paint	Logo	Other	S
Xploder	6977			HK	Flr. Lime			Blk.	RL				150
Xploder	6977			HK	Plum			Blk.	RL				150
Xploder	6977			HK	Pnk.			Blk.	RL				175
Xploder	6977			HK	Red			Blk.	RL				150
Xploder	6977			HK	Dk. Blu.			Blk.	RL				150
Xploder	6977			HK	Or.			Blk.	RL				150
Xploder	6977			HK	Gr.			Blk.	RL				150
XT-3	1484			MAL	Blk.	Yl.			Reg	Red, Yl. & Wht. flames			30
XT-3	4544			MAL	Ivory				Reg	Red & Yl. flames			4
XT-3	1484			MAL	Blk.	Blk.			Reg	Red, Yl. & Wht. flames			30
XT-3		Ralston		MAL	Dk. Prp.				Reg	Blk., Or. & Wht. flames			20
XT-3	1484			MAL	Prp.				Reg	Red, Yl. & Wht. flames			5
XT-3	7531			MAL	Blk.	Yl.			Reg	Yl., Wht. & Red tr.	XT3		5
XT-3	7531 Pre-Pro			MAL	Red				Reg	Blk. & Yl. tr.	XT3	Blk. nose	
XT-3	7531 Pre-Pro			MAL	Red				Reg	Blk. & Yl. tr.	XT3	Red nose	
Z Whiz	9639			FRA	Dk. Gr.				Reg	Red, Yl. & Blk. tr.	Datsun		25
Z Whiz	9639			FRA	Blk.				Reg	Wht. tr.	Datsun		25
Z Whiz	9639			FRA	Dk. Gr.				Reg	Red, Yl. & Blk. tr.	Datsun	Larger RWs	25
Z Whiz	9639			MEX	Gr.				Reg	Red, Yl. & Blk. tr.	Datsun	Larger RWs	25
Z Whiz	9639			HK	Gr.				Reg	Light Gr., Blk. & Wht. tr.	Datsun		8
Z Whiz	9639			HK	Wht.				RL	Or., Blu. & Yl. tr.	Datsun		500
Z Whiz	9639			HK	Grey				RL	Or., Blu. & Yl. tr.	Datsun		25
Z Whiz	9639			MEX	Gr.				Reg	Red, Yl. & Blk. tr.	Datsun		8
Z Whiz	9639			HK	Blu.				Reg	Red, Yl. & Or. tr.	15		30
Z Whiz	9639			HK	Gold				Reg	Or., Wht. & Blu. tr.	Datsun		20
Z Whiz	9639			HK	Grey				Reg	Or., Blu. & Yl. tr.	Datsun		12
Zerder Fact 4	461			MAL	Prp.				HO - Silver				5
Zender Fact 4	461			MAL	Glt. Prp.				UH				5
Zender Fact 4	461			MAL	Glt. Prp.				HO - Silver				5
Zender Fact 4		25th Ann.		MAL	Chr.				UH				5
Zender Fact 4		Revealer		MAL	Sea Gr.				UH - N. Yl.	Yl., Pnk. & grey tr.			5
Zender Fact 4		Revealer		MAL	M. Prp.				UH - N. Gr.	Yl., Pnk. & grey tr.			5
Zender Fact 4		Revealer		MAL	Blk.				UH - N. Yl.	Yl., Pnk. & grey tr.			5
Zender Fact 4		Set		MAL	M. Blu.				UH	Yl. & Prp. tr.		Criss Cross Crash Set	10
Zender Fact 4		Shell		MAL	Red				UH	Yl. Shell tr.	Shell		6
Zender Fact 4		Video Car		MAL	Prp.				UH				10
Zender Fact 4	4407			MAL	N. Gr.	CL			UH	Wht., Yl. & Mgta. tr.			4
Zender Fact 4	4407			MAL	M. Blu.	CL		Grey	UH				4
Zender Fact 4	4407			MAL	N. Gr.	TNT			UH	Wht., Or. & Blk. tr.			4
Zender Fact 4	4407			MAL	M. Blu.	DT		Grey	UH				4
Zender Fact 4	4407			MAL	M. Blu.	CL		Blk.	UH				4
Zender Fact 4	5674			MAL	Silver				HO - Silver				4
Zender Fact 4	5674			MAL	Silver				UH				4
Zencer Fact 4	5674			MAL	Silver				UH			Fact 4 on sides	4
Zender Fact 4	5674			MAL	Silver				UH - Gold				4
Ziploc Racer		Ziploc	Short rear wing	MAL	Blu./Gr.		HW logo		Reg	Wht. & Red tr.	Ziploc		15
Ziploc Racer		Ziploc	Short rear wing	MAL	Blu./Olive		HW		Reg	Wht. & Red tr.	Ziploc		15
Zombot	3852	Speed Demon		MAL	Yl. Chr.				UH				5
Zombot	3852	Speed Demon		MAL	Yl. Chr.				HO - Silver				5
Zombot	3852	Speed Demon		MAL	Blu. Chr.				UH				4